# PEARSON SCIENCE 3

CB120894

## Teacher's Resource

**Linda Aspen-Baxter**
Tisdale Middle & Secondary School
North East School Division

**Annette Brockman**
Carlton Comprehensive High School
Saskatchewan Rivers School Division

**Connie Molnar**
Teacher-Librarian
Lord Asquith School
Prairie Spirit School Division

**Kelsey Shields**
PJ Gillen School
Good Spirit School Division

**Ted View**
École St. Mary
Regina Catholic Schools

Nora Alexander

Steve Campbell

Douglas Hayhoe

Doug Herridge

Carole Moult

Lionel Sandner

Jim Wiese

Beverley Williams

Ricki Wortzman

ISBN-13: 978-0-13-312065-3

EAN

9 780133 120653

PEARSON

PEARSON



Adapted from *Addison Wesley Science & Technology 3 Teacher's Resource* © 2000

*Pearson Science 3, Saskatchewan Edition, Teacher's Resource* was published previously as *Pearson Saskatchewan Science 3, Teacher's Resource*. The content of the two titles is identical.



Feedback on this publication can be sent to editorialfeedback@pearsoned.com.

Pearson Canada Inc.
26 Prince Andrew Place
Don Mills, ON M3C 2T8
Customer Service: 1-800-361-6128

ISBN: 978-0-13-312012-7

Publisher: Reid McAlpine
Research and Communications Manager: Martin Goldberg
Prairie Regional Sales Manager: Doug Franke
Managing Editor: Lee Ensor
Proposal Consultant: Arnold Toutant
Project Manager: Yvonne Van Ruskenveld
Developmental Editors: Louise MacKenzie, Louise McCauley, Keltie Thomas
Copy Editors: Cathy Fraccaro, Linda Jenkins
Senior Production Editor: Susan Aihoshi
Editorial Assistant: Marissa Murray
Senior Production Coordinator: Louise Avery
Cover and Text Design: Alex Li, David Cheung
Composition: Lapiz Digital Services
Cover Photograph: B.W.HOFFMAN / AGSTOCKUSA / SCIENCE PHOTO LIBRARY
Illustrators: David Cheung, Bernadette Lau, ArtPlus Limited
Manufacturing Coordinator: Karen Alley
Vice-President, Publishing: Mark Cobham

The authors and Pearson Canada thank Dr. Glen S. Aikenhead, Dr. Herman Michell, and the staff of the Saskatchewan Ministry of Education for their guidance in the development of this program.

1 2019

Printed and bound in Canada.

# 3 Saskatchewan Science

## Teacher's Resource Contents

UNIT 1

# Plant Growth and Changes

## Table of Contents

## Table of Contents *(continued)*

## Unit Indicators Correlation Chart

| Indicator | Lesson References | Assessment Opportunities |
|---|---|---|
| By the end of grade 3, students will be able to: | | |
| **PL3.1 Investigate the growth and development of plants, including the conditions necessary for germination.** | | |
| a. Pose questions related to plant growth. | Lesson 4<br>Lesson 6<br>Design Project | Communicate, p. 13, q. 3<br>Communicate, p. 17, q .3<br>Work On It, p. 38 |
| b. Observe and explain the function of the major structures of a variety of plants. | Lesson 2<br><br>Lesson 3<br><br>Lesson 6<br><br>Show What You Know | Work On It, p. 9<br>Communicate, p. 9, q. 1, 2, 3<br>Work On It, p. 10<br>Communicate, p. 11, q. 1, 2, 4<br>Work On It, p. 16<br>Communicate, p. 17, q. 2<br>Show What You Know, p. 42, q. 1 |
| c. Relate characteristics such as the number and shape of leaves, flower colour, height, and presence and type of fruit in different types of plants to the plant's environment. | Lesson 8<br><br>Lesson 11 | Work On It, p. 20<br>Communicate, p. 21, q. 2<br>Communicate, p. 29, q. 3 |
| d. Sort and classify plants and/or seeds according to one or more student-selected attributes. | Lesson 8<br><br>Show What You Know | Work On It, p. 20<br>Communicate, p. 21, q. 4<br>Show What You Know, p. 42, q. 2 |
| e. Observe and represent, using written language, pictures, and charts, changes that occur through the life cycle of a flowering plant. | Lesson 2<br>Lesson 4<br>Lesson 7<br><br>Show What You Know | Communicate, p. 9, q. 4<br>Work On It, p. 12<br>Work On It, p. 19<br>Communicate, p. 19, q. 2, 3<br>Show What You Know, p. 43, q. 9 |
| f. Compare the basic needs of plants to the basic needs of animals and humans. | Lesson 5<br><br>Show What You Know | Work On It, p. 15<br>Communicate, p. 15, q. 1, 2, 3<br>Show What You Know, p. 42, q. 4 |
| g. Research ways in which plants rely on animals and abiotic factors to support plant reproduction by dispersing seeds. | Lesson 9 | Work On It, p. 25<br>Communicate, p. 25, q. 1, 2, 3 |
| h. Predict and investigate conditions such as the temperature, available sunlight, available nutrients in soil, and available water, which are necessary for plant germination and growth. | Lesson 4<br>Lesson 6<br>Design Project | Work On It, p. 12<br>Work On It, p. 16<br>Work On It, p. 38 |
| i. Care for a flowering plant throughout its life cycle, tracking its growth and changes. | Lesson 4 | Work On It, p. 12<br>Build On What You Know, p. 13 |
| j. Estimate, record, and display relevant measurements of plant growth, using rulers, tables, and bar graphs. | Lesson 4<br>Lesson 6 | Build On What You Know, p. 13<br>Work On It, p. 16 |

| Indicator | Lesson References | Assessment Opportunities |
|---|---|---|
| k. Suggest explanations for patterns and discrepancies in the growth rate of similar plants grown in varying conditions. | Lesson 4<br>Lesson 6<br>Design Project | Communicate, p. 13, q. 1<br>Communicate, p. 17, q. 1, 2<br>Work On It, p. 38 |
| l. Explain the importance of water and light for the plant growth and the mechanisms by which plants obtain water and light from the environment. | Lesson 3<br>Lesson 4<br>Lesson 6<br>Design Project<br>Show What You Know | Communicate, p. 11, q. 1, 2, 3, 4<br>Communicate, p. 13, q. 2<br>Communicate, p. 17, q. 2<br>Work On It, p. 38<br>Show What You Know, p. 42, q. 3 |
| m. Identify characteristics that remain constant and those that change throughout the life cycle of a flowering plant. | Lesson 2<br>Lesson 7<br><br>Lesson 8 | Communicate, p. 9, q. 4<br>Work On It, p. 19<br>Communicate, p. 19, q. 1, 2, 3<br>Communicate, p. 21, q. 1, 3, 4 |
| n. Pose new questions about conditions necessary for plant growth, based on what was learned. | Lesson 4<br>Lesson 5<br>Lesson 6<br>Lesson 7 | Communicate, p. 13, q. 3<br>Communicate, p. 15, q. 4<br>Communicate, p. 17, q. 3<br>Communicate, p. 19, q. 4 |
| **PL3.2 Analyze the interdependence among plants, individuals, society, and the environment** | | |
| a. Observe, safely and respectfully, plants in local environments. | Lesson 10<br><br>Design Project<br>Show What You Know | Work On It, p. 26<br>Communicate, p. 27, q. 1<br>Work On It, p. 38<br>Show What You Know, p. 43, q. 14, 15 |
| b. Research traditional and contemporary uses of plants or parts of plants, such as food, beverages, medicine, arts, seed banks, shade, wind breaks, erosion protection, cultural celebrations, and for creating products such as dyes, shelter, and clothing. | Lesson 1<br>Lesson 11<br><br>Lesson 12<br><br>Show What You Know | Communicate, p. 7, q.1, 2<br>Work On It, p. 29<br>Communicate, p. 29, q. 1<br>Work On It, p. 31<br>Communicate, p. 31, q. 4<br>Show What You Know, p. 43, q. 11 |
| c. Examine the significance to some First Nations and Métis people of offering tobacco during harvesting and how the purpose differs from using the tobacco plant for smoking. | Lesson 1<br>Ask …<br>Show What You Know | Work On It, p. 7<br>Research, p. 23<br>Show What You Know, p. 43, q. 11 |
| d. Examine the importance of agriculture in Saskatchewan, including the variety of plants and plant-related products. | Lesson 11<br><br>Show What You Know | Work On It, p. 29<br>Communicate, p. 29, q. 2<br>Show What You Know, p. 43, q. 10 |
| e. Describe examples of plant biodiversity in various ecosystems throughout the world. | Lesson 11<br><br>Lesson 12 | Work On It, p. 29<br>Communicate, p. 29, q. 3, 4<br>Work On It, p. 31<br>Communicate, p. 31, q. 3, 4 |

## Unit Indicators Correlation Chart *(continued)*

| Indicator | Lesson References | Assessment Opportunities |
|---|---|---|
| f. Explain how to determine whether plants are healthy and discuss societal and environmental impacts of diseased plants. | Lesson 10<br><br>Lesson 14<br><br>Show What You Know | Work On It, p. 26<br>Communicate, p. 27, q. 2<br>Work On It, p. 35<br>Communicate, p. 35, q.1, 2, 3<br>Show What You Know, p. 43, q. 13 |
| g. Describe ways that plants and animals depend on each other. | Lesson 9<br><br>Show What You Know | Work On It, p. 25<br>Communicate, p. 25, q. 3<br>Show What You Know, p. 42, q. 5, 6, 7 |
| h. Assess the impact of natural and human activity on the biodiversity of plant species. | Lesson 13<br><br>Lesson 14<br>Show What You Know | Work On It, p. 33<br>Communicate, p. 33, q. 1<br>Communicate, p. 35, q. 3<br>Show What You Know, p. 43, q. 12 |
| i. Examine the type and quantity of plants and plant matter in the diets of people who live in various communities and/or represent various cultures. | Lesson 12 | Work On It, p. 31<br>Communicate, p. 31, q. 1, 2, 3, 4 |
| j. Explain how and why plants are replenished naturally and artificially. | Lesson 13 | Communicate, p. 33, q. 2, 3 |
| k. Defend a position related to plant use and protection. | Lesson 15 | Work On It, p. 37<br>Communicate, p. 37, q. 1 |
| l. Imagine a world without plants and describe the impact on animals, people, and the environment. | Lesson 10<br>Lesson 13<br>Show What You Know | Communicate, p. 27, q. 3<br>Communicate, p. 33, q. 4<br>Show What You Know, p. 43, q. 10 |
| m. Respond to and acknowledge the ideas of others regarding the importance of plants to self and society. | Lesson 1<br>Lesson 8<br><br>Ask …<br>Lesson 10<br>Lesson 13<br><br>Show What You Know | Communicate, p. 7, q.1, 2<br>Work On It, p 20<br>Communicate, p. 21, q. 1<br>Research, p. 23<br>Communicate, p. 27, q. 3<br>Work On It, p. 33<br>Communicate, p. 33, q. 1, 4<br>Show What You Know, p. 43, q. 8 |
| n. Research lifestyles and jobs which depend on understanding and working with plants and plant-related products. | Ask … | Research, p. 23 |

## Lesson Planning Chart

Note that estimates of class times are based on 40 min per period.

| Lesson | Type of Activity | Time (number of classes) | Materials Required (for each group) | Line Masters |
|---|---|---|---|---|
| **Unit Opener** | | 1 | chart paper<br>markers<br>pencils | LM 1-1<br>LM 1-2<br>LM 1-3 |
| **Launch:** Plants and You | confirmation inquiry | 1 | pencils | none |
| **1.** How Are Plants Useful? | confirmation inquiry | 1 | pencils | LM 1-4<br>LM 1-5 |
| **2.** Plant Parts | structured inquiry | 1–2 | indoor plant with roots, leaves, and flowers (e.g., carnation)<br>carrot with a stem<br>newspaper<br>magnifying lens<br>branch of a tree (optional)<br>stalk of a rose bush or other shrub (optional)<br>stem of a flower with root attached (optional)<br>pencils | LM 1-6 |
| **3.** Exploring Plant Parts | structured inquiry | 2 | celery stalk with leaves<br>clear container<br>water<br>red food colouring<br>spoon<br>table knife<br>magnifying lens<br>markers<br>pencils | LM 1-7<br>LM 1-8 |
| **4.** How Do Plants Grow? | guided inquiry | 1–2 | 4 bean seeds soaked in water overnight (Soya and black eye beans germinate quickly and are available in health food stores.)<br>4 paper towels<br>water<br>4 resealable plastic bags<br>4 labels<br>marker<br>camera (optional)<br>bird feed (optional)<br>class or students' KWL charts<br>pencils<br>3–4 extra bean seeds (optional)<br>polystyrene foam cup (optional)<br>soil (optional) | LM 1-9<br>LM 1-10 |
| **5.** Basic Needs | structured inquiry | 1 | pencils<br>class or students' KWL charts | LM 1-11 |

## Lesson Planning Chart *(continued)*

| Lesson | Type of Activity | Time (number of classes) | Materials Required (for each group) | Line Masters |
|---|---|---|---|---|
| **6.** Helping Plants Get Water | structured inquiry | 1 | 2 bean plants (from extras planted in Lesson 4)<br>water<br>watering device<br>camera (optional)<br>marker<br>pencils<br>class or students' KWL charts | LM 1-12<br>LM 1-13 |
| **7.** Life Cycles | confirmation inquiry | 1–2 | pencils<br>pumpkin seeds (1 handful, optional)<br>magnifying lenses (optional) | LM 1-14<br>LM 1-15 |
| **8.** Grouping Plants | guided inquiry | 2 | pictures of a variety of leaves (simple—maple, oak, birch; needles—fir, cedar, spruce; compound—honey locust, butternut, hickory)<br>pictures of a variety of flowers (simple flowers—tulips, lilies; flower heads—fireweed, mullein; composite flowers—daisies, sunflowers)<br>camera (optional)<br>glue<br>2 large pieces of paper<br>pencil | LM 1-16 |
| **Ask …** Why is it important to understand plants? | research | 1–2 | pencils | none |
| **9.** How Do Animals Help Plants? | structured inquiry | 1–2 | burr or cattail<br>magnifying lens<br>tweezers<br>pencils | LM 1-17<br>LM 1-18 |
| **10.** Take a Field Trip | guided inquiry | 2 | camera (optional)<br>guide for local plants<br>pencils | LM 1-19 |
| **11.** What Crops Grow in Saskatchewan? | structured inquiry | 1 | variety of empty food boxes and food labels<br>pencils | LM 1-20 |
| **12.** Plants Are Food for the World | structured inquiry | 1 | pencils | LM 1-21 |
| **13.** Nature's Renewal | structured inquiry | 1 | no materials or equipment needed | LM 1-22 |

## Lesson Planning Chart *(continued)*

| Lesson | Type of Activity | Time (number of classes) | Materials Required (for each group) | Line Masters |
|---|---|---|---|---|
| **14.** How Can People Affect Plants? | structured inquiry | 1 | 2 bean plants<br>4 labels<br>marker<br>2 jugs of water (4-L milk jugs)<br>measuring cup<br>rubber gloves<br>spoon<br>500 mL road salt<br>camera (optional)<br>pencils | LM 1-23 |
| **15.** How Can People Help Plants? | structured inquiry | 1 | pencils | LM 1-24 |
| **Design Project:** Create a Garden | open inquiry | 2–3 | Bristol board<br>scissors<br>glue<br>various items, such as coloured paper, seeds, felt, artificial plants, etc., for students to build their model garden<br>pencils | LM 1-25<br>LM 1-26 |

traditional **KNOWLEDGE**

## First Nations Cultural References

The following references provide information on First Nations topics. The information may not be specific to Saskatchewan First Nations and should not be generalized to all First Nations.

- First Nations or Métis Elders and Traditional Knowledge Keepers may be invited into the classroom to share their knowledge about plants. Teachers should follow the "Protocol for Contacting Elders and Traditional Knowledge Keepers" in the Program Overview of this Teacher's Resource.
- Indian and Northern Affairs Canada: www.ainc-inac.gc.ca/ach/lr/ks/gms/gms_dyk-eng.asp#

## Suggested Websites

Please note that website URLs constantly change and the addresses given below may become out of date. In this case, please use the website title and a search engine to find the appropriate website.

- FOSSweb New Plants Module: http://fossweb.com/modulesK-2/NewPlants/index.html
- The Seedy Side of Plants: www.pbs.org/wnet/nature/plants/index.html
- Plants Database United States Department of Agriculture: http://plants.usda.gov/java/
- Plants and Our Environment: http://library.thinkquest.org/3715/?tqskip1=1
- Plant Parts Salad: www.hhmi.org/coolscience/forkids/vegquiz/plantparts.html
- Aggie Horticulture Just For Kids: http://aggie-horticulture.tamu.edu/kindergarden/index.html
- I Can Garden: www.icangarden.com/kidz.cfm
- Gamequarium: Plant Games: www.gamequarium.com/plants.html
- Adventures of the Agronauts: www.ncsu.edu/project/agronauts/
- My First Garden: http://urbanext.illinois.edu/firstgarden/index.cfm
- National Occupational Classification Profiles: www5.hrsdc.gc.ca/NOC/English/NOC/2006/SearchAlphabetical.aspx
- Alberta Occupational Profiles: http://alis.alberta.ca/occinfo/Content/RequestAction.asp?format=html&aspAction=GetHomePage&Page=Home
- Lumberjack: www.absoluteastronomy.com/topics/Lumberjack
- Landscaper Job Descriptions: www.ehow.com/facts_5162768_landscaper-job-descriptions.html
- Gardener Job Descriptions: www.ehow.com/about_5378719_gardener-job-description.html

## Suggested Field Trips

- Lesson 10 suggests taking students on a field trip to observe and record the plants growing in the local area. You will need to make arrangements for a trip to a place where a variety of plants can be observed. This could be an area around your school, a local natural area such as a field or meadow, or a residential neighbourhood with plenty of trees and flowers. Follow any guidelines your school has for field trip safety and permission.
- Consider visiting two local areas where students can observe how different types and numbers of plants grow in different places.
- You may wish to take students to a large grocery store to explore what types of foods from plants are available and where these foods come from (e.g., local and global sources). Afterward, lead a class discussion about how food is shipped around the world, packaged to travel, and kept fresh.
- Here are some other interesting places you may wish to take students during this unit of study:
  - a garden supply store or nursery
  - a greenhouse where students can see how plants are grown indoors
  - a local farm where students can see how seeds are sown, how crops are grown, or how crops are harvested
  - a flour mill, where wheat, oats, peas, or flax is milled
  - a local forest or garden where students can observe a variety of plants

## Suggested Guest Speakers

- You may wish to invite guest speakers who have an interest in or work with plants, such as a gardener, forester, landscaper, green grocer, or horticulturist. Encourage students to prepare some questions ahead of time.
- Invite a First Nations or Métis Elder or Traditional Knowledge Keeper into your classroom to share their cultural beliefs, perspective, and respect for plants as gifts from Creator. Follow the "Protocol for Contacting Elders and Traditional Knowledge Keepers" in the Program Overview of this Teacher's Resource.

## Suggested Additional Student Resources

- *Hungry Planet* by Peter Menzel and Faith D'Aluisio (Ten Speed Press, 2007)
- *Planting a Rainbow* by Lois Ehlert (Voyager Books, 1988)
- *From Seed to Plant* by Gail Gibbons (Holiday House (P), 1993)
- *The Magic School Bus Plants Seeds: A Book About How Living Things Grow* by Joanne Cole (Scholastic Paperbacks, 1995)

## Materials and Equipment Needed for Unit 1

(based on 30 students)

| Launch: Plants and You (p. 4) | |
|---|---|
| **Materials**<br>• pencils | **Equipment**<br>• no equipment needed |
| **1. How Are Plants Useful? (p. 6)** | |
| **Materials**<br>• pencils | **Equipment**<br>• no equipment needed |
| **2. Plant Parts (p. 8)** | |
| **Materials**<br>• 15 indoor plants with roots, leaves, and flowers (e.g., carnation)<br>• 15 carrots with a stem<br>• 15 sheets of newspaper<br>• branch of a tree (optional)<br>• stalk of a rose bush or other shrub (optional)<br>• stem of a flower with root attached (optional)<br>• pencils | **Equipment**<br>• 15 magnifying lenses |
| **3. Exploring Plant Parts (p. 10)** | |
| **Materials**<br>• 15 celery stalks with leaves<br>• water<br>• 2 small bottles of red food colouring<br>• 15 markers<br>• pencils | **Equipment**<br>• 15 clear containers<br>• 15 spoons<br>• 15 table knives<br>• 15 magnifying lenses |
| **4. How Do Plants Grow? (p. 12)** | |
| **Materials**<br>• 120 bean seeds soaked in water overnight<br>• 120 paper towels<br>• water<br>• 120 resealable plastic bags<br>• 20 labels<br>• 30 markers<br>• 15 handfuls of birdfeed (1 for each pair of students) (optional)<br>• class or students' KWL charts<br>• pencils<br>• 90–120 extra bean seeds (optional)<br>• 90–120 polystyrene foam cup (optional)<br>• 90–120 cupfuls of soil (optional) | **Equipment**<br>• camera (optional) |

## Materials and Equipment

*(continued)*

| 5. Basic Needs (p. 14) | |
|---|---|
| **Materials**<br>• pencils<br>• class or students' KWL charts | **Equipment**<br>• no equipment needed |
| **6. Helping Plants Get Water (p. 16)** | |
| **Materials**<br>• 30 bean plants (from extras planted in Lesson 4)<br>• water<br>• 5 markers<br>• pencils<br>• class or students' KWL charts | **Equipment**<br>• 15 watering devices<br>• camera (optional) |
| **7. Life Cycles (p. 18)** | |
| **Materials**<br>• pencils<br>• pumpkin seeds (1 handful for each of 15 pairs of students, optional) | **Equipment**<br>• 15 magnifying lenses (optional) |
| **8. Grouping Plants (p. 20)** | |
| **Materials**<br>• 30 sets of pictures of a variety of leaves (simple—maple, oak, birch; needles—fir, cedar, spruce; compound—honey locust, butternut, hickory)<br>• 30 sets of pictures of a variety of flowers (simple flowers—tulips, lilies; flower heads—fireweed, mullein; composite flowers—daisies, sunflowers)<br>• 30 small bottles of glue or glue sticks<br>• 60 large pieces of paper<br>• pencils | **Equipment**<br>• camera (optional) |
| **9. How Do Animals Help Plants? (p. 24)** | |
| **Materials**<br>• 30 burrs or cattails<br>• pencils | **Equipment**<br>• 30 magnifying lens<br>• 30 pairs of tweezers |
| **10. Take A Field Trip (p. 26)** | |
| **Materials**<br>• 5–6 copies of guide for local plants<br>• pencils | **Equipment**<br>• camera (optional) |

## Materials and Equipment

*(continued)*

| 11. What Crops Grow in Saskatchewan? (p. 28) | |
|---|---|
| **Materials**<br>• 15 sets of a variety of empty food packages and labels<br>• pencils | **Equipment**<br>• no equipment needed |
| **12. Plants Are Food for the World (p. 30)** | |
| **Materials**<br>• pencils | **Equipment**<br>• no equipment needed |
| **13. Nature's Renewal (p. 32)** | |
| **Materials**<br>• pencils | **Equipment**<br>• no equipment needed |
| **14. How Can People Affect Plants? (p. 34)** | |
| **Materials**<br>• 20 bean plants<br>• 40 labels<br>• 10 markers<br>• 20 jugs of water (4-L milk jugs)<br>• 10 pairs of rubber gloves<br>• 5- kg bag of road salt<br>• pencils | **Equipment**<br>• 10 measuring cups<br>• 10 spoons<br>• camera (optional) |
| **15. How Can People Help Plants? (p. 36)** | |
| **Materials**<br>• pencils | **Equipment**<br>• no equipment needed |
| **Design Project: Create a Garden (p. 38)** | |
| **Materials**<br>• 15 sheets of Bristol board<br>• 15 small bottles of glue<br>• 15 sets of various items, such as coloured paper, seeds, felt, artificial plants, etc., for students to build their model garden<br>• pencils | **Equipment**<br>• 15 pairs of scissors |

## Materials and Equipment

*(continued)*

| Overall Unit Requirements | |
|---|---|
| **Materials**<br>• pencils<br>• 15 indoor plants with roots, leaves, and flowers (e.g., carnation)<br>• 15 carrots with a stem<br>• 15 sheets of newspaper<br>• branch of a tree (optional)<br>• stalk of a rose bush or other shrub (optional)<br>• stem of a flower with root attached (optional)<br>• 15 celery stalks with leaves<br>• water<br>• 2 small bottles of red food colouring<br>• 30 markers<br>• 8–10 packages of bean seeds (enough for 120 seeds)<br>• 120 paper towels<br>• 120 resealable plastic bags<br>• 160 labels<br>• 90–120 extra bean seeds (optional)<br>• 90–120 foam cups (optional)<br>• 90–120 cupfuls of soil (optional)<br>• birdfeed (15 handfuls optional)<br>• class or students' KWL charts<br>• 50 bean plants (from extras planted in Lesson 4)<br>• pumpkin seeds<br>• 30 sets of pictures of a variety of leaves (simple—maple, oak, birch; needles—fir, cedar, spruce; compound—honey locust, butternut, hickory)<br>• 30 sets of pictures of a variety of flowers (simple flowers—tulips, lilies; flower heads—fireweed, mullein; composite flowers—daisies, sunflowers)<br>• 30 small bottles of glue or glue sticks<br>• 60 large pieces of paper<br>• 30 burrs or cattails<br>• 5–6 copies of guide for local plants<br>• 15 sets of a variety of empty food packages and labels<br>• 20 jugs of water (4-L milk jugs)<br>• 10 pairs of rubber gloves<br>• 5- kg bag of road salt<br>• 15 sheets of Bristol board<br>• 15 sets of various items, such as felt, coloured paper, seeds, artificial plants | **Equipment**<br>• 30 magnifying lenses<br>• 15 clear containers<br>• 15 spoons<br>• 15 table knives<br>• camera (optional)<br>• 15 watering devices<br>• 30 pairs of tweezers<br>• 10 measuring cups<br>• 10 spoons<br>• 15 pairs of scissors |

# Unit Opener



| Time |
| --- |
| 40 min |

| Line Masters |
| --- |
| • LM 1-1<br>• LM 1-2<br>• LM 1-3 |

traditional **KNOWLEDGE**

In this unit, students will explore and investigate plant growth and changes. As students explore a variety of plants, they will come to understand the similarities and differences among the physical characteristics of different plant species and the changes that take place in different plants as they grow. Students will also investigate the requirements of plants and the effects that changes in environmental conditions have on plants. Students will describe ways in which plants are important to other living things, and the effects of human activities on plants.

Scientists use categories such as "living" and "non-living" to make sense of the world, but First Nations and Métis peoples describe things in a different way. They understand that everything in nature is alive with Spirit. For example, rocks, animals, rain, and people have Spirit. They also categorize the world based on survival. A plant can be described as "poisonous" or "non-poisonous." They tell us that when everything in nature is living, our relationship with nature is more personal.

Many plants are sacred to First Nations and Métis peoples. While the types of plants that are considered sacred vary among North American First Nations and Métis peoples, the plains people in Saskatchewan agree on four main sacred plants: sweetgrass, sage, cedar, and tobacco. These plants are also considered medicines and strict protocols govern their use.

When these four sacred plants are harvested, traditional First Nations and Métis people offer tobacco to Mother Earth before picking them. The plants are dried and used later in special ceremonies. Tobacco is smoked only in pipe ceremonies. Sweetgrass, sage, and cedar are mainly used in smudges. Smudges are sacred ceremonies that include the burning of the sacred plants. As the plants burn and the flames that consume them die, smoke is produced that many First Nations people believe carries prayers to Creator.

First Nations and Métis people teach their children about the respect that must be shown for plants, because plants have Spirit (the spirit of Creator) and some plants, such as the four sacred plants, are particularly special. They honour Spirit in plants with tobacco offerings. They also teach children to leave plants undisturbed unless the plants are needed for food, medicines, or ceremonies. For more information on tobacco and its use among First Nations and Métis people, see the Background Information in Lesson 1.

## Assessing Prior Knowledge

- Read the opening text and examine the photograph on page 2 with students. Initiate a discussion about students' knowledge of plants by posing questions, such as: *How are plants used? How do plants affect the quality of your life? Do you rely on plants to survive?*

- Share with students that plants are living things that are a very important part of our world. Challenge students to think of and suggest reasons why plants are important for the world we live in. As students suggest different reasons, record them on a piece of chart paper for future reference. If a student suggests a reason that others do not understand, have that student expand on the reason and see if the rest of the class agrees. As you progress through the unit, invite students to continue to add to the list of why plants are important.

## Introduce the Unit

- Explain to students that in this unit they will be taking an in-depth look at plants and how plants grow by:
  - examining the ways First Nations and Métis peoples view plants
  - looking at the similarities and differences between types of plants
  - studying how plants change as they grow
  - investigating what plants need to survive and how plants respond to changes in the environment
  - exploring how people use plants, and how they can affect and help plants
- Invite students to look for pictures of interesting plants or potted plants at home that they may be able to bring to class for the unit. Ensure students ask permission from their parents to bring these items to school. Also, encourage students to observe in and around their neighbourhoods any unique plants that they can photograph or describe to share with the class. Ask the class if anyone knows a person who works in a field related to plants, such as a forestry, gardening, farming, or green groceries, who might be willing to visit the class.
- Once you have determined students' prior knowledge, you may want to hand out LM 1-1 Unit 1 Summary and LM 1-2 Unit 1 Vocabulary to help students record their understanding of the unit and key terms.

## Introduce the Design Project

Briefly describe the end-of-unit Design Project. Explain to students that they will use what they learn about plants in the unit to create a garden. Tell students that in this unit they will learn about what plants need to survive and how to care for plants. They will work with a partner to plan a garden that will sustain healthy plants. Then, they will create a model of their garden to show what plants need to grow and how they plan to help plants grow.

| Time |
| --- |
| 40 min |
| **Skills** |
| • communicating |
| **Grouping** |
| class/individuals |
| **Materials and Equipment** |
| • chart paper<br>• markers<br>• pencils |
| **Line Masters** |
| • LM 1-3 |

## Looking Forward

- Use a KWL chart to stimulate student interest, connect new learning to existing knowledge, generate inquiry questions, and help determine students' background knowledge. You may choose to have students work on the chart as a group or as individuals.
- **As a whole group activity:** post a large sheet of chart paper, title it "Plants," and divide it into three columns to replicate LM 1-3 Plants KWL Chart. Label the columns "What I Know About Plants," "What I Want to Know About Plants," and "What I Learned About Plants."
- Invite the class to brainstorm for facts they know about plants, which will help you to assess students' prior knowledge. Record students' responses in the first column of the KWL chart. Next, ask students what they want to know about plants and record their responses in the second column. Guide students to suggest questions such as the following:
  - How do plants grow?
  - What do plants need to grow?
  - How are plants different?
  - How are plants the same?
  - How can we learn about plants?
  - How are plants useful?
  - How are plants important to people and animals?
  - Can people affect plants?
  - How can people care for plants?
  - Why is it important to understand plants?
- Inform students that they will return to this KWL chart throughout the unit to record what they have learned about plants. Post the chart where it can be easily seen and added to.
- **As an individual activity:** Hand out LM 1-3 Plants KWL Chart. Have students work individually to record facts they know about plants in the first column of the chart. Provide students with an opportunity to share their facts with the class. Before recording each fact on a master KWL chart, ask the class if everyone agrees that the statement is true. If students cannot agree, rephrase the fact as a question and record it in the second column of the master chart.
- Have students write a list of questions about what they want to know about plants in the second column of their charts. Invite students to share their questions with the class and record them on the master KWL chart.
- Explain that students will return to the KWL chart throughout the unit to record answers to their questions and to complete the third column with what they learn about plants. Keep students' KWL charts in a folder or a binder where they can be easily accessed. Post the master KWL chart where it can be seen and easily added to throughout the unit.

| Time |
|---|
| 40 min |

## Focus on Literacy

### *During Reading: Asking Questions*

Tell students that graphical texts, such as photographs, diagrams, drawings, and maps, can provide a lot of information in a very concise way. Say, *The text on this page tells us that we would not survive without plants, because people rely on them for many things. The pictures on these pages show us many familiar situations in which we encounter plants or things made from plants. Let's take a closer look.*

Have students quickly preview the pictures on page 4 to name and identify the different situations depicted (e.g., supermarket, drugstore, flower shop, home). Repeat this process for the pictures on page 5 (e.g., a school setting, clothing store, bakery/restaurant).

Say, *By breaking down the text on each page into smaller parts, we will be better able to focus our attention and read the text. As we examine these drawings, let's practise a strategy that good readers use while reading: asking questions. This will help us stay engaged with the pictures and interact with them in a meaningful way. To help us ask some good questions, we are going to look at each part of the drawing with two questions in mind: "What does it say or show?" and "What does it not say or show?"*

On the board or chart paper, create a three-column chart. Label the first column "What it says/tells us," label the second column "What it does not say/tell us," and leave the third column blank for now. Model how to read the supermarket part of the picture on page 4. Say, *I notice a lot of our food, such as cucumbers, juices, and tomatoes, comes from plants. I'm going to record this in the first column. This brings a few questions to mind for me, such as "Who grows all this food?" and "What do they do if we do not buy all this food?"*

Record your questions in the second column of the chart. Invite pairs of students to continue reading each part of the pictures on pages 4 and 5, and pause to have them share their thinking and questions after each part. Continue to record students' thinking on the chart.

### *After Reading: Sorting Questions to Identify Additional Information Needs*

Use the third column of the three-column chart (see above) to work with students to identify which of the questions recorded in the second column they think may be answered in this unit. Brainstorm with students ways to figure this out (e.g., by viewing the table of contents for the unit, or looking through the unit lessons to get an idea of what is covered). Discuss how the class can find answers to any remaining questions in the second column (e.g., through further research). Questions in the second column can become opportunities for student research based on personal interest. Revisit these questions as answers are discovered throughout the study of the unit.

## Get Started ▶

- Many students do not realize that without plants they would not exist, because plants produce the world's oxygen, as well as food and other useful materials.
- Before reading the text on page 4, have students brainstorm ways in which they use plants. Compile a class list of students' ideas.

| Time |
| --- |
| 40 min |
| **Learning Context** |
| inquiry |
| **Level of Inquiry** |
| confirmation |
| **Skills** |
| • observing<br>• interpreting<br>• comparing<br>• communicating |
| **Grouping** |
| individuals |
| **Materials and Equipment** |
| • pencils |

## Work On It

### Purpose

To provide an opportunity for students to consider how people use plants every day

### Activity Notes

- Questions 1 and 2 guide students to examine the pictures on pages 4 and 5. Provide time for students to view, consider, and list the ways plants are used in the picture and compare their lists with those of classmates.
- Instruct students to create a web of the different ways plants are used (e.g., plants provide oxygen, beauty, medicine, and foods such as fruits, vegetables, and juices; they are used to make desks, chairs, tables, paper, pencils, clothes, baked goods; they are burned for heat).

## Communicate

1. Students' answers may vary and depend on the season but could include grass, dandelions, lilies, birch trees, and poplar trees. Encourage students to add to the class list of different types of plants as they work through the unit.
2. Students' answers may vary but could include clothes, paper, pencils, desks, and chairs.
3. Students' answers may vary but could include fruit, juice, cereal, and toast.

## DI Differentiating Instruction

### *For EAL/ELL*

Ensure that EAL/ELL students can name and identify all the items shown in the pictures on pages 4 and 5. Have them use drawings to list and show ways people use plants.

### *For Reteaching*

Have students look through magazines to find photos of ways that plants are used. Students can cut out the photos and create a collage of the different ways plants are used.

## Assessment *for* Learning

| What to Look for in Student Work | What to Do |
|---|---|
| Students can identify ways people use plants. | • Observe students as they work on the activity in Work On It and check the lists they create.<br>• Check students' responses to Communicate questions 2 and 3. |

# 1 How Are Plants Useful?

Page 6

**Time**

40 min

**Line Masters**

- LM 1-4
- LM 1-5

## Indicator Assessment Chart

| Indicator | Assessment Opportunities |
|---|---|
| **PL3.2 b.** Research traditional and contemporary uses of plants or parts of plants, such as food, beverages, medicine, arts, seed banks, shade, wind breaks, erosion protection, cultural celebrations, and for creating products such as dyes, shelter, and clothing. | • Communicate, p. 7, q. 1, 2 |
| **PL3.2 c.** Examine the significance to some First Nations and Métis people of offering tobacco during harvesting and how that purpose differs from using the tobacco plant for smoking. | • Work On It, p. 7 |
| **PL3.2 m.** Respond to and acknowledge the ideas of others regarding the importance of plants to self and society | • Communicate, p. 7, q. 1, 2 |

## Lesson Goal

To explore how people use plants

## Background Information

Plants and plant products are used by humans all over the world. While wood products such as furniture are numerous and well known, there are many more products that come from trees, including chemicals, cork, rubber, and gum. Other non-food plant products include cotton and linen, a variety of medicines and herbal remedies, and straw.

One of the most used plant products is paper. Trees contain cellulose, a large molecule found in the cell walls of wood and lignin. Cellulose and lignin bind together to give wood strength and flexibility. Pulp mills separate the lignin and cellulose from trees to make pulp, which is used to make paper. With the lignin gone, the cellulose fibres combine with water to make a sludge that is strained through a thick screen that leaves the cellulose fibres on the screen. They are dried with heat and pressure, and then rolled into paper.

traditional ***KNOWLEDGE***

Tobacco is considered sacred among First Nations and Métis peoples. Traditional tobacco contains a mixture of many sacred plants, including bearberry. The Cree called it *kinikinik*. It is believed that smoke from the sacred plants—tobacco, cedar, sweetgrass, and sage—carries prayers to Creator. Tobacco is used in many important ceremonies including the pipe ceremony. Contrary to Western beliefs, tobacco is a sacred medicine often believed to cleanse.

*continued →*

Tobacco offerings are ways that First Nations and Métis people communicate their profound respect and gratitude for a gift or a teaching. They teach their children to give tobacco as a sign of gratitude. In the community when one needs help from another, especially Elders, protocols must be followed in order to gain the required assistance. These protocols always include a tobacco offering.

Tobacco is the means to show gratitude for the spirit of a living being. A tobacco offering expresses appreciation for the gifts that Mother Earth and Creator provide. All First Nations and Métis people believe that all things, even those that Western science might consider abiotic, possess a spirit. Hence, things like rocks and fire have spirit. A tobacco offering is a way that First Nations and Métis people show gratitude to that spirit. Thus, when a tree is cut, an animal is killed, a rock is removed for use in a ceremony, or a plant is harvested, the spirit in that tree, animal, rock, or plant is thanked with tobacco.

## Curriculum Connections

In this lesson, students have the opportunity to develop skills and concepts in these areas:

### *Social Studies*

DR3.3 a. Research the view of land as held by indigenous peoples in communities studied.

### *English Language Arts*

CR3.2 b. Select and use appropriate strategies (before, during, and after) to construct and confirm meaning when viewing.

CC3.3 a. Use oral language to clarify and extend personal understanding, interact courteously with others (e.g., share ideas and opinions, complete tasks, discuss concerns or problems), and sustain conversations by extending others' contributions.

## Focus on Literacy

### *Before Reading/Writing: A to Z Brainstorm to Activate Prior Knowledge*

Provide copies of LM 1-4 A to Z Brainstorm. Say, *Before we begin reading today, let's refresh our memories with what we already know about plants. On this sheet, you will find 26 boxes, one for each letter of the alphabet. Your task is to think about our topic, "Plants," and write down in the boxes as many words that relate to plants as you can. Use the alphabet to help you. For example, if are thinking about a birch tree, record the words in the box for the letter B.*

Give students three or four minutes to work independently to record as many words as they can for as many letters as they can. Next, have students share their A to Z brainstorm with a partner and record words from their partner to fill in any empty boxes on their sheets.

Continue the activity by saying, *The goal of today's lesson is to explore how people use plants. With your partner, revisit your alphabet boxes and this time look at the words you have recorded. If you know of a use for a plant you have recorded, record it in the same box as the plant. For example, in the "B" box I wrote "birch tree," and I know First Nations and Métis peoples used birchbark to make canoes. So I am going to write "canoe" in this box as well.*

In a whole class discussion, invite students to share all the uses of plants that they came up with and record them on the board or chart paper.

## Get Started ▶

- Invite students to look at the photographs on page 6 of the student book and identify the uses of plants shown. Read the text with students.
- Return to the class list of plant uses created in the Before Reading activity and have students add any uses discovered in the text. Ask students to also consider plant products that are used in and around the school and add them to the list. You may wish to post the list in the classroom so that it can be added to throughout the unit.

| Time |
| --- |
| 40 min |
| **Learning Context** |
| cultural perspectives |
| **Level of Inquiry** |
| confirmation |
| **Skills** |
| • interpreting<br>• communicating |
| **Grouping** |
| groups |
| **Materials and Equipment** |
| none |
| **Line Masters** |
| • none |

## Work On It

### Purpose

To have students examine some ways that First Nations and Métis peoples have been using plants over thousands of years

### Activity Notes

- Before students begin the activity, hold a class discussion in which you share the traditional knowledge about tobacco, its uses, and its meaning as a sacred plant among First Nations and Métis peoples that is provided in the Background Information section of this lesson. Ensure students understand that traditional tobacco, called *kinikinik* by the Cree, does not actually contain tobacco or nicotine. Sharing this background knowledge is important so that students can appreciate the significance and role of tobacco within First Nations and Métis cultures.
- You may wish to use one or more of the following strategies to lead the class discussion:
  - **Think-Pair-Share:** Pairs of students sit cross-legged, facing each other. Students have one minute to reflect about what they think or have learned after you read aloud each caption about traditional uses of plants on page 7 of the student book. Partners then take turns sharing their thinking with each other. When students have finished sharing, have them come together as a class to debrief about ideas they have shared.

*continued* →

traditional ***KNOWLEDGE***

- **Comparison Table:** Present the relevant captions from page 7 of the student book in a table, so that students can compare traditional ways that First Nations and Métis peoples have used plants with the ways we use plants today.

| Uses for Plants | First Nations and Métis Peoples | Our Society |
|---|---|---|
| Art, decorating, and aesthetics | Some First Nations and Métis people create patterns by biting birchbark. This is used for decorating clothing made from animal skins. Today, birchbark biting is an art. | Our society uses plants to create bouquets, corsages, gardens, and landscapes for decorative and aesthetic purposes. |
| Medicines | Some First Nations and Métis people use the purple coneflower for pain relief. | Our society uses some plants for medicine but derives many medicines from chemicals. |
| Transportation | Most First Nations and Métis people used to make canoes out of birchbark. They used spruce tree roots and spruce gum or sap to hold the bark together. | Our society has used plants to make boats and rafts. Today we make these items with metal and/or high-tech materials. |
| Ceremonies | Many First Nations and Métis people use plants for special ceremonies that link them to their ancestors or offer respect to Mother Earth. | Our society uses flowers in ceremonies, such as weddings and funerals. |
| Homes and shelters | First Nations used tamarack, lodge pole pine, and other available woods to make shelters, lodges, and tipis. The Métis made their homes out of logs much as the Europeans did. | Our society uses lumber in combination with other materials to make shelters. |
| Food | First Nations people ate berries and roots. Some eastern First Nations grew squash, corn, beans, and wild rice. | Our society grows and harvests plants for food through wide scale agriculture and farming. |

- **Venn Diagram:** With the class, create a Venn diagram like the one on the opposite page to compare the ways we use plants today with the traditional ways First Nations and Métis peoples have used plants. Have students to consider key questions, such as: *How might we use plants differently today than First Nations and Métis people did in the past? How is our view of plants the same as that of First Nations and Métis people? How is it different? What other ways do we (and First Nations and Métis people) use plants that are not mentioned in the book?* Alternatively, you may wish to have small groups of students create their own Venn diagrams and share their work with the class.

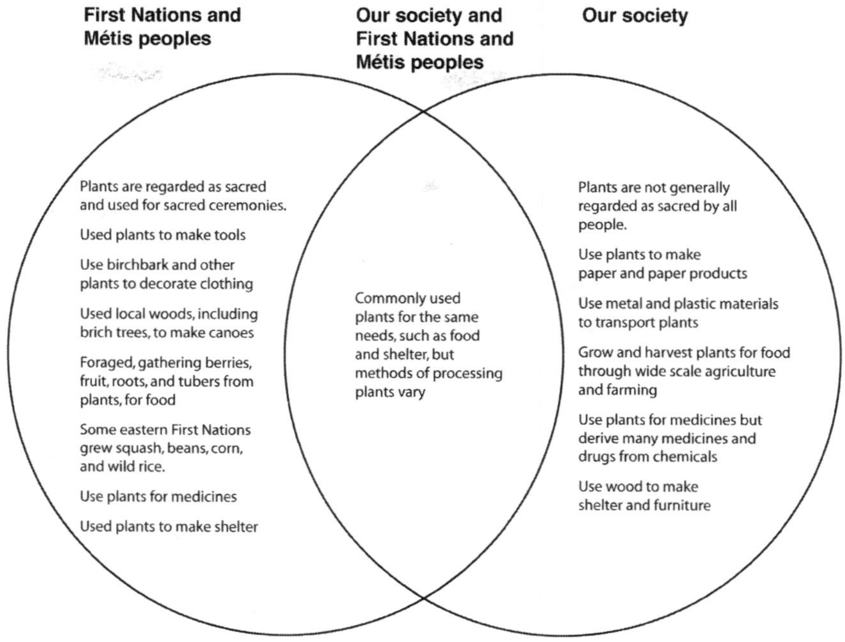


## Additional Activity

Students may enjoy making some recycled paper from toilet paper by following the step-by-step instructions on LM 1-5 Paper Making.

## Communicate

Have small groups of students work together to complete these questions. You may wish to have students use the Indian and Northern Affairs Canada website to search for the answer to question 2: www.ainc-inac.gc.ca/ach/lr/ks/gms/gms_dyk-eng.asp#

1. Students' answers may vary but could include three of the following examples: First Nations and Métis people make traditional tobacco from a mixture of dried plants and willow bark; used birchbark to make canoes; used spruce tree roots, gum or sap to hold the bark of the canoes together; use birchbark to create patterns to decorate clothes; use purple coneflower for pain relief.
2. Students' answers may vary but could include that First Nations and Métis peoples have also used willow bark for pain relief and to treat fevers.

Tobacco is sacred for the Cree (*Nehiyawak*) people. Traditional tobacco is considered a medicine and used in special ceremonies. See Traditional Knowledge in the Background Information and Activity Notes for this lesson.

### BUILD ON WHAT YOU KNOW

At the end of the unit, students will complete a Design Project to create a garden. Use the Build On What You Know activities throughout the unit to help students prepare for the project. Wrap up this lesson by having students record their ideas about how people might use the plants that grow in the garden they will create (e.g., for food, medicine, building materials, decoration). Encourage students to use pictures or words to record their ideas. Collect students' work and give students ample opportunity to review their ideas before they begin to work on the end-of-unit Design Project.

## DI Differentiating Instruction

### *For EAL/ELL*

Pair EAL/ELL students with students who are proficient speakers and writers of English so they may receive effective modelling of the English language as small groups of students read and discuss the photo captions.

### *For Enrichment*

Invite an Elder or Traditional Knowledge Keeper to visit your classroom and share his or her knowledge and experience with using plants. Follow the "Protocol for Contacting Elders and Traditional Knowledge Keepers" in the Program Overview of this Teacher's Resource.

## Assessment *for* Learning

| What to Look for in Student Work | What to Do |
|---|---|
| Students can identify traditional and contemporary uses of plants or parts of plants. | • Observe students as they work on the Get Started and Work On It activities.<br>• Check students' responses to Communicate questions 1 and 2. |
| Students can acknowledge the importance of plants to others and to themselves. | • Observe students as they share and discuss during the Get Started and the Work On It activity. |
| Students can examine the traditional use of tobacco to some First Nations and Métis peoples. | • Observe students as they work on the Work On It activity.<br>• Check students' responses to Communicate question 1. |

# 2 Plant Parts

Page 8

| Time |
| --- |
| 40–80 min |

**Vocabulary**

- roots
- stem
- leaves
- chlorophyll
- seeds
- flowers

**Line Masters**

- LM 1-6

## Indicator Assessment Chart

| Indicator | Assessment Opportunities |
| --- | --- |
| **PL3.1 b.** Observe and explain the function of the major structures (i.e., root stem, flower, leaf, and fruit or seed) of a variety of plants. | • Work On It, p. 9<br>• Communicate, p. 9, q. 1, 2, 3 |
| **PL3.1 e.** Observe and represent, using written language, pictures, and charts, changes that occur through the life cycle of a flowering plant. | • Communicate, p. 9, q. 4 |
| **PL3.1 m.** Identify characteristics that remain constant and those that change throughout the life cycle of a flowering plant. | • Communicate, p. 9, q. 4 |

## Lesson Goal

To look at and compare parts of different plants

### Background Information

Plants have five main parts: roots, stem, leaves, seeds, and flowers. The roots anchor the plant in the ground and provide moisture and nutrients for the plant. In some cases, such as potatoes and carrots, the roots also store energy for the plant. Tap roots, such as dandelions and carrots, are a main central root with small root hairs attached. Other plants have a fibrous root system that consists of many equal-sized roots going in different directions. These have many secondary roots and small root hairs spreading out beneath the plant.

The stem of the plant holds the leaves and flowers and contains a transport system for moving water, nutrients, and food between the roots and the rest of the plant. Stems can be woody, as in trees, or herbaceous, as in daisies and lilies.

The leaves of the plant contain chlorophyll and are where photosynthesis takes place. Most leaves are green because of the chlorophyll, but some plants have leaves that are not green. These leaves still contain chlorophyll but have a higher concentration of other pigments. Leaves come in all shapes and sizes. The needles of evergreen trees are leaves with a waxy coating.

The flower of a plant is where the organs for reproduction are located. Flowers are self-pollinated or are pollinated by insects or the wind. Once the flower has been pollinated, it begins to form seeds for future plants. Seeds are small embryonic plants enclosed in a covering called a seed coating. The seed coating usually also contains some stored food.

## Curriculum Connections

In this lesson, students have the opportunity to develop skills and concepts in these areas:

### *English Language Arts*

CR3.2 b. Select and use appropriate strategies (before, during, and after) to construct and confirm meaning when viewing.

### *Visual Arts*

CP3.8 a. Observe visual details, and include details to enhance depictions of animals, people, and objects.

**Get Started ▶**

- Show students the branch of a tree, the stalk of a rose bush, and the stem of a flower (or other examples of plant stems). Ask, *Does anyone know what these parts of plants are called? Does anyone know why they are important for the plant?*
- Discuss students' responses and explain that the stem of a plant holds the plant up and carries water and nutrients from the roots to the leaves of the plant.
- Read the text and examine the illustration on page 8 of the student book with students. Use questions such as the following to engage students in a discussion about the key parts of the plants shown:
  - *Are the roots of all plants the same?* (No. Some plants, such as carrots, have one main root while others have groups of smaller roots that branch out in all directions).
  - *Do all plants have flowers?* (No. Some plants, such as moss and evergreen trees, do not have flowers.)
  - *What is the purpose of the leaves of a plant?* (to trap energy from sunlight to make food for the plant)
- For each plant part, have students suggest examples that they are familiar with, such as:
  - roots: carrots, grass roots, tree roots under a cliff overhang
  - stems: tree trunks and branches, celery stalks, flower stalks
  - leaves: grass, oak and maple leaves, pine and spruce needles
  - flowers: tulips, apple blossoms, roses
  - seeds: peach pits, sunflower seeds, cucumber seeds
- Discuss with students how the parts of plants may look different in different types of plants and may even have different features, but they perform the same functions in all types of plants.

**Time**

40–80 min

**Learning Context**

inquiry

**Level of Inquiry**

structured

**Skills**

- classifying
- observing
- comparing

**Grouping**

pairs

**Materials and Equipment**

(per pair)

- indoor plant with roots, leaves, and flowers (e.g., carnation)
- newspaper
- magnifying lens
- carrot with a stem
- branch of a tree (optional)
- stalk of a rose bush or other shrub (optional)
- stem of a flower with root attached (optional)

**Line Masters**

- LM 1-6

## Work On It

### Purpose

To have students identify the parts of plants

### Activity Notes

- Have students examine the indoor plant and compare it to the diagram of plant parts on page 8 of the student book. Ask, *What do the leaves of these plants look like? What do the stems of these plants look like?* Through discussion, students should note that they can see the stem and leaves, and the roots (or the roots may be hidden in the soil). Depending on the type of indoor plant, students will note flowers or the lack of flowers. If the plant does not have flowers, ensure you explain to students that at one point the plant had, or will have, flowers.
- Encourage students to observe the plant carefully and to draw and label the different parts of the plant as accurately as possible. Provide copies of LM 1-6 Plant Parts for students to record their drawings.
- Have students examine the carrot and compare it to the diagram of plant parts on page 8. Ask, *What do the leaves of these plants look like? What do the stems of these plants look like?* Through discussion, students should note that the part of the carrot they eat is the root of a carrot plant.
- Encourage students to observe the carrot carefully and to draw and label the different parts of the carrot as accurately as possible on their copy of LM 1-6 Plant Parts.

## Additional Activity

Students can bring to class a variety of pictures that show different parts of plants. The pictures can be organized into displays for each plant part.

## Communicate

1. Students should suggest that plants have similar parts, such as seeds, leaves, roots, and a stem.
2. Students' answers may vary but could include visual differences among plant parts, such as the size and shape of leaves and the size and number of roots (e.g., the carrot has one big thick root and the indoor plant has several thin roots).
3. Roots – Roots hold the plant in the ground. They absorb water and nutrients. Some roots can store food for the plant.

   Stem – The stem holds the plant up. It carries water and nutrients from the roots to the leaves. Sometimes stems can store food.

   Leaves – The chlorophyll in leaves can trap energy from sunlight to make food for the plant.

   Flowers – Flowers contain parts to produce seeds.

   Seeds – New plants grow from seeds.
4. Students' answers may vary but could include that leaves bud on trees in the spring, are present in the summer, may turn colour and fall off in the fall, and may not be present on trees in the winter.

## DI Differentiating Instruction

### *For EAL/ELL*

EAL/ELL language learners require direct instruction of new vocabulary. Provide students with practice in pronouncing the words introduced in the lesson. Tie the new vocabulary to prior learning and use visuals to reinforce the meaning of each new word. Create a word wall to help expose EAL/ELL students to the new vocabulary on a continuous basis.

### *For Reteaching*

Draw a diagram of the parts of a sunflower plant on chart paper and write captions for each part on cards. Students can use string and glue or tape to attach each card to the corresponding part of the sunflower.

### *For Enrichment*

Students can find an interesting plant at home or on the school grounds and sketch a diagram of this plant. Using their knowledge of plant parts, students could then label the plant parts on their diagram.

## Assessment *for* Learning

| What to Look for in Student Work | What to Do |
| --- | --- |
| Students can identify the parts of a plant. | • Observe students as they complete the Work On It activity.<br>• Check students' responses to Communicate questions 1 and 2. |
| Students can identify the purpose of different plant parts. | • Check students' responses to Communicate question 3. |
| Students can draw and identify plant parts. | • Observe students as they complete the Work On It activity and check their drawings.<br>• Check students' responses to Communicate question 4. |

# 3 Exploring Plant Parts

Page 10

| Time |
|---|
| 80 min |
| **Line Masters** |
| • LM 1-7<br>• LM 1-8 |

## Indicator Assessment Chart

| Indicator | Assessment Opportunities |
|---|---|
| **PL3.1 b.** Observe and explain the function of the major structures (i.e., root, stem, flower, leaf, and fruit or seed) of a variety of plants. | • Work On It, p. 10<br>• Communicate, p. 11, q. 1, 2, 4 |
| **PL3.1 l.** Explain the importance of water and light for plant growth and the mechanisms by which plants obtain water and light from the environment. | • Communicate, p. 11, q. 1, 2, 3, 4 |

## Lesson Goal

To explore the parts of plants and what they do

### Background Information

The stem of a plant has two main functions. It contains a transport system for moving materials between the roots and the leaves. Maple syrup is produced from the sap of the maple tree moving between the roots and the leaves in the early spring. The transport system is composed of many tiny tubes through which liquid materials move. The stem in many plants also provides the plant with support. This is especially evident in trees, where the stem is woody and permits trees to grow to great heights.

## Curriculum Connections

In this lesson, students have the opportunity to develop skills and concepts in these areas:

***English Language Arts***

CR3.4 f. Follow simple written multi-step instructions (e.g., how to assemble a product or play a board game) and functional and instructional messages in the environment (e.g., instructions, menus, invitations, announcements).

## Misconceptions

A celery stalk is often mistakenly referred to and misidentified as a stem. A celery stalk is a leaf part, and "stalk" is short for "leafstalk." If you remove all of the stalks from a bunch of celery, a stem will remain.

## Get Started ▶

- Review with students what they learned about the parts of plants in Lesson 2, and the role that each part plays in the survival of plants. Invite students to share examples of plants they are familiar with and what the parts of these plants look like. Ask them some of the following questions:
  - *Why do plants need to produce seeds?*
  - *Do all plant seeds look the same?*
  - *How do the leaves of plants help the plant survive?*
  - *Why is the stem of the plant important?*
- Have students examine the photograph of seeds, flowers, and roots on page 10 of the student book. Invite them to identify the different plant parts and how each part helps all plants survive. You may want to ask students if all leaves (or roots or flowers) shown are the same, and in what ways the plant parts shown are similar or different to the ones they are familiar with or have seen around the school.

!

The trunk of a tree can tell you a lot about the tree, including the tree's age. The cut end of a tree trunk (stem) reveals a pattern of rings known as growth rings. One light-coloured ring and one dark-coloured ring indicate one year of growth. In the spring and early summer, trees grow very fast and create a light-coloured ring. During late summer and fall, trees begin to grow slowly and create a dark-coloured ring. So if you start at the middle of the trunk, the oldest part of the tree, and count the pairs of rings outward, you can determine the age of the tree.

**Time**

80 min

**Learning Context**

inquiry

**Level of Inquiry**

structured

**Skills**

- inferring
- observing
- comparing
- classifying

**Grouping**

pairs

**Materials and Equipment**

- celery stalk with leaves
- clear container
- water
- red food colouring
- spoon
- table knife
- marker
- magnifying lens
- pencils

**Line Masters**

- LM 1-7

## Work On It

### Purpose

To explore the importance and functions of plant parts

### Activity Notes

- Show the class a celery stalk complete with leaves. Point out where the root was cut off from the bottom of the plant. Ask the class how many of them have ever eaten celery and how they usually eat it.
- Explain to the class that they will be conducting an investigation to observe and learn more about the parts of plants. Students should be reminded to follow the instructions in the student book carefully.
- Ensure students are careful when mixing the water and food colouring, and when marking the level of the water in the container. When they return to observe the plant on subsequent days, be sure their records include the changes to the celery and the water level in the container. Encourage students to make careful observations and record them in detail on LM 1-7 Exploring Plant Parts.
- Students may need some assistance in using the magnifying lenses appropriately to get detailed observations of the plant parts. You may need to demonstrate how to hold the magnifier close to the plant and then slowly move it away until the object is enlarged and in focus.

**SAFETY CAUTION!**
Ask your teacher to help you cut the celery with the knife.

- You may wish to have students work in pairs or individually to conduct the investigation. After 24 hours, students should easily be able to see the food colouring in the cut celery stalk. The dots of food colouring that they observe are the tubes used by the stalk to transport water and nutrients to the leaves of the plant. The stalk is the stem of the celery leaf and all stems have structures that perform this function.

## Communicate

1. Students should be able to identify the following plant parts and reasons why the parts are important:
   - stem: transports material from the roots to the leaves and gives structure to the plant
   - leaves: catch the light from the Sun to help the plant grow
2. Students should describe how the coloured water could be seen in the small tubes in the celery stalk.
3. Students should observe that the water level in the container dropped.
4. Students should explain that water travels up the stem of a plant. The evidence they have for this is that the coloured water went up the stalk (the stem of the celery leaf) and changed the colour of the leaves.

## DI Differentiating Instruction

### *For EAL/ELL*

Pair EAL/ELL students with students fluent in speaking and reading English. Encourage these students to read the step-by-step instructions aloud for their EAL/ELL partners and to follow the text with their finger so their partner can associate the spoken word to the written word.

### *For Reteaching*

Students who have difficulty understanding the function of the stem as a transport system can use a white carnation and coloured water to further observe the function of the stem. Provide LM 1-8 Coloured Flowers, which details step-by-step instructions for students to conduct the activity.

### *For Enrichment*

Students may enjoy researching how sap from maple trees is collected and made into maple syrup. Sap, which is tapped from the stem of trees, runs between the roots and the leaves in the spring. Students can find out why the trees are tapped in the spring and what the sap does for trees.

## Assessment *for* Learning

| What to Look for in Student Work | What to Do |
|---|---|
| Students can examine and identify the function of a celery stalk. | • Observe students during the Work On It activity.<br>• Check students' responses to Communicate questions 1 to 3. |
| Students can explain how a plant obtains water. | • Observe students during the Work On It activity.<br>• Check students' responses to Communicate question 4. |

# 4 How Do Plants Grow?

Page 12

**Time**

40–80 min, then daily short observations

**Line Masters**

- LM 1-9
- LM 1-10

## Indicator Assessment Chart

| Indicator | Assessment Opportunities |
|---|---|
| **PL3.1 a.** Pose questions related to plant growth (e.g., How do very young plants look different from grown plants? How much water do plants need to grow? Do all plants grow in the same way?). | • Communicate, p. 13, q. 3 |
| **PL3.1 e.** Observe and represent, using written language, pictures, and charts, changes that occur through the life cycle of a flowering plant. | • Work On It, p. 12 |
| **PL3.1 h.** Predict and investigate conditions such as the temperature, available sunlight, available nutrients in soil, and available water, which are necessary for plant germination and growth. | • Work On It, p. 12 |
| **PL3.1 i.** Care for a flowering plant throughout its life cycle, tracking its growth and changes. | • Work On It, p. 12<br>• Build On What You Know, p. 13 |
| **PL3.1 j.** Estimate, record, and display relevant measurements of plant growth, using rulers, tables, and bar graphs. | • Build On What You Know, p. 13 |
| **PL3.1 k.** Suggest explanations for patterns and discrepancies in the growth rate of similar plants grown in varying conditions. | • Communicate, p. 13, q. 1 |
| **PL3.1 l.** Explain the importance of water and light for plant growth and the mechanisms by which plants obtain water and light from the environment. | • Communicate, p. 13, q. 2 |
| **PL3.1 n.** Pose new questions about conditions necessary for plant growth, based on what was learned. | • Communicate, p. 13, q. 3 |

## Lesson Goal

To find out what a seed needs to begin to grow

## Background Information

Seeds like a dandelion seed germinate in the spring, grow into a flower, and produce a seed head that releases seeds that are carried by the wind to start new plants. All seeds follow a similar pattern, although the time between germination and the production of new seeds varies from plant to plant.

Seeds can begin germination as soon as they find suitable conditions, or they can remain dormant until the necessary conditions for growth are evident. Seeds require appropriate temperature and moisture to germinate. Seeds have three basic parts. They have a seed coating that protects a baby plant inside them. They also have a food supply inside them that provides energy for the baby plant to grow.

## Curriculum Connections

In this lesson, students have the opportunity to develop skills and concepts in these areas:

### *Mathematics*

SP3.1 e. Answer questions related to the data presented in a bar graph or line plots.

### *English Language Arts*

CR3.4 f. Follow simple written multi-step instructions (e.g., how to assemble a product or play a board game) and functional and instructional messages in the environment (e.g., instructions, menus, invitations, announcements).

## Get Started ▶

- Give each pair of students a small amount of bird feed made up of several different types of seeds. Ask students what the feed is used for and how many different types of plants they think they are looking at. Students should be able to sort the bird feed into the different types of seeds and suggest the number of different plants that are represented in their bird feed.
- Ask students what bird feed could be used for other than feeding birds. You may need to remind them that the seeds could all be planted and they would eventually grow into plants.
- Have students look at the seeds in the photograph on page 12 of the student book and invite them to identify any that they recognize. Some students may be able to pick out peanut or pumpkin seeds, and the maple key. Have them describe the plants or the products that these seeds eventually produce (e.g., peanut plant, pumpkins, and a maple tree). Ask students how they think a small seed, such as a pumpkin seed, can produce such a large fruit, or how an acorn can produce something as big and strong as an oak tree.
- The seeds shown in the photograph (from left to right, in rows) are: peanuts, peas, lettuce, corn, beet, black locust, pine, linden, carrot, hazelnut, pumpkin, radish, and maple.

First Nations and Métis peoples have different words for different trees. There are general terms and specific terms, and the words as well as meaning of the words vary among different groups. For example, the Woodland Cree word for tree is *mistik*, and the Plains Cree word for tree is *mitos*.

**Time**

40–80 min, then short daily observations

**Learning Context**

inquiry

**Level of Inquiry**

guided

**Skills**

- observing
- hypothesizing
- interpreting
- comparing

**Grouping**

pairs/individuals

**Materials and Equipment**

- 4 bean seeds soaked in water overnight
- paper towels
- water
- 4 resealable plastic bags
- labels and marker
- camera (optional)
- bird feed (optional)
- class or students' KWL charts
- pencils
- 3–4 extra bean seeds (optional)
- polystyrene foam cup (optional)
- soil (optional)

Note: Soya and black eye beans germinate quickly. They can be purchased from a health food store.

**Line Masters**

- LM 1-9

## Work On It

### Purpose

To have students investigate what seeds need to grow

### Activity Notes

- Ask the class if any of them have ever seen a seed start to sprout. Some students may have eaten sprouts from different plants, such as beans, onions, or radishes. These sprouts are seeds that have a relatively short life cycle and have started to grow. Plants like trees have a much longer life cycle and the seeds of these plants germinate and "sprout" or grow over a much longer time.
- Have students observe the soaked bean seeds and provide them with an extra seed so they can carefully open it up to see the seed coat, baby plant, and food supply. Remind them of the purpose of these three parts of the seed: the seed coat protects a baby plant, and the food supply provides energy for the baby plant to start growing.
- As students prepare to set up their seed for observation of the germination, you should make sure of the following:
  - The paper towels should be damp but not soaking wet (this can be done by soaking the paper towel and then squeezing it out). The paper towel can be kept damp by pouring small amounts of water in the bag and letting the paper towel soak it up.
  - Students should choose several seeds since some may mould.
  - The seeds should placed midway between the top and bottom of the bag to allow students to observe the emergence of both the roots and the stem.
  - The seeds should not be placed in direct sunlight (in most cases the germinating seeds can be left on the students' desks).
  - Students draw a diagram of the seed at the beginning of the investigation and then on each of the next five days. Warn students that they may not notice a change every day.
  - Alternatively, students can use a camera to take pictures of their seed over the five days to create a visual record of the changes taking place.
  - You may also wish to begin germinating extra bean seeds (3 or 4 per student) for use in further lessons.
- Provide copies of LM 1-9 How Do Plants Grow? for students to record their observations.

## Communicate

1. Students can expect to find that the seed in the warm place with low light (e.g., not in direct sunlight) grew the best. The seed in the warm place with bright light may not have grown as well because it became too hot. The seed in the warm place with no light may have sprouted also. The seed in the cold place with no light may not have sprouted because it did not have enough warmth.
2. Students should identify warmth and water as necessary for germination.
3. Students' answers will vary. Students should understand that seeds do not need soil to germinate because they have a food supply inside the seed. Once this food supply is exhausted, seeds need to obtain nutrients and moisture from soil.

### BUILD ON WHAT YOU KNOW

Poke holes in the bottom of polystyrene foam cups, one for each student. Students will then plant one of their sprouted bean seeds in the cup and care for the plant for the remainder of the unit. Have students also plant three or four other bean seeds for use in further lessons. Instruct students to use the table on LM 1-10 How My Plant Is Growing to record the date and height of their plant every two days for two weeks. Students can then plot and display these data in a bar graph on LM 1-10. You may also wish to have students take photographs of their bean plants every two days and use their photos to create a display of their plants' growth after two weeks.

## DI Differentiating Instruction

### *For EAL/ELL*

Use a cooperative learning strategy and have EAL/ELL students work alongside students proficient in reading and writing English to allow students to share and discuss key concepts.

### *For Reteaching*

If students have difficulty obtaining or interpreting results, you may wish to repeat the activity as a demonstration and note observations and conclusions with the whole class.

### *For Enrichment*

Encourage students to ask questions about the germinating seeds, and have them suggest investigations to answer some of their questions. Possible student questions to investigate include:

- Do all seeds germinate the same way?
- Will the root of a plant always go down?
- Will the stem of the plant always go up?
- How important is the Sun for seed germination?

## Assessment *for* Learning

| What to Look for in Student Work | What to Do |
|---|---|
| Students can explain the importance of water and light for plant growth. | • Observe students during the Work On It activity.<br>• Check students' responses to Communicate questions 1, 2, and 3. |
| Students can follow step-by-step instructions to carry out an inquiry. | • Observe students complete the Work On It activity. |
| Students can care for a flowering plant. | • Observe students as they work on the Build On What You Know activity. |
| Students can record and display measurements of plant growth in a table and bar graph. | • Check students' completed work from the Build On What You Know activity. |
| Students can pose new questions about plant growth based on what they have learned. | • Check students' responses to Communicate question 3. |

# 5 Basic Needs

Page 14

| Time |
|---|
| 40 min |

| Line Masters |
|---|
| • LM 1-11 |

## Indicator Assessment Chart

| Indicator | Assessment Opportunities |
|---|---|
| **PL3.1 f.** Compare the basic needs of plants to the basic needs of animals and humans. | • Work On It, p. 15<br>• Communicate p. 15, q. 1, 2, 3 |
| **PL3.1 n.** Pose new questions about conditions necessary for plant growth, based on what was learned. | • Communicate, p. 15, q. 4 |

## Lesson Goal

To compare the needs of plants and animals

## Background Information

Plants and animals are living things. All living things need energy and water to grow and change. Non-living things do not grow, so they do not need energy. Plants and animals also need space in which to grow, as well as shelter from harsh conditions and other living things around them so they can reproduce. Plants are different from animals in that they produce their own food energy and do not move around, while animals eat plants or other animals to get their food energy and are able to freely move from one location to another.

traditional ***KNOWLEDGE***

Many scientists are dismissive of the concept of Spirit. Spirit is intangible, and therefore cannot be understood with the senses, quantified, or studied. However, for many First Nations and Métis people, Spirit, or the spirit of Creator, is very real and it permeates all living things. As teachers, we need to be sensitive to this belief and to respect it as a valid way of knowing the created world for First Nations and Métis people as well as other beliefs that students may bring to the classroom from other cultures. Teachers need to be fully open to this First Nations and Métis perspective, so that all students may appreciate how profoundly the belief in Spirit influences First Nations and Métis cultures.

For many First Nations and Métis people, many things that scientists consider non-living have Spirit and, thus, are considered living. For example, fire, rock, air, and water all have Spirit. Some Elders consider these elements, which can give life and take life, to be imbued with a living energy. Thus, teachers must be aware that some students in their classroom may have a distinctly different worldview regarding fire, rock, air, and water than the one espoused by our Eurocentric society.

*continued* →

Many First Nations and Métis people also believe that plants and animals possess Spirit, and they give thanks to this Spirit after a harvest or hunt. The stories of many First Nations and Métis peoples reflect this belief. Many Plains groups, for example, tell the story of a great sacrifice at the beginning of time. As Creator fashioned the fish, insects, birds, and animals, many animal spirits, such as the buffalo and the elk, gave up their lives to clothe, shelter, and feed people.

Elders often finish their prayers with the expression "all my relations." This simple phrase describes the relationship of many First Nations and Métis people to all living things. It acknowledges the humble existence of humans and how we rely on the land and everything on it for survival.

## Curriculum Connections

In this lesson, students have the opportunity to develop skills and concepts in these areas:

### *English Language Arts*

CR3.2 a. Determine main ideas in visual and multimedia texts including safe websites designed for children (including First Nations and Métis resources).
CR3.2 b. Select and use appropriate strategies (before, during, and after) to construct and confirm meaning when viewing.

## Get Started ▶

- Ask the class to consider what plants and animals need to survive. Ask, *Does anyone have a pet or a garden at home? What types of things does your pet (garden) need to survive? How does your family provide for the pet? Do all pets need the same things? How is the garden cared for so the plants can grow? Are there any plants inside your home? Do they need different things from plants in a garden?*
- Have the class look at the illustrations of the plants and animals on page 14 of the student book. Ask them what the different animals and plants need to survive and how they get these things. As the class discusses the different needs of plants and animals, pose some of the following questions to stimulate students' thinking:
  - *How are the needs of plants and animals similar? How are they different?*
  - *How does a poplar tree get what it needs to grow? Is this similar to how animals get what they need to grow?*
  - *How does a polar bear get what it needs to survive?*
  - *How are the basic needs of a poplar tree and a polar bear similar? How are they different?*

| Time |
| --- |
| 40 min |
| **Learning Context** |
| inquiry |
| **Level of Inquiry** |
| structured |
| **Skills** |
| • classifying<br>• comparing<br>• inferring |
| **Grouping** |
| pairs |
| **Materials and Equipment** |
| • pencils<br>• class or students' KWL chart(s) |
| **Line Masters** |
| • LM 1-11 |

## Work On It

### Purpose

To provide an opportunity for students to compare the basic needs of plants and animals

### Activity Notes

- Distribute copies of LM 1-11 Basic Needs for students to record their work for steps 1, 2, and 3 of the Work On It.
- While students consider what plants and animals need to survive, remind them that they should be considering what is absolutely essential and not what they would like to have. Ask, *What could you not live without? Do you absolutely need a television, or is it just something that you want to have?*
- Record students' ideas and suggestions on chart paper or the board. If students are unfamiliar with Venn diagrams, draw an example on the board and explain how they can record information for plants and animals individually and together in the circles.
- Encourage student partners to share the tasks of suggesting ideas and recording the information.
- As students discuss and complete their Venn diagrams, you will have an opportunity to gauge how well they understand the basic needs of living things. For those experiencing difficulty understanding these basic needs, provide support by asking questions, such as:
  - *What happens to a plant when it does not rain?*
  - *Why do most plants in Saskatchewan not grow in the winter?*
  - *How do people make sure the plants they have in their gardens continue to stay healthy?*
  - *Why do you eat lunch and dinner?*
  - *What would happen to a kitten if it did not eat anything?*
- Students should conclude that both plants and animals need energy (e.g., plants get energy from sunlight and animals get energy from food) water, shelter, and space to survive. Help students to understand that similar groups of plants and animals are found living together in different places because they depend on each other to survive. For example, some animals eat plants, and some plants depend on animals or insects to help them reproduce.

## Communicate

1. Students should understand that plants, like animals, need air, water, and nutrients to survive. Some students may also suggest that plants need space to grow and other living things so they can reproduce.
2. Students should recognize that plants and animals both need air, water, and food (nutrients) to survive.
3. Students' answers will vary but could include examples such as cows eat grass and squirrels eat nuts.
4. Students' answers will vary but could include questions such as: Can plants and animals help each other survive? Can plants survive without animals?

## BUILD ON WHAT YOU KNOW

As students continue to care for their bean plants, they will discover that the plants and the garden that they will create have many needs. Encourage students to think about how they will ensure that their garden provides all of the basic needs of plants. Students may suggest ideas, such as locating the garden near a water source, having a water hose nearby, locating the garden in a tree-less area to provide ample sunlight, and providing compost to add nutrients to the soil.

## DI Differentiating Instruction

### *For EAL/ELL*

Have EAL/ELL students identify plant and animal needs shown in the illustration on page 14 of the student book. Write the needs they identify on small cards or sticky notes for students to place on the illustration to associate words with the images.

### *For Reteaching*

Have students complete a class Venn diagram to compare the needs of animals and plants, but this time use pictures from magazines, newspapers, and so on. Create a large Venn diagram to compare the needs of animals and plants, post it in the classroom, and encourage students to find visual examples to complete it.

## Assessment *for* Learning

| What to Look for in Student Work | What to Do |
| --- | --- |
| Students can compare the basic needs of plants and animals. | • Observe students during the Work On It activity.<br>• Check students' responses to Communicate question 2. |
| Students can identify the needs of plants and animals. | • Check student responses to Communicate questions 1, 2, and 3. |
| Students can pose new questions about the needs of plants based on what was learned. | • Check students' responses to Communicate question 4. |

# 6 Helping Plants Get Water

Page 16

| Time |
| --- |
| 40 min |
| **Line Masters** |
| • LM 1-12<br>• LM 1-13 |

## Indicator Assessment Chart

| Indicator | Assessment Opportunities |
| --- | --- |
| **PL3.1 a.** Pose new questions related to plant growth (e.g., How do very young plants look different from grown plants? How much water do plants need to grow? Do all plants grow in the same way?). | • Communicate, p. 17, q. 3 |
| **PL3.1 b.** Observe and explain the function of the major structures (i.e., root, stem, flower, leaf, and fruit or seed) of a variety of plants. | • Work On It, p. 16<br>• Communicate, p. 17, q. 2 |
| **PL3.1 h.** Predict and investigate conditions such as the temperature, available sunlight, available nutrients in soil, and available water, which are necessary for plant germination and growth. | • Work On It, p. 16 |
| **PL3.1 j.** Estimate, record, and display relevant measurements of plant growth, using rulers, tables, and bar graphs. | • Work On It, p. 16 |
| **PL3.1 k.** Suggest explanations for patterns and discrepancies in the growth rate of similar plants grown in varying conditions. | • Communicate, p. 17, q. 1, 2 |
| **PL3.1 l.** Explain the importance of water and light for plant growth and the mechanisms by which plants obtain water and light from the environment. | • Communicate, p. 17, q. 2 |
| **PL3.1 n.** Pose new questions about conditions necessary for plant growth, based on what was learned. | • Communicate, p. 17, q. 3 |

## Lesson Goal

To explore how plants need water

### Background Information

Plants have adapted to a variety of different locations and environmental conditions all over the world. However, while plants may have adaptations that allow them to survive in very harsh conditions, they all have the same basic needs—air, sunlight, water, space, minerals, and nutrients. Seeds require appropriate temperature and moisture to germinate. Once embryonic plants have consumed the food supply inside the seed coat, they start to grow and have the same basic needs as a mature plant. Plants require water, but too much water may drown them and harm their growth.

## Curriculum Connections

In this lesson, students have the opportunity to develop skills and concepts in these areas:

### *English Language Arts*

CR3.4 b. Select and use appropriate strategies (before/during/and after) to construct and confirm meaning when reading.
CR3.4 f. Follow simple written multi-step instructions (e.g., how to assemble a product or play a board game) and functional and instructional messages in the environment (e.g., instructions, menus, invitations, announcements).
CC3.1 d. Communicate ideas, findings, and information pertaining to topics, problems, questions, or issues by creating easy-to-follow visual, oral, and written formats with a clear purpose (e.g., short report, explanation of a procedure).
CC3.2 a. Demonstrate understanding of the topic, problem, question, or issue in a variety of ways (e.g., dance pieces, visual representations, drama in context, diagram, demonstration, chart).

## Focus on Literacy

### *Before Writing: Planning to Write an Explanation*

Introduce the activity by saying, *Writers need to make a few decisions before they begin writing. They need to know what their purpose is, and they need to identify the audience who they are writing for. We know that the audience of this lesson is us, a grade 3 class.* Ask students to identify some things that the writer included on page 16 of the student book for grade 3 readers (e.g., a picture, words at our level, not too many unfamiliar words, just a few paragraphs of information).

Tell students, *The title and goal of this lesson tells us the writer's purpose—to explain how plants get water.* Ask students to think about how they would explain something familiar to a classmate, such as how to make a peanut butter and jelly sandwich or how to wrap a present. Have students share their thinking and record their ideas (e.g., draw a picture and label it, give step-by-step instructions) on the board or chart paper. Then ask students to use the ideas on the chart to plan how they would rewrite this lesson.

### *During Writing: Writing an Explanation*

Have students work with a partner to write an explanation of how plants get water. Remind students to consider that the purpose of an explanation is to explain how something works and that their explanation could include:

- a variety of text types, pictures, captions, step-by-step instructions
- a description of the part of the process
- any other interesting features they think will help the reader understand the information

## Misconceptions

Some students may think that if the leaves of a plant start to turn yellow, it means that the plant is not getting enough water. However, when there is too much water on the roots of plants, their leaves sometimes turn yellow.

## Get Started ▶

- As a class, examine the bean plants that have been growing in the classroom. Have students identify reasons why these plants are growing successfully in the classroom (e.g., conditions that meet the basic needs of the plants). Ask questions such as the following:
  - *Why are our bean plants growing?*
  - *What part have you played in the successful growth of these plants?*
  - *What would happen if we took away some of the water (or light, or nutrients) that the plants are receiving?*
- Invite students to examine the photo of the roots of a plant shown on page 16 of the student book. Discuss and review with them the role that roots play in the survival of a plant.

**Time**

40 min

**Learning Context**

inquiry

**Level of Inquiry**

structured

**Skills**

- inferring
- observing
- interpreting
- experimenting
- comparing
- predicting

**Grouping**

pairs

**Materials and Equipment**

(per group)
- 2 bean plants
- water
- watering device
- camera (optional)
- marker
- pencils
- class or students' KWL charts

**Line Masters**

- LM 1-12

## Work On It

### Purpose

To provide an opportunity for students to investigate and compare a plant that receives water and a plant that does not

### Activity Notes

- Have students use the extra bean plants planted earlier in the unit for this investigation as one of the plants will wither and die.
- Provide copies of LM 1-12 Helping Plants Get Water for students to use to record their predictions and observations.
- Review the steps in What You Will Do with students before they begin and clarify any misconceptions students might have. Observe them as they work to ensure they are following the directions and working together cooperatively.
- As students observe the plants over the next two weeks and record their observations in drawings, encourage them to include as much detail as possible of what the two plants look like. Students could also colour their drawings to show the changes taking place. You may also wish to have students take photos or videos to record their observations. If students shoot videos, encourage one partner to film while the other describes and points out their observations in front of the camera.

## Additional Activity

Students can use their knowledge of plants' basic needs and how these needs can be met to design and build a watering device to help people care for and grow healthy plants. Provide LM 1-13 Design a Watering Device and instruct students to work with a partner to design a watering device using a collection of a variety of items. This open inquiry will allow students to develop procedures and create conclusions based on evidence they compile. Encourage students to follow the steps on the line master, design and sketch their ideas, and decide what materials they need to build their device.

!

The rainforests on Canada's west coast have access to plenty of water, but in the summer the weather is notably drier. However, the west coast gets lots of fog in the summer, and the plants in the rainforests can absorb the moisture in the fog through their leaves. The trees are so efficient at trapping moisture that fog can provide them with three-quarters of all the water they need. Fog is an important source of water in many ecosystems. Fog allows plants to stay hydrated even during droughts. Fog may condense and drop to the soil where plants roots can take it up.

## Communicate

1. Students' answers will vary based on their predictions. Students' descriptions of what happened should include that the unwatered plant began to wilt and die and that the plant they watered continuously survived (as long as students did not overwater it). Some students might have noticed that the colour of the watered plant's leaves began to turn yellow, which may indicate overwatering.
2. Water is important to plants because they cannot survive or grow without it.
3. Students' answers may vary but could include that when plants do not get water they do not grow and they die, or that when plants cannot meet one of their basic needs they cannot survive. New questions may include: What would happen if plants could not get any nutrients from the soil or got some water but not enough?

### BUILD ON WHAT YOU KNOW

Students should have discovered that their garden will require a consistent supply of water. Discuss with students what they think would happen if they overwater their garden. Some students might have experienced this throughout this lesson. Encourage students to brainstorm ideas about how often they will water their garden and record them in their notebooks.

## DI Differentiating Instruction

### *For Reteaching*

Students can use a magnifying lens to closely observe any changes in the structure or colour of both plants. Discuss with students the changes they are observing with a magnifying lens as compared to the changes they saw with the naked eye and how these changes may relate to the amount of water each plant is receiving.

### *For Enrichment*

Students can measure and record the number of millilitres of water that they give the plant they are watering. Keeping track of the specific amounts will provide students with an accurate account of how much water their bean plant needs for survival. It will also allow students to adjust the amount water if the plant shows signs of receiving too much water (e.g., yellowish leaves, soggy soil).

## Assessment *for* Learning

| What to Look for in Student Work | What to Do |
|---|---|
| Students can predict and investigate conditions necessary for plant growth. | • Observe students during the Work On It activity. |
| Students can record and display relevant measurements of plant growth. | • Observe students during the Work On It activity. |
| Students can suggest explanations for patterns and discrepancies in the growth of plants grown in varying conditions. | • Check students' responses to Communicate questions 1 and 2. |
| Students can explain the importance of water to plants. | • Check students' responses to Communicate question 2. |
| Students can pose new questions related to plant growth and based on what was learned. | • Check students' responses to Communicate question 3. |

# 7 Life Cycles



**Time**

40–80 min

**Vocabulary**

- life cycle

**Line Masters**

- LM 1-14
- LM 1-15

## Indicator Assessment Chart

| Indicator | Assessment Opportunities |
| --- | --- |
| **PL3.1 e.** Observe and represent, using written language, pictures, and charts, changes that occur through the life cycle of a flowering plant. | • Work On It, p. 19<br>• Communicate, p. 19, q. 2, 3 |
| **PL3.1 m.** Identify characteristics that remain constant and those that change throughout the life cycle of a flowering plant. | • Work On It, p. 19<br>• Communicate, p. 19, q. 1, 2, 3 |
| **PL3.1 n.** Pose new questions about conditions necessary for plant growth, based on what was learned. | • Communicate, p. 19, q. 4 |

## Lesson Goal

To explore the life cycles of plants

### Background Information

All plants have life cycles that lead to the production of new plants. Seeds, rhizomes, or shoots from existing plants, root in suitable material and begin to grow a new plant. This plant will eventually produce a stem, leaves, and flowers to start the cycle over again. Some seeds germinate, grow as a plant, and produce new seeds in a very short time, while others take many years. Plants that start and complete their life cycle in one year germinate in the spring when the soil warms up, then grow to produce leaves and eventually flowers through the summer, and then produce seeds during the late summer or early fall to start the cycle over again the following year. Some plants, such as dandelions, have a faster life cycle. Other plants, such as trees, have life cycles that are much longer.

traditional ***KNOWLEDGE***

All First Nations and Métis peoples of Saskatchewan regard the tree as a symbol of life. Trees provided the Plains people with fuel for fires; wood for shelters; materials for transportation, implements, weapons, and tools; and wood for the framework of many sacred lodges. Many First Nations groups view trees, such as cedar and willow trees, as sacred. Cedar, for example, is shaved or ground up to make a smudge.

Birch was used to fashion canoes and many First Nations groups, such as the Dené and the Cree, adorned their clothing with birchbark that bore skilfully made patterns created by biting. (Please note that although Westerners call birchbark biting, beadwork, moccasin making, and similar cultural works art, many First Nations and Métis people do not consider them art at all. In fact, an equivalent word for *art* does not exist in some First Nations languages, including Cree.

The tree is also a symbol of life among other First Nations in Canada. Among west coast First Nations, trees became a record of their teachings, symbols, and spirituality, since skilled carvers fashioned totem poles from trees. Among eastern Canadian First Nations, a tree of life figures prominently in many creation stories. For example, the Wendat (Huron) believe that the sky people uprooted the tree of life, the sky woman fell to Earth, and all humans originated from the sky woman.

The stages of a tree's life cycle are labelled on the circle graphic that represents a First Nations Medicine Wheel on page 18 of the student book. However, it is important to note that not all First Nations and Métis groups in Saskatchewan accept the concept of a Medicine Wheel as a traditional teaching in their cultures. For example, among the Cree and the Dakota in Saskatchewan, few Knowledge Keepers (if any) teach about the Medicine Wheel. Instead, Cree and Dakota Elders teach about the four directions and have four directions teachings.

Not all Elders teach the concept the Medicine Wheel. This particular teaching has been adopted only recently by First Nations in Canada. Most Elders believe that these teachings originated from the United States in the last century or so. Other Saskatchewan Elders, such as some Saulteaux Elders, have used the Medicine Wheel as a vehicle to encapsulate some of their teachings. As teachers, we need to be careful not to generalize this kind of teaching across all groups. In some instances, ideas that belong in particular quadrants of the Medicine Wheel vary from band to band, reserve to reserve, and perhaps even from Elder to Elder. However, teachers may include the tree as a symbol of life in this lesson in the following ways:

- Lead a class discussion about why First Nations and Métis peoples might choose trees as a symbol of life. Ask, *Why do you think First Nations and Métis people might see trees as a symbol of life? What might be some of the reasons?* Students' answers may include that as a tree's leaves fall off, or die, in the fall and then bud in the spring the tree is "reborn."
- You may also wish to open up the class discussion to include symbols of life from other cultures and the roles trees may play in them. Invite students of other cultures to share their culture's symbols, views, and relevant stories.
- You might have students craft their own symbols of life from other types of plants, such as flowers, wheat, or other items they choose.

## Curriculum Connections

In this lesson, students have the opportunity to develop skills and concepts in these areas:

### *English Language Arts*

CC3.3 a. Use oral language to clarify and extend personal understanding, interact courteously with others (e.g., share ideas and opinions, complete tasks, discuss concerns or problems), and sustain conversations by extending others' contributions.

### *Visual Arts – Drama*

CP3.3 d. Use language purposefully when speaking and writing in role.
CP3.4 b. Work together within dramatic contexts.
CP3.4 f. Demonstrate respect for the contributions of others.

### Get Started ▶

- Discuss with students the changes that they have observed in their bean plants as the plants have been growing. Invite students to share the drawings or photographs they have compiled to record the changes. Ask students if they think all plants go through these changes as they grow.
- Have the class list their birthdays and discuss some of the changes they have undergone so far in their lives. Extend the discussion to include some of the further changes that they will go through as they grow to become adults. Explain to the class that these changes are part of what is called a life cycle, and that all living things undergo changes during their life cycles.
- Read the text on page 18 of the student book with students and stop to interpret the circular visual presented that shows the four stages of the oak tree's life cycle. Discuss with students the idea that a circle is continuous (it has no beginning or end) and that the visual may represent the Circle of Life, which is continuous. Students should understand that there is no true beginning or end to the Circle of Life.
- Have students look at the photographs on page 18 and suggest other plants they are familiar with that undergo similar changes. Encourage students to identify how the oak tree is changing in each stage shown.
- Invite a few students to informally share the progress of their bean seed growth and compare the stages they have observed to the stages shown of the oak tree's life cycle. Ask, *How did your bean seed change from a seed into a seedling? How do you think it will change from a seedling into a plant?*

**traditional KNOWLEDGE**

First Nations and Métis people in Saskatchewan regard the tree as a symbol of life. They believe there are four aspects to a person—emotional, physical, mental, and spiritual—and that these aspects are developed throughout the stages of a person's life. These stages are similar to the stages in the life cycle of a tree. For example, a child is like a seed and develops a person's emotional aspect. A teenager is like a seedling and develops the physical aspect. An adult is like a young tree and develops the mental aspect. An elder is like a mature tree and develops the spiritual aspect.

| Time |
|---|
| 40–80 min |
| **Learning Context** |
| inquiry |
| **Level of Inquiry** |
| confirmation |
| **Skills** |
| • comparing<br>• observing<br>• inferring |
| **Grouping** |
| pairs |
| **Materials and Equipment** |
| • pencils<br>• pumpkin seeds (optional)<br>• magnifying lenses (optional) |
| **Line Masters** |
| • LM 1-14 |

## Work On It

### Purpose

To have students examine and identify the different stages of a pumpkin's life cycle

### Activity Notes

- Read aloud the text on page 19 of the student book. Have students examine and discuss the photographs of a pumpkin's life cycle. Ask questions such as the following:
  - *What are the changes that the pumpkin plant goes through in its life cycle?*
  - *How are those changes similar to the changes the oak tree goes through?*
  - *How is the life cycle of the pumpkin different than the life cycle of the oak tree?*
  - *What reasons can you suggest for the two plants having different life cycles?*
- Students should identify the stages of the pumpkin life cycle as follows: seed, seedling, flowering plant, plant with fruit (and seeds). Students should discover that both pumpkins and oak trees start as seeds and go through a series of stages to become a mature plant that produces seeds. Provide LM 1-14 Life Cycles for students to record their work.
- As students draw the life cycle of a plant that they are familiar with, encourage them to add as much detail as possible, including notes.

## Additional Activity

Provide pumpkin seeds for students to examine with magnifying lenses. Have students draw pictures to record their observations and ask them to describe how pumpkin seeds are similar to and different from the bean seeds they planted. You may also wish to have students follow the step-by-step instructions on LM 1-15 Drying and Roasting Pumpkin Seeds to make a seed treat to eat.

## Communicate

1. Students should recognize that a pumpkin develops green leaves during the seedling stage and that its leaves stay consistent through the flowering plant and plant with fruit stages. The texture of the pumpkin is relatively consistent from the flowering stage to the plant with fruit stage, although the skin gets rougher as the pumpkin enters the latter stages.
2. Changes that occur during a pumpkin's cycle include its colour, which changes from green to orange as it goes from the flowering plant stage to the fruit stage. The size of a pumpkin also changes as it progresses through its life cycle, including the size of its stem, which becomes progressively thicker.
3. Students' answers will vary but skits should include the four stages of a plant's life cycle: seed, seedling, young plant, mature plant. You may wish to develop a common set of criteria for students' skits with the class to use for assessment and student self-assessment.
4. Students' answers will vary but could include: What do a poplar tree's seeds look like? Is the life cycle of a poplar tree as long as the life cycle of an oak tree?

## DI Differentiating Instruction

### *For EAL/ELL*

Provide extra support for EAL/ELL students to compare and contrast the life cycles of a pumpkin and an oak tree. You can assist these students by helping them organize their observations into categories, such as:

- ways that the plants are the same (e.g., Are there stages when both plants look the same? Are there stages that both plants have?)
- ways that the plants are different (e.g., Are there times when one plant looks very different from the other? Are there stages that one plant goes through that the other plant does not?)

### *For Enrichment*

Challenge students to design a structure that will speed up the early spring growth of plants. Show students or describe an example of such a structure, such as a clear glass or plastic structure that can be placed over cold soil to increase the temperature of the soil. Then challenge students to design and build a model of a miniature greenhouse that will provide a stable warm (not too hot or too cold) enclosure for a plant to get an early start at growing in the spring. Have students test their models to see if they can provide a stable warm environment.

## Assessment *for* Learning

| What to Look for in Student Work | What to Do |
|---|---|
| Students can relate characteristics in different types of plants to the plants' environment. | • Observe students during the Work On It activity.<br>• Check students' responses to Communicate questions 1 and 2. |
| Students can observe and represent, using written language, pictures, and charts, changes that occur through the life cycle of a flowering plant. | • Observe students during the Get Started and Work On It activities.<br>• Check students' responses to Communicate questions 2 and 3. |
| Students can identify characteristics that remain constant and those that change throughout the life cycle of a flowering plant. | • Observe students during the Work On It activity.<br>• Check students' responses to Communicate questions 1, 2, and 3. |
| Students can pose new questions about conditions necessary for plant growth, based on what was learned. | • Check students' responses to Communicate question 4. |

# 8 Grouping Plants

Page 20

| Time |
|---|
| 80 min |
| **Line Masters** |
| • LM 1-16 |

## Indicator Assessment Chart

| Indicator | Assessment Opportunities |
|---|---|
| **PL3.1 c.** Relate characteristics such as the number and shape of leaves, flower colour, height, and presence and type of fruit in different types of plants to the plant's environment. | • Work On It, p. 20<br>• Communicate, p. 21, q. 2 |
| **PL3.1 d.** Sort and classify plants and/or seeds according to one or more student-selected attributes. | • Work On It, p. 20<br>• Communicate, p. 21, q. 4 |
| **PL3.1 m.** Identify characteristics that remain constant and those that change throughout the life cycle of a flowering plant. | • Communicate, p. 21, q. 1, 3, 4 |
| **PL3.2 m.** Respond to and acknowledge the ideas of others regarding the importance of plants to self and society. | • Work On It, p. 20<br>• Communicate, p. 21, q. 1 |

## Lesson Goal

To look at and compare characteristics of different plants

## Background Information

Scientists use a number of different features to classify plants, including flower structure, type of bark, root structure, and leaf size, shape, and structure. Leaves can be classified as simple or compound. A simple leaf is one leaf by itself. A compound leaf is several leaves together in a cluster. Leaves can also be classified by shape (oval, triangular, or palmate), or by leaf edge (straight or serrated). While most plants have a consistent leaf structure as they grow, some plants, such as English ivy, have different juvenile and mature leaf forms.

Flowers can be classified as simple or composite. A simple flower has one flower head on a stalk. A composite flower has many different flower heads on a single stalk. Flowers can also be classified as regular and irregular. A regular flower (lily, tulip, trillium) is one that has its parts arranged in a circle (whorl) and is radially symmetrical like the spokes of a bicycle wheel. Each petal is similar in size, shape, and colour. An irregular flower (violet, jack-in-the-pulpit, snapdragon) is not radially symmetrical and its petals are not the same.

traditional **KNOWLEDGE**

The ways that First Nations and Métis people group and classify plants are not necessarily the same as the ways that scientists group and classify plants. First Nations and Métis people often group plants according to where they are found and the survival needs that they help people meet. The Cree people, for example, group plants by survival or dependency on the environment. Plants are grouped according to plants for medicines, land medicines, plants that grow in specific areas, and connectedness in where plants are found (e.g., lake plants).

It is very important in First Nations and Métis cultures not to interfere with nature. When studying plants, for example, it is important to take pictures of tree leaves rather than pulling them off trees. Trees and all plants need to be shown respect, because they contain Spirit just as people do. The belief is that by not picking the leaves, the tree will continue to have life and continue to grow. Taking pictures of fallen leaves rather than removing them for study is also important as fallen leaves decompose and contribute to new life that grows, such as seedlings.

## Curriculum Connections

In this lesson, students have the opportunity to develop skills and concepts in these areas:

***Social Studies***

IN3.1 c. Make inferences about how the culture of the local community is reflected by its customs and celebrations.

***English Language Arts***

CR3.4 f. Follow simple written multi-step instructions (e.g., how to assemble a product or play a board game) and functional and instructional messages in the environment (e.g., instructions, menus, invitations, announcements).

CC3.2 a. Demonstrate understanding of the topic, problem, question, or issue in a variety of ways (e.g., dance pieces, visual representations, drama in context, diagram, demonstration, chart).

## Get Started ▶

- Remind students of the conversation they had earlier about their own life cycle. Explain to them that while they will undergo changes as they grow, there are some features of themselves that will not change. For example, they will always have 10 fingers. Have the class suggest other features that will remain constant as they grow and change.
- Have students read the text on page 20 of the student book and study the photographs. Ask them to suggest other features of plants that might remain constant as they go through their life cycle.

- Once students have some understanding that some features remain constant through a plant's life cycle, ask them if they can think of any way to use these features to group plants into different groups. As they suggest different features and ways to use them, record these on the board and have the class discuss which features would be good for classifying plants. Encourage students to give good reasons to support their choice of features to be used. Features may include leaves, flowers, and/or roots.

!

The white birch (*Betula papyrifera*), a deciduous hardwood tree, was chosen as the official tree of Saskatchewan in 1988. The white birch is a fast-growing tree that is easily recognized by its chalk-white, papery bark.

**Time**

80 min

**Learning Context**

inquiry

**Level of Inquiry**

guided

**Skills**

- observing
- comparing
- classifying
- communicating

**Grouping**

individuals

**Materials and Equipment**

(per group)
- pictures of a variety of leaves (simple – maple, oak, birch; needles – fir, cedar, spruce; compound – honey locust, butternut, hickory)
- pictures of a variety of flowers (simple flowers – tulips, lilies; flower heads – fireweed, mullein; composite flowers – daisies, sunflowers)
- camera (optional)
- glue
- 2 large pieces of paper
- pencils

**Line Masters**

- LM 1-16

## Work On It

### Purpose

To provide an opportunity for students to sort and classify plants according to features that they select

### Activity Notes

- Read the introductory text as a class. Share with students that humans use plants and plant products for many different things, including food, different products, and medicines. Some plants, such as poison ivy, contain chemicals and other things that can make people very uncomfortable and sick. Therefore, scientists need a way to tell plants apart from each other.
- Challenge the class to name different plants they know or have learned about through this unit. Record these plants on the board for all to see. When there are about 10 plants listed, ask students to group the plants in some way. Have several students share the groups they created and explain the criteria they used. When different groupings are suggested, ask students how certain plants could be in two different groups and whether this would confuse people.
- Explain that while scientists use some very sophisticated methods of classifying plants, they also use some basic features to sort plants into groups.
- Have collections of photos of leaves and photos of flowers ready to distribute in the class. You may wish to have students work in small groups or individually, depending on how many samples you have for them to work with. As students sort the leaves, remind them that each leaf should end up in a category based on some feature of the leaf, and that they should be able to describe the leaf in detail. Their description should include words that use the features of the leaf.

| Sorting Leaves |
| --- |
| shape |
| size |
| leaf edge |
| leaves are single or in groups |

- You may wish to hand out LM 1-16 Grouping Plants for students to record their groups.
- Students can repeat the classification with the photos of the flowers. They may find that they need to develop a different set of features.

| Sorting Flowers |
| --- |
| flowers are single or in groups<br>size of flowers<br>number of petals<br>arrangement of petals<br>shape of petals |

- Encourage students to go beyond sorting by colour. Help them to focus on the features of the flowers.
- You may have students go on a scavenger hunt in the schoolyard to take pictures of a variety of leaves and flowers to add to your collection of photos. Remind students of the First Nations and Métis beliefs about not disturbing these plants and being respectful of the life they represent. Students should not collect these leaves or flowers. The flowers and leaves help plants grow and reproduce and, when they fall off, they decompose and contribute to new life that grows in the soil.

## Communicate

1. Students' answers may vary but should include the fact that leaves are good for classifying plants because they are a feature that all plants have. Another reason that students may suggest is that leaves remain constant regardless of the plant's age.
2. Students should suggest that there are several seasons when using leaves to classify plants is difficult. Some of the reasons may include:
   Spring — leaves have not formed yet
   Fall — leaves of some trees change colour and fall off; many plants are finished their life cycle and thus cannot be observed
   Winter — many plants do not have leaves or flowers, so classifying will be difficult
3. Students should suggest that the structures of roots and flowers remain constant on plants whether plants are young or old.
4. Students' answers will vary but could include that flowers could be used to group plants, but they only appear on plants for part of the life cycle. Roots cannot be used because they are in the ground. Thus, they are not easily visible and they may look very similar from plant to plant.

## DI Differentiating Instruction

### *For EAL/ELL*

You can support EAL/ELL students as well as their language and culture by providing pictures of leaves and flowers that are common in their country of origin. Students will feel comfortable working with these plants as they are familiar with them.

### *For Enrichment*

Some students may enjoy the challenge of establishing a photo collection of all the leaves on trees in the local area. They can begin their collection with trees in the schoolyard and then move more into the community surrounding the school. Students can take photos, classify the leaves, and describe the leaves in their own words. They can consult a guide that contains pictures of leaves of trees found in the community to learn the actual names of the trees. Students should respect the trees they are working among.

## Assessment *for* Learning

| What to Look for in Student Work | What to Do |
|---|---|
| Students can relate characteristics, such as the number and shape of leaves, in different types of plants to the plants' environment. | • Check students' responses to Communicate question 2. |
| Students can compare the characteristics of different plants. | • Observe students during the Work On It activity.<br>• Check students' responses to Communicate question 4. |
| Students can sort and classify plants according to one or more student-selected attributes. | • Observe students during the Work On It activity, and check their completed classification tables. |
| Students can identify characteristics that remain constant and those that change throughout the life cycle of a flowering plant | • Check students' responses to Communicate questions 1 and 3. |
| Students can acknowledge the ideas of others regarding the importance of plants to self and society. | • Observe students during the Work On It activity.<br>• Check students' responses to Communicate question 1. |
| Students will understand First Nation and Métis respect for all plants. | • Observe students as they gather information for their table in the schoolyard. |

# Ask … Why is it important to understand plants?

Page 22

| Time |
| --- |
| 40–80 min |
| **Line Masters** |
| • none |

## Indicator Assessment Chart

| Indicator | Assessment Opportunities |
| --- | --- |
| **PL3.2 c.** Examine the significance to some First Nations and Métis people of offering tobacco during harvesting and how that purpose differs from using the tobacco plant for smoking. | • Research, p. 23 |
| **PL3.2 m.** Respond to and acknowledge the ideas of others regarding the importance of plants to self and society. | • Research, p. 23 |
| **PL3.2 n.** Research lifestyles (e.g., farming, fishing, and logging) and jobs (e.g., florist, crop scientist, landscaper, gardener, fruit grower, ecologist, logger, and nursery worker) which depend on understanding and working with plants and plant-related products. | • Research, p. 23 |

## Focus on Literacy

### *Before Reading: Quick Write to Activate Prior Knowledge*

Activating prior knowledge is an important part of the reading process. Good readers continually try to connect to what they already know and have experienced in order to make sense of the text they are reading. Giving students opportunities to activate this prior knowledge helps them construct new meaning and deepen understanding. It also engages students in the task of reading and affirms that they have something to bring to the process of reading as well.

The "quick write" strategy helps students get their ideas down on paper and activate their prior knowledge. Use the lesson title "Why is it important to understand plants?" as a writing prompt. Then, have students complete this quick write exercise in their notebooks according to the following rules:

- Begin and finish writing at the teacher's established signal.
- Write continuously for three minutes.
- Write as fast as you can.
- Do not correct or erase anything.
- Do not lift your pencil from the paper or remove your hands from the computer.
- Do not stop until the stop signal! If you get stuck, jump-start your brain by writing the topic title and extending it into a sentence.

Have students share their quick write, or ideas from it, with a partner. Provide time for students to share with the whole class, and to predict what they will be reading about in this lesson. Draw attention to any careers or jobs that students may have highlighted in their quick writes as a way to introduce this feature in the student book, so that students will start to associate the "Ask" feature with profiles of various careers.

## A Florist

- Read the profile of Cherryl McNair on page 22 of the student book with students. Use the following questions to guide a whole discussion:
  - *What is the role of a florist?*
  - *Based on your knowledge of grouping plants, why do you think Cherryl needs to understand colour and texture?*
  - *Why do you think it's important for a florist to create a visually appealing basket or bouquet?*
- Guide students to record notes about why it is important for a florist to understand plants. Students' notes should address:
  - how Cherryl chooses plants for a basket or bouquet
  - how plants can influence how people feel

## A Farmer

- Read Aaron Rathgeber's profile on page 22 with students. Ask the following questions to guide a whole class discussion:
  - *How do you think Aaron knows when it is a good time to plant his crops?*
  - *How often do you think Aaron needs to check on his crops for wheat midge, or orange bugs? If he does not check his crops, what do you think might happen to the plants?*
  - *If the conditions needed for Aaron's crops to grow are not met, what do you think might happen to his crops?*
- Guide students to record notes about why it is important for a farmer to understand plants. Students' notes should address:
  - how Aaron maintains healthy crops
  - how Aaron needs to be aware of the needs of plants for his crops to survive

traditional **KNOWLEDGE**

## A Cultural Advisor

- It is important to note that Murray Ironchild is an Elder but chooses to use the title of Cultural Advisor. Most Elders are recognized by their community and would not consider adopting this title.
- Profiles like this one present First Nations and Métis people and their culture in positive and hopeful ways. They also help students appreciate a perspective from another culture—in this case, a Cree Elder's point of view. Help students appreciate the profound sense of respect that many First Nations and Métis people, as well as their Elders and other Traditional Knowledge Keepers, have for the land. Elder Ironchild describes the act of offering tobacco for the plants he harvests. You may wish to read the background information about traditional tobacco in First Nations and Métis cultures in Unit 2 of this Teacher's Resource for further information.

- In addition to the various ways that his people, the Cree, have used plants for millennia, Murray Ironchild emphasizes a relationship with the land. Ensure students understand that Cree people see themselves as part of the created order—not set apart as humans are within a biblical perspective. Thus, they have a relationship with all living things. In large part, to honour this relationship, they offer tobacco to thank animals or plants that give up their life to feed people. The Cree believe that it is the willingness of the buffalo spirit, the tree spirit, the sweetgrass spirit, and the deer spirit that allow themselves to be slain or harvested for medicines and food. Some great Cree hunters do not believe that deer fall to their arrows or their bullets due to their skill but rather that the deer spirit in the deer die freely to feed people. This understanding of relationship guides Elders to conclude their prayers with the phrase "all my relations" to signify our relatedness to each other, to animals and plants, to Mother Earth, and to Creator.
- In teaching this profile, observe the following cautions:
  - Medicines are made with sacred plants. These plants need to be harvested in appropriate ways, following centuries old protocols. Students must be taught to pay the same respect to plants and not to pick or uproot plants unnecessarily.
  - Some ceremonies that Murray Ironchild mentions, particularly the sweat lodge, are sacred, and it is inappropriate for anyone apart from Elders, including teachers, to describe what happens in them. Elders ask teachers to respect the sanctity of their ceremonies. The inner workings of a ceremony are revealed to those who really desire to follow a traditional path and are not meant to be an object of curiosity. In fact, Elders never turn anyone away from the sweat lodge door.
- Read the profile of Murray Ironchild with students. Pose the following questions to guide a whole discussion:
  - *Why does Murray leave a gift after picking a plant?*
  - *How do you think Murray has learned about these teachings? Who do you think his teachers are?* (Students should respond with Elders, as Elders are teachers and share their knowledge.)
  - *How do you think Murray's life would be affected if there were not any plants?*
- Guide students to record notes about why it is important for a cultural advisor to understand plants. Students' notes should address:
  - What do plants teach Murray?
  - What do plants provide Murray with?
  - What do plants provide people with?
- Consider inviting a First Nations or Métis Elder or Traditional Knowledge Keeper into your classroom to share his or her knowledge about plants with students. Ensure you follow the "Protocol for contacting Elders and Traditional Knowledge Keepers" in the Program Overview of this Teacher's Resource.

## Research

- Students will gather and synthesize information as they research one of the lifestyles or jobs listed on page 23 of the student book. Students may have to use what they already know about plants to infer how plants are important to these various lifestyles and jobs.
- Suggested websites for student research include the following:
  - National Occupational Classification Profiles: www5.hrsdc.gc.ca/NOC/English/NOC/2006/SearchAlphabetical.aspx
  - Alberta Occupational Profiles: http://alis.alberta.ca/occinfo/Content/RequestAction.asp?format=html&aspAction=GetHomePage&Page=Home
  - Lumberjack: www.absoluteastronomy.com/topics/Lumberjack
  - Landscaper Job Descriptions: www.ehow.com/facts_5162768_landscaper-job-descriptions.html
  - Gardener Job Descriptions: www.ehow.com/about_5378719_gardener-job-description.html
- Students' answers may vary but could include that landscapers have to understand the light and water needs of different plants in order to plan and build gardens. Gardeners need to understand what plants need to grow and what seeds need to sprout.

## Assessment *for* Learning

| What to Look for in Student Work | What to Do |
|---|---|
| Students can examine the significance to some First Nations and Métis people of offering tobacco during harvesting. | • Observe students as they read and discuss the profiles. |
| Students can respond to acknowledge the ideas of others regarding the importance of plants to self and society. | • Observe students as they read and discuss the profiles. |
| Students can research lifestyles and jobs that depend on understanding and working with plants and plant-related products. | • Observe students as they read and discuss the profiles.<br>• Check students' completed research. |

# 9 How Do Animals Help Plants?

Page 24

**Time**

40–80 min

**Vocabulary**

- nectar
- pollen
- stamen
- pistil
- pollination

**Line Masters**

- LM 1-17
- LM 1-18

## Indicator Assessment Chart

| Indicator | Assessment Opportunities |
|---|---|
| **PL3.1 g.** Research ways in which plants rely on animals and abiotic factors (e.g., gravity, wind, and water) to support plant reproduction by dispersing seeds. | • Work On It, p. 25<br>• Communicate p. 25, q. 1, 2, 3 |
| **PL3.2 g.** Describe ways that plants and animals depend on each other. | • Work On It, p. 25<br>• Communicate, p. 25, q. 3 |

## Lesson Goal

To find out how animals help plants

### Background Information

Animals and plants have many ways of helping each other meet their basic needs. Plants provide food for animals, places to live, shelter from the weather, and space to live and grow in. Animals help plants in many ways, but one of the most important ways is helping to distribute seeds. Burrs and other "hitchhikers" that attach to animals are carried away from the parent plant. They eventually drop into soil and wait for the correct growing conditions to germinate. Animals carry other seeds when they eat the fruit of plants. They digest the fruit but not the seeds, which are excreted and can then germinate. Wind carries other seeds, such as milkweed and dandelion. Animals, such as bees and butterflies, pollinate some flowers, which leads to the production of the seeds. The colour and scent of the flowers attract the insects that then fly from one flower to another looking for nectar. In the process, they pollinate the flowers they stop at.

## Curriculum Connections

In this lesson, students have the opportunity to develop skills and concepts in these areas:

### *English Language Arts*

CR3.2 e. Identify design, layout, and other features (e.g., colour, bold typeface, and sounds effects) that help to understand grade-appropriate visual and multimedia texts (including First Nations and Métis resources)
CR3.2 g. View and identify purpose for visual features used.
CR3.4 f. Follow simple written multi-step instructions (e.g., how to assemble a product or play a board game) and functional and instructional messages in the environment (e.g., instructions, menus, invitations, announcements).

### *Visual Arts*

CP3.8 a. Observe visual details, and include details to enhance depictions of animals, people, and objects

## Get Started ▶

- Show the class a jar of honey and ask students what they know about how honey is produced. Most students should know that honey comes from bees and is a product of their collecting nectar from different plants. Honey is an example of a product that animals (e.g., bees and humans) get from plants. Challenge students to name other products that humans and other animals use that come from plants.
- Ask the class if anyone is allergic to pollen and whether they know what pollen is. Have students learn a little more about pollen and why it is important to plants. Invite the class to look at the illustrations on page 24 of the student book to see one way in which animals help plants. Ask, *What would happen if there were no bees around to help pollinate the flowers?* (This actually did occur in some apple orchards in Japan. The government brought in members of the army to pollinate the apple trees by hand.) *Would the plants producing the flowers be able to survive without being pollinated?*
- Before reading the text with students, discuss the purpose of the boldface text used in the illustration captions. Elicit that boldface highlights new vocabulary and that these words are important in understanding the pollination of flowers.
- Ask students what the purpose of the drawings on page 24 is. Discuss with students what these graphic visuals represent and how they help to outline the pollination process step by step, using a combination of illustrations and text.
- Invite students to study the pictures and read the information on pollination of plants by insects. Explain that many flowers are adapted (colour, shape of the flower, scent) to attract different insects that will then fly to other similar plants and pollinate them.

**Time**

40–80 min

**Learning Context**

inquiry

**Level of Inquiry**

structured

**Skills**

- observing
- inferring
- interpreting

**Grouping**

individuals

**Materials and Equipment**

(per group)
- burr or cattail
- magnifying lens
- tweezers
- pencils

**Line Masters**

- LM 1-17

**SAFETY CAUTION!**

Burrs can be sharp. Use tweezers to handle them.

## Work On It

### Purpose

To have students investigate ways that animals help plants

### Activity Notes

- All plants produce seeds to ensure that new plants will grow in the next life cycle. Some plants have seeds that are carried by the wind, and others rely on animals to transport their seeds. Ask students if they have ever walked through a meadow or valley and had burrs stick to their clothing. *How do the burrs attach themselves to clothes? What else would they stick to? Why do they stick to materials?*
- Have students use the magnifying lens to closely observe the burrs or cattails. Encourage them to observe in detail by asking questions such as
  - *What does the surface of the burr (cattail) feel like?*
  - *What are the ends of the small spikes of the burr shaped like?*
  - *How could the shape of the ends of the burr help it stick to an animal's fur?*
- Provide copies of LM 1-17 How Do Animals Help Plants? for students to record their observations. As students open the burr or cattail and draw their diagrams to show what the inside and outside of the burr or cattail look like, encourage them to include as much detail as possible. Have them label the parts they observe, including the seeds. Students' responses to step 5 about how animals help plants that produce burrs or cattails should include helping plants spread seeds to new locations.

## Additional Activity

Students can complete the activity outlined on LM 1-18 How Can Wind and Water Spread Seeds? to discover how these elements can affect the dispersal of seeds. As students predict whether wind or water will best spread particular seeds, encourage them to consider the size and weight of the seeds.

In step 3, students should observe that the lightest seeds, such as the grass seed, are moved or spread by wind (the fan) the most easily. The stronger the wind, the heavier the seed that wind can move and the farther that seeds will travel. In step 4, students should observe that the lighter seeds float on the top of the water. If students leave the seeds in the water for a long period of time, they may notice that some of the seeds become water logged and sink to the bottom of the bucket.

Students should conclude that the lightest seeds are most likely to be spread by wind, because they are small and light. Students should also conclude that any of the seeds could probably be spread by water. The nuts in shells should float best, since air trapped inside the shells helps the nuts to float. The very light seeds will also float until they become water logged and sink.

## Communicate

1. Students should recognize that for pollination to take place, pollen needs to be dispersed and that wind is a force that can carry pollen.
2. Students should recognize that water can disperse seeds as it flows from one area to another. Students might identify that flowing rivers carry floating seeds to other areas.
3. Students' answers may vary but could include dandelion or grass seeds dispersed by wind, different types of nuts dispersed by squirrels, and different types of berry seeds dispersed by birds.

## DI Differentiating Instruction

### *For EAL/ELL*

Support the EAL/ELL student learners' language skills development through the use of scaffolding. Break down the steps of the Work On It activity into simpler one- or two-word instructions. Use visuals to help these students associate written words with pictures of what the words mean.

### *For Reteaching*

Students who have difficulty understanding how animals help plants distribute their seeds may enjoy looking inside different fruits and seeing the seeds that are stored. Each seed is capable of producing a new plant. When animals (humans included) eat the fruit and dispose of the seeds, they are in some ways planting a seed. Students should remember that the seeds will only germinate if the proper growing conditions occur.

### *For Enrichment*

Students may be interested in researching where the idea for Velcro™ came from and how it is related to burrs.

## Assessment *for* Learning

| What to Look for in Student Work | What to Do |
| --- | --- |
| Students can research ways in which plants rely on animals and abiotic factors to support plant reproduction by dispersing seeds. | • Observe students during the Work On It activity.<br>• Check students' responses to Communicate question 3. |
| Students can describe ways that plants and animals depend on each other. | • Observe students during the Work On It activity.<br>• Check students' responses to Communicate question 3. |

# 10 Take a Field Trip

Page 26

| Time |
| --- |
| 80 min |
| **Line Masters** |
| • LM 1-19 |

## Indicator Assessment Chart

| Indicator | Assessment Opportunities |
| --- | --- |
| **PL3.2 a.** Observe, safely and respectfully, plants in local environments (e.g., classroom, flower garden, school yard, community garden, forest, field, park, and nature preserve). | • Work On It, p. 26<br>• Communicate, p. 27, q. 1 |
| **PL3.2 f.** Explain how to determine whether plants are healthy and discuss the impacts of diseased plants on society and the environment. | • Work On It, p.26<br>• Communicate p. 27, q. 2 |
| **PL3.2 l.** Imagine a world without plants and describe the impact on animals, people, and the environment. | • Communicate, p. 27, q. 3 |
| **PL3.2 m.** Respond to and acknowledge the ideas of others regarding the importance of plants to self and society. | • Communicate, p. 27, q. 3 |

## Lesson Goal

To discover plants in your neighbourhood

### Background Information

Plants are an integral part of many Canadian neighbourhoods. There is great diversity in the types of plants grown in different regions of the country, which is determined by the weather patterns and soil conditions. In many different locations plants are grown for many similar reasons, including:

- as wind rows to provide houses, buildings, and roads some protection from strong winds and drifting snow
- for shade to keep homes cooler in the summer
- for food to eat
- to improve the appearance of homes and properties

traditional **KNOWLEDGE**

In this lesson, you may describe and positively compare ways that scientists and First Nations and Métis people use observation to better understand nature. First Nations people teach their children to observe very early in life. Many First Nations Elders and traditional midwives teach that babies swaddled and carried in moss bags on their mother's back learn these skills very early. Often Elders and Knowledge Keepers teach by asking their young to observe patiently.

*continued →*

Observation is a skill that ensured the survival of many hunter-gatherer societies. Through careful observation, hunters understood the behaviours, tracks, and patterns of animals. For example, hunters could observe and understand the behaviour and patterns of wild geese to know when to collect and harvest eggs and when to hunt the geese to avoid depopulating a local flock. Gatherers knew when certain types of berries could be harvested. Through observation, First Nations peoples, such as the Dené, knew when to travel over ice safely if needed. Through careful observation of weather patterns, landforms, celestial events, and star patterns, some groups knew when certain types of ceremonies were best performed, when to move their camps, and where they should go.

A few cautions should be observed. You need to help students understand the important First Nations values of respect for the land and to take wildlife from the area only if needed. Thus, any area that students visit needs to remain as untouched as possible. Emphasize a strict "look only" philosophy among students, and encourage students to take pictures where possible.

## Curriculum Connections

In this lesson, students have the opportunity to develop skills and concepts in these areas:

### *Social Studies*

IN3.2 c. Make inferences about how the culture of the local community is reflected by its customs and celebrations.

DR3.3 b. Identify ways in which people in communities studied interact with the land (e.g., meeting needs and wants, how land is protected or neglected).

### *English Language Arts*

CC3.2 a. Demonstrate understanding of the topic, problem, questions, or issue in a variety of ways (e.g., dance pieces, visual representations, drama in context, diagram, demonstration, chart).

## Get Started ▶

- Have students study the two photos at the top of page 26 of the student book. As they are looking at the photos, ask them to work with a partner to compare what the photos show with respect to number of plants, types of plants, and the reason that the plants are there.
- Have student pairs share their ideas with the rest of the class to discuss how city and rural neighbourhoods are similar and different with respect to the plants that grow in them. Have students suggest reasons for why these differences occur.

**Time**

80 min

**Learning Context**

inquiry
cultural perspectives

**Level of Inquiry**

guided

**Skills**

- observing
- classifying
- inferring

**Grouping**

groups

**Materials and Equipment**

(per group)
- pencils
- camera (optional)
- guide for local plants

**Line Masters**

- LM 1-19

## Work On It

### Purpose

To provide an opportunity for students to discover and observe plants that grow locally

### Activity Notes

- Ask students what type of plants they have in and around their home: *What type of plants are they? How big are the plants? What are some of the reasons the plants are there?* Have the class make a list of the different reasons that people have plants in and around their homes. Are there any reasons that can be added to the list when they consider the plants around the school?
- Explain that they will be going on a field trip through the neighbourhood to observe and record the different types of plants that are found in the area around the school. Students can classify the plants in a variety of ways when listing the types of plants they observe. They can label plants as grasses, flowers, crops, gardens, shrubs, and trees, and include a rough estimation of the sizes of the plants they see. Use LM 1-19 My Field Trip Notes for students to record their observations.
- If you have a camera or video camera available, you may wish to visually record the plants found in their specific locations to aid students when determining the function of the plants. This will give students an opportunity to reflect on real-world pictures or videos. You can then use this collection of pictures and videos for students to create a digital slide presentation to show and share their findings.
- You may want to break the field trip into two parts and use the first part to observe the school and the grounds around it. Students can list, draw pictures, or take pictures of the plants they see and tell the function of the plants in their locations. The second part of the field trip could be travelling through a residential neighbourhood near the school. If you intend to go off the school property, you should check with the office to see if a letter of permission is required.
- Invite an Elder or Traditional Knowledge Keeper to guide your students on the field trip to extend the cultural perspective of this activity. Then students may experience First Nations and Métis beliefs in regard to the significance of observation and respect for Mother Earth first-hand. An Elder or Traditional Knowledge Keeper may also discuss edible plants that can be found in Saskatchewan and what they are often used for. Follow the "Protocol for Contacting Elders and Traditional Knowledge Keepers" in the Program Overview of this Teacher's Resource.

**!** The western red lily (*Lilium philadelphicum andinum*) is Saskatchewan's provincial flower. This flower is currently on the endangered species list and is illegal to pick. The western red lily can survive extreme weather conditions. This lily is also found as a symbol on the Saskatchewan provincial flag.

## Communicate

1. Students' answers may vary but could include flowers growing around houses because people have planted them there; larger trees in older areas of town; younger trees growing in newer areas; and wild plants, such as dandelions, that have sprouted in some areas.
2. Students' answers may vary but could include discoloured plants, plants that are withering because of a lack of water, and plants with small holes in their leaves due to bug infestation. Students should recognize that plants without signs of disease like these are most likely healthy.
3. Students' answers may vary but could include that a world without plants would affect the food chain. Plants are a main food supply for humans today as well as animals. Some students might recognize that without green plants there would not be any oxygen produced. The beauty of the environment, solidity of soil, privacy, and so on would all be affected with the lack of plants.

### BUILD ON WHAT YOU KNOW

After students go on the field trip, they will have seen a variety of trees, flowers, and weeds. Encourage students to brainstorm a list of plants that they would like to have in the garden they design at the end of the unit. Students should recognize that some plants have a purpose in gardens. For example, trees might provide wind protection for any vegetables and fruits they might choose to grow. Encourage students to choose a variety of plants, including some they have observed thriving in the neighbourhood, which is a good indication that those plants can survive in similar environmental conditions at the school.

## DI Differentiating Instruction

### *For EAL/ELL*

When placing students in groups for the field trip, place EAL/ELL students with students who are proficient speakers of English and enjoy sharing and interacting verbally. Encourage these students to use words to describe their observations during the field trip to help immerse EAL/ELL students in the language. Encourage these groups of students to interact verbally as much as possible.

### *For Enrichment*

Students may be interested to learn more about the plants that live in other cities and towns found across Canada. They could research what types of plants are grown in different places of the country and how these plants differ from the ones they have found growing in their area.

## Assessment *for* Learning

| What to Look for in Student Work | What to Do |
|---|---|
| Students can observe plants safely and respectfully in local environments. | • Observe students during the Work On It activity.<br>• Check students' responses to Communicate question 1. |
| Students can explain how to determine whether plants are healthy. | • Observe students during the Work On It activity.<br>• Check students' responses to Communicate question 2. |
| Students can imagine a world without plants and describe the impact on animals, people, and the environment. | • Check students' responses to Communicate question 3. |
| Students can respond to and acknowledge the ideas of others regarding the importance of plants to self and society. | • Observe students during the Work On It activity.<br>• Check students' responses to Communicate question 3. |

# 11 What Crops Grow in Saskatchewan?

Page 28

| Time |
|---|
| 40 min |
| **Line Masters** |
| • LM 1-20 |

## Indicator Assessment Chart

| Indicator | Assessment Opportunities |
|---|---|
| **PL3.1 c.** Relate characteristics such as the number and shape of leaves, flower colour, height, and presence and type of fruit in different types of plants to the plant's environment. | • Communicate, p. 29, q. 3 |
| **PL3.2 b.** Research traditional and contemporary uses of plants or parts of plants, such as food, beverages, medicine, arts, seed banks, shade, wind breaks, erosion protection, cultural celebrations, and for creating products such as dyes, shelter, and clothing. | • Work On It, p. 29<br>• Communicate, p. 29, q. 1 |
| **PL3.2 d.** Examine the importance of agriculture in Saskatchewan, including the variety of plants and plant-related products. | • Work On It, p. 29<br>• Communicate, p. 29, q. 2 |
| **PL3.2 e.** Describe examples of plant biodiversity (e.g., trees, shrubs, bushes, herbs, grasses, vines, and mosses) in various ecosystems throughout the world. | • Work On It, p. 29<br>• Communicate, p. 29, q. 3, 4 |

## Lesson Goal

To investigate foods made with wheat

## Background Information

Saskatchewan produces a variety of plant crops for different purposes. Wheat is the largest crop grown in the province. Wheat, which belongs to the grass family, is used in many products and sold all over the world. The most common wheat grown is hard red spring wheat, which is usually used for bread and other baked goods. Durum wheat, which is also popular, is used mainly for pasta.

Canola is Saskatchewan's second largest crop. Canola seeds are used for salad oil, cooking oil, and margarine. Saskatchewan is also a large producer of flax, an oilseed crop used in paint, varnish, linoleum, linen clothing, and other products. Napkins, towels, sheets, and clothes are sometimes made with linen and, therefore may contain flax seed.

Oats are also produced in Saskatchewan as feed for horses, hogs, and cattle. Rolled oats and oatmeal are used to make cookies and other products as well.

Saskatchewan farmers produce rye, a cereal crop that can be used to make flour. This flour is then used to make rye bread. Rye is also used for cattle feed and hog feed. Barley is another cereal grain produced in Saskatchewan. Barley is often used in soups and grown for livestock feed.

Saskatchewan also produces nearly half of the world's supply of mustard seed. Mustard seed is used as a spice and to make the condiment mustard that many people put on hamburgers and hot dogs.

Sunflowers are another widespread crop in Saskatchewan. Sunflower seeds are used to make cooking oil and salad oil. They are also packaged as a snack food.

traditional **KNOWLEDGE**

Northern Saskatchewan is a large producer of wild rice. Wild rice is a type of grass that can grow to be about 2.5 m tall. This crop grows in shallow waters in the northern lakes, rivers, and streams of the province. As soon as the ice melts in the spring, wild rice is seeded in the shallow waters with a seeder. The First Nations and Métis traditional way of seeding and harvesting the rice was by hand from a canoe. Today, people of the Lac La Ronge First Nation usually harvest wild rice with an airboat, in late August or early September. The rice is then taken to a processing plant where it is cleaned and stored in bags to be sold all over the world. The Lac La Ronge First Nation harvests and exports more than 450 000 kg of wild rice annually.

## Curriculum Connections

In this lesson, students have the opportunity to develop skills and concepts in these areas:

***Social Studies***

IN3.3 c. Identify products produced locally and sold elsewhere.

**Get Started ▶**

- Ask students to bring a variety of empty food packages and labels to class (e.g., cereal boxes, soup can labels, bread bags, cracker boxes, cookie packages). Explain that on every box or label, the ingredients of the food are listed and that students will be examining the ingredients of different foods. Remind students to get permission from their parents before bringing in the boxes or labels.
- Before reading the text, ask students if they have ever read the label on any food products they have eaten. Show students a variety of food packages and labels and ask them to find the list of ingredients. Students may need clarification about the role of food labels (e.g., to identify the ingredients and the place where the product was made).

Discuss with students some of the ingredients found on the labels and where they think the foods are produced.

- As students read through Get Started on page 28 of the student book, stop and discuss whether they have eaten the foods that are mentioned. Elicit what they already know about these foods. Have students list other foods that they have eaten that might contain the mentioned foods as ingredients.
- Ask students how they think Saskatchewan affects their diet and the diets of people around the world. Elicit or explain that Saskatchewan is a major producer of the plants that are used for food throughout the world. Encourage students to connect the idea that the crops grown in Saskatchewan, such as wheat and rice, make up part of their daily diet as well as the daily diet of many people in the world.
- Discuss with students the First Nations and Métis traditional ways of harvesting wild rice as well as the use of modern technology. Have students examine the photo on page 37 of the student book, which shows wild rice being seeded in a traditional way, and the photo on page 28, which shows wild rice being harvested from an airboat.

Saskatchewan contains 44 percent of Canada's total cultivated farmland. Wheat is the most important field crop in Saskatchewan. It grows on more than half the farmland in the province. Barley is an important secondary grain. Other grains, such as canola, flax, rye, oats, peas, lentils, canary seed, and barley are also produced.

| Time |
| --- |
| 40 min |
| **Learning Context** |
| inquiry |
| **Level of Inquiry** |
| structured |
| **Skills** |
| • interpreting<br>• comparing |
| **Grouping** |
| groups |
| **Materials and Equipment** |
| (per group)<br>• variety of empty food packages and labels<br>• pencils |
| **Line Masters** |
| • LM 1-20 |

## Work On It

### Purpose

To have students identify a variety of foods that contain the plant product wheat

### Activity Notes

- **Note:** Malt and gluten are products of wheat.
- Read through the steps with students and ensure they understand what to do. Select one food label to discuss with students and model what to look for (the ingredients list and wheat products listed). Tell them that the ingredients flour, malt, and gluten are all wheat products.
- Distribute copies of LM 1-20 What Crops Grow in Saskatchewan? for students to use to record their work.
- Students may have a difficult time reading some names of ingredients. Remind students not to get frustrated, but to ask for help.
- Invite students to choose an area to research that they have a connection to. If you have any students who have immigrated from another country, they may be interested in researching the trees, shrubs, grasses, and crops that grow there. Other students may know people who live in other areas of the world and may be interested in researching those areas.
- Encourage students to find at least four types of trees, shrubs, grasses, and crops that grow in the area they research. Making a Venn diagram may help them compare the plants they find with those in Saskatchewan.

## Communicate

1. Students' answers may vary but could include that they were surprised that malted milk powder (e.g., Ovaltine) and some soups have wheat.
2. Students' answers may vary but should include that Saskatchewan relies heavily on successfully growing plants and producing a variety of plant products to sell in world markets. Without these plant products, people might not have jobs and the population of the province might decrease. Students might also recognize that if Saskatchewan did not produce these plant products, there would be less of the products to go around and the prices of them might increase.
3. Oranges and bananas are not harvested in Saskatchewan, because of the climate. These fruit do not grow in such cool and dry conditions.
4. Students' answers may vary but should include examples of trees, shrubs, grasses, and crops that grow in the area they researched, along with ways that they are similar to and different from those found in Saskatchewan. Those who choose areas with climates very different from Saskatchewan's will find the greatest difference in plants.

## DI Differentiating Instruction

### *For EAL/ELL*

Use visual cues with EAL/ELL students as necessary to clarify and reinforce the concepts. Vocabulary can be complex when working with food ingredients, so visual cues will assist these students in understanding.

### *For Enrichment*

Students may be interested in researching how the wheat crops in Saskatchewan are harvested. Students could work in small groups to create a computer slide presentation of photos that represent the harvesting process, including combining, hauling grain, and storage. Students could collect personal photos of family members or friends harvesting or collect such photos on the Internet.

## Assessment *for* Learning

| What to Look for in Student Work | What to Do |
| --- | --- |
| Students are able to examine and understand the importance of agriculture to Saskatchewan. | • Observe students during Get Started.<br>• Check students' responses to Communicate question 2. |
| Students are able to describe examples of plant biodiversity in various ecosystems throughout the world. | • Observe students during the Work On It activity.<br>• Check students' responses to Communicate questions 3 and 4. |

# 12 Plants Are Food for the World

Page 30

| Time |
| --- |
| 40 min |
| **Line Masters** |
| • LM 1-21 |

## Indicator Assessment Chart

| Indicator | Assessment Opportunities |
| --- | --- |
| **PL3.2 b.** Research traditional and contemporary uses of plants or parts of plants, such as food, beverages, medicine, arts, seed banks, shade, wind breaks, erosion protection, cultural celebrations, and for creating products such as dyes, shelter, and clothing. | • Work On It, p. 31<br>• Communicate, p. 31, q. 4 |
| **PL3.2 e.** Describe examples of plant biodiversity (e.g., trees, shrubs, bushes, herbs, grasses, vines, and mosses) in various ecosystems throughout the world. | • Work On It, p. 31<br>• Communicate, p. 31, q. 3, 4 |
| **PL3.2 i.** Examine the type and quantity of plants and plant matter in the diets of people who live in various communities and/or represent various cultures. | • Work On It, p. 31<br>• Communicate p. 31, q. 1, 2, 3, 4 |

## Lesson Goal

To find out about plants people eat in different parts of the world

## Background Information

Life on Earth depends on plants. All food that animals, including humans, eat comes from plants directly or indirectly. When we eat meat, for example, we are eating animals that have fed on plants or fed on other animals that have fed on plants.

Millions of people around the world rely on cereal grains from plants to survive. Wheat, for example, is an important food staple in the Western world. Likewise, corn is important in the Americas, and rice is essential in Asia. Some tubers, such as potatoes, are eaten almost everywhere in the world. In addition, cassava, another tuber, is a staple food in tropical areas.

Fruit, vegetables, and nuts—the staples of a healthy human diet—all come from plants. Fruit and vegetables contain vitamins, minerals, carbohydrates, and fibre. Nuts contain vitamins, minerals, protein, and fatty acids.

Oranges are the most-consumed fruit in the world. What's more, in developing countries, bananas are the fourth most-consumed plant product after rice, wheat, and maize.

## Curriculum Connections

In this lesson, students have the opportunity to develop skills and concepts in these areas:

### *Social Studies*

DR3.1 a. Demonstrate an understanding that the surface of the Earth can be represented through maps, aerial photographs, and satellite images.

### *English Language Arts*

CR3.4 b. Select and use appropriate strategies (before, during, and after) to construct and confirm meaning when reading.

## Get Started ▶

- Read the title on page 30 of the student book to introduce the lesson and ask, *What types of plants does the world depend on for food?* Compile a list of students' suggestions on the board or on chart paper for students to refer back to after reading the text.
- Read the text with students and ask, *Is there anything we should add or correct on our list of plants the world depends on for food?* Then accept and record students' suggestions as necessary.
- With students, examine the photos of the three families on page 30. Have students look for and identify similarities and differences in the food shown in the photos and suggest reasons for these similarities and differences.

**Time**

40 min

**Learning Context**

cultural perspectives

**Level of Inquiry**

structured

**Skills**

- inferring
- interpreting
- comparing

**Grouping**

pairs

**Materials and Equipment**

(per pair)
- pencils

**Line Masters**

- LM 1-21

## Work On It

### Purpose

To have students identify plants, parts of plants, and food made from plants eaten by people who live in other parts of the world

### Activity Notes

- Read the introductory text with students and invite them to brainstorm what types of plants are eaten by people who live in different parts of the world. Record students' ideas and discuss why they think the plants in the diets of people around the world may be so different.
- Draw students' attention to the world map shown on page 31 of the student book. Talk about how the map can help them see where the families shown in the photos live. Explain to students that Earth's surface can be represented with a map. Ask students to identify the purpose of the stick pins shown on the map and what they represent. Have students locate Saskatchewan on the map and compare its location to the places where the three families live (e.g., not near the equator, landlocked rather than near an ocean).

*continued* →

- The photos in the student book come from the book *Hungry Planet* by Peter Menzel and and Faith D'Aluisio. You may wish to order copies of the book from the library to have on hand for students to look at.
- Review the steps in Work On It with students before they begin to work with their partners. Students may also view the photos online at What the World Eats, Part 1, A Time Photo Essay: www.time.com/time/photogallery/0,29307,1626519,00.html.
- Observe students throughout the investigation to ensure they are able to identify the types of plants shown in the photos. Encourage students to work together to try to identify the plants shown and to be ready to share their thoughts.
- Provide LM 1-21 Plants Are Food for the World for students to record their work.
- Circulate among student pairs and remind them to look for foods made of plant parts and plant products as well as plants. Bring the class together to share their findings. You may also wish to share the following points with students.
- The Ukita family of Kodaira City, Japan, spends 37,699 Yen, or $317.25, on food each week. Their favourite foods are sashimi (raw fish cut into thin slices), fruit, cake, and potato chips. They also eat tomatoes, watermelon, bananas, flour, rice, packaged fruits and vegetables, bok choy, potatoes, broccoli, and chives, which all come from plants.
- The Aboubakar family of Breidjing Camp in Chad spends 685 CFA Francs, of $1.23, on food each week. Their favourite food is soup with fresh sheep meat. They also eat rice and beans, which come from plants.
- The Ayme family of Tingo, Ecuador, spends $31.55 on food each week. Their favourite food is potato soup with cabbage. They also eat bananas, lemons, onions, rice, carrots, potatoes, and cabbage, which all come from plants.

Many food products are produced from trees. Cinnamon is a popular spice that is obtained from the inner bark of several trees from the genus *Cinnamomum*. This family of trees are native to Southeast Asia. Cinnamon is harvested by scraping off the outer bark of the branches of these trees. Hammering the branches evenly loosens the inner bark. The long rolls of inner bark are dried and then cut into smaller lengths for sale.

## Communicate

1. Students' answers may vary but could include fruit, vegetables, pasta, cereal, and bread.
2. Students' answers may vary but could include pasta, cereal, and cake.
3. Students should conclude that the environment and climate in different places will affect the diets of families who live in those places. Some foods grow in hot climates while others grow in cooler climates. Students should also conclude that families' diets often reflect the foods that are most abundant in the area where they live.
4. Students' answers will vary but could include:
   - Ecuador: the wild cashew tree, a large tree that grows up to 45 m tall and bears kidney-shaped fruit 2 to 3 cm long—the fruit are poisonous uncooked, but people roast and eat the nuts; the cacao tree that bears fruit known as pods, which contain 20 to 60 cocoa beans. People use the cocoa beans to make chocolate.

- Japan: bamboo, a giant woody grass that people use to build buildings and other structures, to make arts and crafts, and to eat as a delicacy; the cherry tree that has pink blossoms, which people use for decoration and ornamental purposes, and to flavour food.
- Chad: peanuts are grown as food crops for local consumption; cotton is grown and sold to make a living. Around the world, people use the fibres of cotton plants to make fabrics, clothes, sheets, towels, furniture, and other products.

## DI Differentiating Instruction

### *For Enrichment*

Students can take a photo of their family that includes the food that their family eats in a typical week. Students could then compare their family's diet to those shown in the photos in the student book and to those of classmates.

## Assessment *for* Learning

| What to Look for in Student Work | What to Do |
| --- | --- |
| Students can research traditional and contemporary uses of plants or parts of plants. | • Observe students during the Work On It activity.<br>• Check students' responses to Communicate question 4. |
| Students can describe examples of plant biodiversity in various ecosystems throughout the world. | • Observe students during the Work On It activity.<br>• Check students' responses to Communicate questions 3 and 4. |
| Students can examine the type and quantity of plants and plant matter in the diets of people throughout the world. | • Observe students during the Work On It activity.<br>• Check students' responses to Communicate questions 1, 2, 3, and 4. |

# 13 Nature's Renewal

Page 32

| Time |
| --- |
| 40 min |
| **Line Masters** |
| • LM 1-22 |

## Indicator Assessment Chart

| Indicator | Assessment Opportunities |
| --- | --- |
| **PL3.2 h.** Assess the impact of natural (e.g., animal migration, fire, competition, and decay) and human activity (e.g., burning land, logging, fertilization, soil compaction, and picking endangered plants) on the biodiversity of plant species. | • Work On It, p. 33<br>• Communicate, p. 33, q. 1 |
| **PL3.2 j.** Explain how and why plants are replenished naturally (e.g., forest fires, and pollination) and artificially (e.g., tree farms, planting seedlings, and seed banks). | • Communicate, p. 33, q. 2, 3 |
| **PL3.2 l.** Imagine a world without plants and describe the impact on animals, people, and the environment. | • Communicate, p. 33, q. 4 |
| **PL3.2 m.** Respond to and acknowledge the ideas of others regarding the importance of plants to self and society. | • Work On It, p. 33<br>• Communicate, p. 33, q. 1, 4 |

## Lesson Goal

To research how forest fires affect plants

## Background Information

On average, about 9100 forest fires occur in Canada every year. Human activities start 60 percent of them and most of these are sparked unintentionally. Lightning causes 35 percent of Canada's forest fires. Forest fires caused by lightning are usually 10 times as large as those caused by humans and often less accessible to fire-fighting crews.

Fire helps to naturally shape Canadian forests, since some trees rely on fire for replenishment. For example, the black spruce, jack pine, trembling aspen, and white birch are all adapted to regenerate after a fire. Some of these trees regenerate directly from their root systems, while others sprout from the base of dead trees.

## Curriculum Connections

In this lesson, students have the opportunity to develop skills and concepts in these areas:

### *English Language Arts*

CR3.4 d. Ask questions and support answers by connecting prior knowledge with literal information found in, and inferred from, texts including First Nations and Métis resources.

## Get Started ▶

- Ask students to consider the positive and negative aspects of fire. Record their ideas on the board or chart paper. Students may suggest that fire is beneficial for cooking, heating, and special ceremonies, and that fire is harmful when it burns people and their homes and destroys animals and plants.

traditional ***KNOWLEDGE***

- Read the text with students. Then, have students explain to a partner what they learned from the text. You may also wish to have small groups of students enact the scene described in the text.

**!**

When a forest fire starts naturally, some First Nations people say that Spirit in fire visits the forest to renew what needs to be renewed. In the Cree worldview, there is a natural law that keeps everything in balance in the world. Everything is always in flux and nothing is permanent in the world.

| Time |
| --- |
| 40 min |
| **Learning Context** |
| decision making |
| **Level of Inquiry** |
| structured |
| **Skills** |
| • interpreting<br>• comparing<br>• communicating |
| **Grouping** |
| groups |
| **Materials and Equipment** |
| (per group)<br>• pencils |
| **Line Masters** |
| • LM 1-22 |

## Work On It

### Purpose

To have students investigate how forest or prairie fires can help or harm plants

### Activity Notes

- Review the steps of the Work On It with students. Encourage them to be open-minded to the ideas and opinions of all group members as they discuss the helpful or harmful effects of a forest or prairie fire. Provide copies of LM 1-22 Nature's Renewal for students to record their research.
- Discuss with students your expectations for their group presentations. You may wish to work with students to create a class list of evaluation criteria, so that they have a clear outline of what is expected in terms of group work, information presented, and the final presentation form.

## Communicate

1. Students' answers may vary but could include that fires are necessary for generating new growth in some plants, and that fires can kill plants and eliminate entire forests, including populations and habitats of animals that live there.
2. New trees will sometimes sprout where old ones have burned down.
3. People can plant new seedlings or plants in burnt areas.
4. Students' answers may vary but could include that a lack of trees would affect the aesthetic of the landscape; the amount of wind in areas, since trees would no longer be present as wind blocks; and soil erosion, since soil might blow away.

## DI Differentiating Instruction

### *For Enrichment*

Students can research a plant that has a life cycle that is dependent on fire, such as the jack pine that grows in Saskatchewan. Have students design a storyboard to illustrate the life cycle of the plant, and the role that fire plays in helping it complete its life cycle.

## Assessment *for* Learning

| What to Look for in Student Work | What to Do |
|---|---|
| Students understand the impact of natural and human activity on the biodiversity of plant species. | • Observe students during the Work On It activity.<br>• Check students' responses to Communicate question 1. |
| Students can explain how plants are replenished naturally and artificially. | • Check students' responses to Communicate questions 2 and 3. |
| Students can respond to and acknowledge the ideas of others regarding the importance of plants to self and society. | • Observe students during the Work On It activity.<br>• Check students' responses to Communicate questions 1 and 4. |

# 14 How Can People Affect Plants? *Page 34*

| Time |
|---|
| 40 min |

| Vocabulary |
|---|
| • endangered |

| Line Masters |
|---|
| • LM 1-23 |

## Indicator Assessment Chart

| Indicator | Assessment Opportunities |
|---|---|
| **PL3.2 f.** Explain how to determine whether plants are healthy and discuss the impacts of diseased plants on society and the environment. | • Work On It, p. 35<br>• Communicate, p. 35, q. 1, 2, 3 |
| **PL3.2 h.** Assess the impact of natural (e.g., animal migration, fire, competition, and decay) and human activity (e.g., burning land, logging, fertilization, soil compaction, and picking endangered plants) on the biodiversity of plant species. | • Communicate, p. 35, q. 3 |

## Lesson Goal

To investigate how road salt can affect plants

## Background Information

Humans can affect plants in many ways, some of which are positive and some of which are negative. Because plants and animals have often lived and evolved in areas together, they have created a balance in many ecosystems that they share. However, when humans enter an ecosystem, big changes can occur. Over time, humans have changed the world's environment through the rapid population growth of our species and the development of technology. For example, the demands of an increasing human population and changes in technology have led to the destruction of large tracts of the world's rainforests for commercial purposes. Global climate change due to human activity and the drying up of water supplies for irrigation are also of ongoing concern, as is air pollution from our use of fossil fuels for energy.

Human activities, such as picking endangered plants and fertilizing lawns and gardens, also affect plants at the local level. As well, non-native organisms unintentionally or intentionally introduced into areas by humans may interact with native organisms in ways that negatively affect plants in the ecosystem. For example, non-native plants may grow taller than native plants, capturing and blocking out available sunlight.

*continued →*

Salting icy roads is another human activity of concern for many scientists. These scientists do not advocate using road salt and are trying to find ways to decrease its impact on plants. Not only can road salt kill plants alongside roads, but it can also dissolve in melting snow and ice and thereby flow into water sources and other areas, where it can negatively affect plants farther afield. Road salt can also attract animals, such as deer and moose, which may cause collisions on roads. Scientists have also learned that some amphibians will not cross salted roads and, as a result, can become separated from their breeding grounds.

## Curriculum Connections

In this lesson, students have the opportunity to develop skills and concepts in these areas:

### *English Language Arts*

CR3.4 f. Follow simple written multi-step instructions (e.g., how to assemble a product or play a board game) and functional and instructional messages in the environment (e.g., instructions, menus, invitations, announcements).

### *Social Studies*

DR3.2 a. Identify the influences that geography has on societies (e.g., location of settlements, transportation of goods and people, types of industry such as farming, ranching, forestry, mining, tourism, and manufacturing).

## Get Started ▶

- Invite students to preview the text and photos on page 34 of the student book. Have students create a three-column table in their notebooks. In the first column, based on their preview, have students write down two or three questions that they would expect to find answers to as they read the text.
- In the second column of the table, have students record what they previewed in the text that caused them to think of their questions. Then, read the text with students and encourage them to determine whether the text answers their questions and record any answers in the third column of their table.
- Afterward, in a class discussion, invite students to share their questions and answers and to pose any of their questions that were not answered.
- Discuss with students other ways they think people can affect plants positively and negatively. Record their suggestions on the board or on chart paper.

| Time |
| --- |
| 40 min |
| **Learning Context** |
| inquiry |
| **Level of Inquiry** |
| structured |
| **Skills** |
| • observing<br>• interpreting<br>• experimenting<br>• comparing |
| **Grouping** |
| groups |
| **Materials and Equipment** |
| (per group)<br>• 2 bean plants<br>• 4 labels<br>• marker<br>• 2 jugs of water (4-L milk jugs)<br>• measuring cup<br>• rubber gloves<br>• spoon<br>• road salt<br>• camera (optional)<br>• pencils |
| **Line Masters** |
| • LM 1-23 |

**SAFETY CAUTION!**
Wear rubber gloves to handle the road salt.

## Work On It

### Purpose

To have students investigate how the human activity of salting roads can affect plants

### Activity Notes

- Review the step-by-step instructions with the groups. Remind students to wear rubber gloves when handling the road salt. You may choose to assist students with the measuring and mixing of the salt with the water. Try to use jugs that have caps so the water and salt mixture can be mixed and/or shaken daily prior to watering the plants, since the salt may settle on the bottom of the jug.
- Remind students of the importance of following the labels on each bean plant to water the plants. Students will need to water each plant consistently with the appropriate water (clean water or water with road salt) to see the expected results.
- Provide copies of LM 1-23 How Can People Affect Plants? for students to record their observations. Students can also use a camera to document the changes in the bean plants, and then use the photos to create a visual representation of their findings once the activity is complete.

## Communicate

1. Students' answers may vary but should include that the plant watered with the road salt mixture started to wilt and die.
2. Students' answers may vary but should include that the plant that received clean water seemed healthy because it stood tall, did not wilt, and grew, and that the plant that received the road salt mixture seemed unhealthy because it began to wilt and change colour.
3. Salting our highways can make nearby plants wilt and die.

## DI Differentiating Instruction

***For EAL/ELL***

Introduce EAL/ELL students to the visuals and hands-on materials in the activity. This may provide a secure learning environment and the opportunity for EAL/ELL students to take risks in their learning.

## Assessment *for* Learning

| What to Look for in Student Work | What to Do |
|---|---|
| Students can explain how to determine whether plants are healthy, and discuss societal and environmental impacts of diseased plants. | • Observe students during the Work On It activity.<br>• Check students' responses to Communicate questions 1, 2, and 3. |
| Students can assess the impact of road salt on plants. | • Observe students during the Work On It activity.<br>• Check students' responses to Communicate question 3. |

# 15 How Can People Help Plants? Page 36

| Time |
| --- |
| 40 min |
| **Line Masters** |
| • LM 1-24 |

## Indicator Assessment Chart

| Indicator | Assessment Opportunities |
| --- | --- |
| **PL3.2 k.** Defend a position related to plant use (e.g., picking plants, harvesting crops, fertilization, and planting invasive species) and protection (e.g., establishing conservation areas, planting native species, and developing alternatives to plant-based products). | • Work On It, p. 37<br>• Communicate, p. 37, q. 1 |

## Lesson Goal

To explore how people can help plants grow

## Background Information

Plants grow all over the world. While human activity has many negative effects on plants and their habitats, some of people's actions can help plants grow. These actions include watering plants, naturally enriching the soil plants live in, maintaining clean air and water, protecting and preserving spaces for plants to grow, not over-picking plants, and not moving plants from their natural habitats. Other positive actions include planting trees, shrubs, and other plants native to specific areas.

## Curriculum Connections

In this lesson, students have the opportunity to develop skills and concepts in these areas:

### *English Language Arts*

CR3.3 i. Listen attentively and courteously to each other in discussions and to guest speakers; show respect for the ideas, language, and communication styles of others; and give sensitive and thoughtful responses.
CC3.3 d. Organize and present ideas chronologically or around major points of information.

## Get Started ▶

- Take a class poll of how many students have plants or gardens at home. Then, have students make a list of the different types of plants and/or gardens that they have at home. Ask students what types of things their families do to help their plants survive. For each action students suggest, encourage them to explain how the action helps plants grow and survive.

- Read the introductory text together. Then examine the photos and read the four situations listed on page 36 of the student book. Give students a few minutes to work with a partner to list ways to remedy each of the situations. Have students share and compare their ideas on how to help plants grow in these situations. For each solution students suggest, have them identify how their idea helps meet plants' basic needs.
- Invite students to think of areas around the school that are difficult for plants to grow in and meet their basic needs. Ask, *What could you do to help plants grow in these areas?*

**Time**

40 min

**Learning Context**

decision making

**Level of Inquiry**

structured

**Skills**

- inferring
- hypothesizing
- communicating

**Grouping**

groups

**Materials and Equipment**

(per group)
- pencils

**Line Masters**

- LM 1-24

## Work On It

### Purpose

To have students identify ways that people can help plants grow

### Activity Notes

- Review with students the basic needs of plants, and list these needs on the board. Have students suggest ways that people can help plants meet each of these needs and record their suggestions beside the need as in the example below.

| Basic Needs of Plants | Meeting the Needs |
|---|---|
| Water | Rain, watering can, sprinkler |
| Good soil | Compost, fertilizer, peat moss |
| Air | Clear space in the garden, windows |
| Space to grow | Gardens, pots |
| Shelter from harsh weather | Cover for the plants, indoor pots |

- Have small groups of students look at the five pictures on student book page 37 and explain how each action shown helps plants meet their basic needs. Students may have some difficulty understanding how a conservation area and a "Stop Dutch Elm Disease" sign help plants meet their basic needs. You may want to ask them what happens when a road or building is constructed on forested land or the land of a meadow. Ask, *What happens to the trees and shrubs that used to grow in the forest?* Similarly, you can ask what happens when garbage and chemicals seep into ponds and rivers: *Is polluted water good for plants? Will it still help the plants grow?*
- As students look at the photos, ensure they understand that the man in the canoe is seeding wild rice by hand, a traditional way used by First Nations and Métis peoples.
- As students discuss the various situations shown in the photos, assess how well they understand the impact of human actions on plants and plant growth. You can help students develop these connections more fully by asking questions such as:
  - *How can people help plants grow?*
  - *What would happen if we used up all the plants in the world?*
  - *What types of things can people do to help make sure there are always places where plants will be able to grow?*
- As students build their list of actions and ways to help plants meet their basic needs, make sure they include how the action will help the plant(s).

- Provide LM 1-24 How Can People Help Plants? for students to record their lists and the positive and negative ways that the action of their choice affects plants. Encourage groups to brainstorm all the positive and negative effects of the action they choose. You may also wish to provide time for students to research the positive and negative effects.

## Communicate

1. Students' answers may vary but could include the following positive and negative effects:
   - Harvesting crops: material left behind from harvested crops, such as straw in a wheat field, restores nutrients to the soil for future crops; removes plants from the ground, and then the plants may not reproduce naturally
   - Fertilizing crops: can make plants grow faster and bigger; fertilizer can affect plants negatively if it runs off into water in natural areas where plants grow
   - Protecting some areas of plants growth: can provide endangered plants a safe, clean place to grow and reproduce; these areas can become overgrown and, as a result, some plant species can be squeezed out

## DI Differentiating Instruction

### *For EAL/ELL*

To help EAL/ELL students or any other students having difficulty with terminology, pose questions such as the following to elicit specific vocabulary:

- *Where is the boy putting bits of fruit and vegetables?* (in a composter)
- *What do you call the material in a composter once it breaks down?* (compost or humus)
- *What's another word for protect?* (conserve)
- *What do you call a park where plants and animals are protected?* (a conservation area)

Record these words on chart paper and encourage students to refer to them as they answer the questions in this section.

### *For Enrichment*

Students may enjoy finding the locations of local conservation areas, parks, reserves, or other areas nearby that have been established and maintained for plants to grow. They can also research how the area benefits local plants.

## Assessment *for* Learning

| What to Look for in Student Work | What to Do |
|---|---|
| Students can describe ways in which people's actions help plants grow and defend a position related to plant use. | • Observe students during the Work On It activity.<br>• Check students' responses to Communicate question 1. |

DESIGN PROJECT

# Create a Garden

Page 38

**Time**

80–120 min

**Learning Context**

inquiry

**Level of Inquiry**

open

**Skills**

- making models
- communicating

**Grouping**

pairs

**Materials and Equipment**

(per pair)
- Bristol board
- scissors
- glue
- various items, such as coloured paper, seeds, felt, artificial plants, etc., for students to build their model garden
- pencils

**Line Masters**

- LM 1-25
- LM 1-26

## Curriculum Indicators

| Indicators Met in Design Project |
|---|
| **PL3.1 a.** Pose questions related to plant growth (e.g., How do very young plants look different from grown plants? How much water do plants need to grow? Do all plants grow in the same way?) |
| **PL3.1 h.** Predict and investigate conditions such as the temperature, available sunlight, available nutrients in soil, and available water, which are necessary for plant germination and growth. |
| **PL3.1 k.** Suggest explanations for patterns and discrepancies in the growth rate of similar plants grown in varying conditions. |
| **PL3.1 l.** Explain the importance of water and light for the plant growth and the mechanisms by which plants obtain water and light from the environment. |
| **PL3.2 a.** Observe, safely and respectfully, plants in local environments (e.g., classroom, flower garden, school yard, community garden, forest, field, park, and nature preserve). |

## Background Information

Plants require sunlight, air, space, nutrients from soil, and water in varying amounts and intensities in order to grow. The amounts they need of each of these elements may also vary throughout different stages of their life cycles, such as germination and flowering. Growing and maintaining plants is a hobby for many people, while others seem to lack interest. Although all plants have the same basic needs, the fact that all plants do not need the exact same amounts of sunlight, water, or nutrients from the soil can make gardening interesting as well as challenging. With time, patience, and some understanding of the needs of specific plants, most people are able to grow and maintain healthy plants.

## Curriculum Connections

In this project, students have the opportunity to develop skills and concepts in these areas:

### *Visual Arts*

CP3.7 e. Discuss how the plan and visual exploration is evolving, and adjust decisions accordingly.
CP3.8 a. Observe visual details, and include details to enhance depictions of animals, people, and objects.
CP3.8 e. Use three-dimensional materials such as clay to create real textures.

## Get Started ▶

- The Design Project provides an opportunity for students to demonstrate, apply, and synthesize what they have learned about plant growth in the unit (basic needs of plants, conditions seeds need to sprout, and how to care for plants).
- Have students review their investigations of seed germination and plant growth. Ask them to explain what they have learned about how to take care of a plant and keep it healthy.
- Discuss with students the types of plants they observed during the field trip in Lesson 10. Make a list of these plants for students to consider including in their garden designs.
- Create a tabletop display of the materials students might use to build their model gardens. Encourage students to examine the display to help them decide what materials they want to use to make their models.

## Work On It

### Purpose

To provide an opportunity for students to use what they have learned about plant growth and changes to design a garden

### Activity Notes

- Discuss the Design Project with students. Provide copies of LM 1-25 Design Project Planner: Create a Garden to help students plan their gardens step by step and to record their ideas. Review the steps with students to ensure they understand what to do.
- Encourage students to use a variety of materials to construct a three-dimensional model of their garden. Remind students that their garden design must provide the basic needs of plants, and that they must be able to explain how the elements of their design provide these basic needs.
- You may wish to use LM 1-26 Design Project Rubric: Create a Garden to assess students' projects and to distribute for students to use for self-assessment.
- Visit students as they work and encourage them to explain how they are designing their gardens. Pose questions to help students refine their designs as necessary. Encourage students to share their ideas and question each other. Through such discussion, students may think of ways to improve their plans.

## Communicate

1. Students' answers may vary but could include how their garden design provides water, access to sunlight, nutrients from soil, and wind breaks for plants, as well as the types of plants they have included. Students might also include composting, signage, rocks, or decorations.

## DI Differentiating Instruction

### *For Enrichment*

Students can plant a real garden on school grounds or in containers in the classroom. Students can then be responsible for caring for the plants in this garden based on what they have learned in the unit. Scout out an area in the schoolyard where students may create gardens, or have students bring in containers from home to create container gardens. Collect materials, such as soil and digging trowels, and have students create a garden for the beans plants that they have been growing throughout the unit. Students may also wish to include other plants.

## Assessment *for* Learning

| What to Look for in Student Work | What to Do |
|---|---|
| Students can use what they have learned about plant growth and caring for plants to create a garden that provides the basic needs for plants. | • Observe students during the Work On It activity.<br>• Check students' responses to Communicate question 1. |
| Students can explain the importance of water and light for plant growth. | • Check students' responses to Communicate question 1. |

## Unit 1 Summary

Page 40

Students may wish to use the unit summary as a study guide. The Unit 1 Summary is available as a line master (LM 1-1 Unit 1 Summary).

## Show What You Know

Page 42

You may wish to use the review questions in the following ways:

- Use the questions as a guide to an oral class discussion and review.
- Use a jigsaw approach to review the unit. Organize students in small groups and assign each group a selection of questions (e.g., Group 1: questions 1, 6, and 11; Group 2: questions 2, 7, and 12) to discuss and answer. Each group can present their responses during a sharing session. Provide an opportunity for students from other groups to add to or comment on the group's response to each question.
- Organize students in small groups. Have groups take turns drawing a question from a hat or jar. The group then has 30 seconds to begin to answer the question. Otherwise, a volunteer from another group has a chance to answer the question. Have other groups listen to the answer and provide an opportunity for them to add to and/or correct the answer. Then award points for the answer (e.g., 3 points for a full and complete answer, 2 points for a correct but incomplete answer) and points to groups who add to and/or correct answers (e.g., 1 point for completing an answer, 2 points for correcting an answer). Keep score and the group who collects the most wins.

**1.** Students should clearly label the following parts of a plant and describe the function of each part:
**a)** flower — produces seeds for new plants
**b)** seeds — new plants grow from seeds
**c)** leaves —trap energy from sunlight to make food for the plant
**d)** stem — holds the plant upright and carries water and nutrients between the leaves and the roots
**e)** roots —hold the plant in the ground, take in water for the plant, and store food for the plant

**2.** Students' answers may vary but could include a group of foods that contain seeds and a group that do not contain seeds, or groups of foods that are the same plant part. For example, foods that are leaves would go in one group, and so on:
leaves — lettuce, spinach
flowers (fruit) — tomato, cucumber, cauliflower, apple, broccoli tops
roots — carrot
stem — broccoli

**3.** Seeds require water and warmth to sprout.

**4.** Humans and plants both need energy, water, space to grow, and shelter. Plants need sunlight to produce their own energy. Unlike plants, humans cannot produce their own energy. Humans need to eat plants or animals to get the energy they need.

5. Students' answers may vary but could include plant products, such as wooden furniture, paper, cotton or linen cloth, medicines, and perfumes or other scented items made from petals or oils from plants.
6. Students' answers may vary but could include that insects help pollinate flowers so plants can produce new seeds, or that animals help plants spread their seeds to new areas to grow.
7. Students' answers may vary but could include three of the following examples of how plants help people:
   - provide shade from the Sun
   - produce oxygen for humans to breathe
   - provide food to eat
   - provide products that humans use
   - provide recreational places like forests
   - can be a hobby for some people (gardening)
8. First Nations and Métis people respect plants and animals because they understand that everything in the world is a gift from Creator. Everything is alive because Spirit flows through everything. Plants and animals deserve our respect, because they contain Spirit, just as we do.
9. Students' pictures may vary but should include details to show that the size, colour, and presence of flowers, buds, and leaves can vary throughout the plant's life cycle, but the shape of its leaves is the same whether the plant is young or old.
10. If Saskatchewan's wheat crops were not harvested this year, there would be less wheat to make foods that contain wheat. So people around the world would have less of these foods to eat. Because less of these foods would be available, their prices might go up.
11. Students should identify tobacco, sage, cedar, and sweetgrass as four plants that are sacred to many the First Nations and Métis peoples. (Tobacco is offered to Mother Earth in return for harvested plants and used in special ceremonies. Sage and sweetgrass are used in smudging ceremonies. Cedar is used for healing properties and to build ceremonial structures, such as sweat lodges.)
12. If a campfire is left unattended, it is a danger to plants because fire can spread easily and quickly and destroy entire plant populations.
13. If a plant looks wilted and its leaves are dry, it probably needs water. I could water it, but not overwater it, to make it healthy again.

## Looking Back

Self-evaluation allows students to communicate their learning and their feelings about it. Seeing how students view their learning can give you insight and information on which to base your programming decisions.

Ask students to answer these questions individually, and then to share their answers with the class. Some students will likely find some areas of this unit easier than other areas. This exercise may help students identify who can give them assistance to understand difficult concepts.

# Unit 1 Line Masters

## Table of Contents

## Table of Contents *(continued)*

Name: ______________________________

# Unit 1 Summary

| Most First Nations and Métis people see plants as gifts from Creator. | |
|---|---|
| **SUMMARY**<br>□ Plants and animals deserve our respect because they contain Spirit, just as humans do. | **MY STUDY NOTES** |

| Plants have similar parts and needs. | |
|---|---|
| **SUMMARY**<br>□ Plants have parts that are alike that help them survive.<br>□ Plants need sunlight, water, nutrients from soil, air, and space to grow. | **MY STUDY NOTES** |

| Plants change as they grow. | |
|---|---|
| **SUMMARY**<br>□ Plants grow and change through their life cycles. But some parts of plants are always the same. | **MY STUDY NOTES** |

| Plants are important to living things. | |
|---|---|
| **SUMMARY**<br>□ Plants are one of the few living things that can make their own food. This makes them an important source of food for other living things. | **MY STUDY NOTES** |

| Plants and the environment affect each other. | |
|---|---|
| **SUMMARY**<br>□ Different places have different types and numbers of plants. | **MY STUDY NOTES** |

| People can affect plants. | |
|---|---|
| **SUMMARY**<br>□ Human actions can affect plants. Some actions are helpful to plants and some actions are harmful. | **MY STUDY NOTES** |

Name: ______________________________

# Unit 1 Vocabulary

Check off each vocabulary term below as you learn it in this unit.

After you check off all the terms, make a concept map using as many terms as you can. Start your concept map with this word in the centre: "plants". Use the back of this page or a separate page for your concept map.

- □ chlorophyll, p. 8
- □ endangered, p. 34
- □ flowers, p. 8
- □ leaves, p. 8
- □ life cycle, p. 18
- □ nectar, p. 24
- □ pistil, p. 24
- □ pollen, p. 24
- □ pollination, p. 24
- □ roots, p. 8
- □ seeds, p. 8
- □ stamen, p. 24
- □ stem, p. 8

Name: ______________________________

# Plants KWL Chart

| What I KNOW About Plants | What I WANT to Know About Plants | What I LEARNED About Plants |
|---|---|---|
| | | |

Name: ______________________________

# A to Z Brainstorm

You have one box for each letter of the alphabet below. Think about plants. In the boxes, write as many words about plants as you can. Use the alphabet to help you. For example, if you are thinking about the word "apple," record it in the box for the letter "A."

| | | |
|---|---|---|
| A | B | C |
| D | E | F |
| G | H | I |
| J | K | L |
| M | N | O |
| P | Q | R |
| S | T | U |
| V | W | X |
| Y | Z | |

Name: ______________________________

# Paper Making

### What You Need

- 6–8 squares of toilet paper
- large plastic bowl
- water
- wooden spoon
- fine wire screen
- 2 pieces of felt (you might use old newspaper instead of felt)
- rolling pin

### What You Will Do

1. Rip the toilet paper into small pieces. Drop the pieces into a large bowl half-filled with water.
2. Stir the pieces in the water until they are all wet.
3. Carefully place the wire screen into the bowl. Swirl the paper and water mixture until the screen is covered in wet paper fibres.
4. Lift the screen out of the bowl. Shake it gently so that some of the water runs off the screen but the fibres stay in place.
5. Carefully flip the screen over so the fibres are against one piece of felt. Gently lift the screen away from the fibres.
6. Cover the wet fibres with the other piece of felt. Then use the rolling pin to squish out as much water as you can.
7. Gently remove the top sheet of felt. Let the new piece of paper dry.

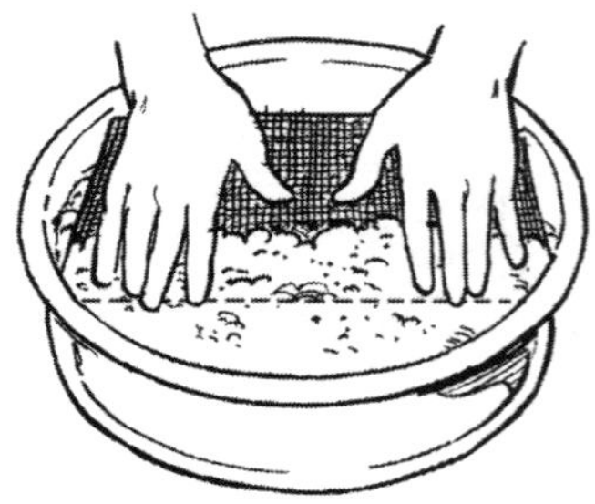

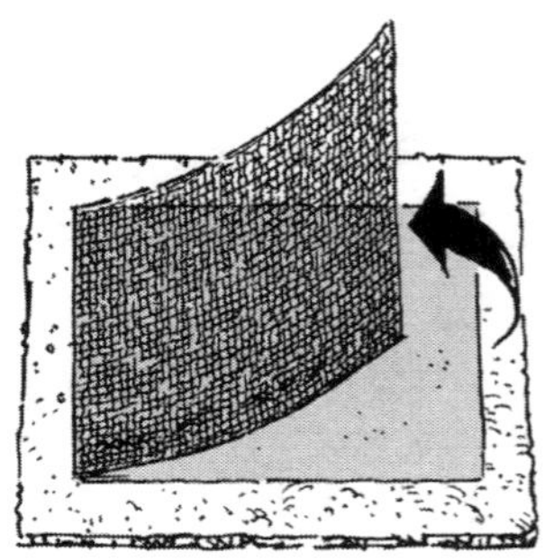

### What Did You Find Out?

1. How well did it work? What would you do differently next time?

_____________________________________________

_____________________________________________

2. Try to make new paper from bits of magazines, paper towels, or newspapers.

Name: ______________________________

# Plant Parts

Draw and label the parts of the indoor plant and the carrot.

**Indoor Plant**

**Carrot**

Name: ______________________________

# Exploring Plant Parts

Draw a picture of the piece of celery. Label the two plant parts you can see in it.

Ask your teacher to cut across the middle of the celery. Draw a picture of what you see.

Name: ______________________________

# Coloured Flowers

You know that the stem of a plant carries water and nutrients from the roots to the leaves. Does it carry the water and nutrients anywhere else? Try this investigation to find out.

**What You Need**

- food colouring
- water
- tall vase
- white flower

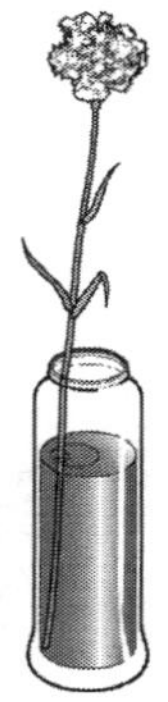

**What You Will Do**

1. Add a few drops of food colouring to the water in the vase.
2. Place the flower in the vase.
3. Let the flower sit in the water for two days.
4. Draw and describe any changes that happen to the flower:

**What Did You Find Out?**

1. What happened to the flower?

_______________________________________________

_______________________________________________

2. Do you think you could get half of the flower to be one colour and the other half to be a different colour? How would you do this? Try it.

Name: ______________________________

# How Do Plants Grow?

What do you think will happen to each seed? Write down your predictions in the table below.

| | |
|---|---|
| **Warm place with bright light** | |
| **Warm place with low light** | |
| **Warm place with no light** | |
| **Cold place with no light** | |

Over the next five days, check if the seeds have changed. In the table below, draw a picture of what you see each day.

| Location | Warm Place with Bright Light | Warm Place with Low Light | Warm Place with No Light | Cold Place with No Light |
|---|---|---|---|---|
| **Day 1** | | | | |
| **Day 2** | | | | |
| **Day 3** | | | | |
| **Day 4** | | | | |
| **Day 5** | | | | |

Name: ___________________________

# How My Plant Is Growing

In the table below, record the date and height of your bean plant every two days for the next two weeks.

| Date | Height of My Bean Plant (cm) |
|---|---|
| | |
| | |
| | |
| | |
| | |
| | |
| | |

Which days showed the most growth in your bean plant?

______________________________________________

______________________________________________

______________________________________________

Using the data you collected in the table on the previous page, create a bar graph to show the growth of your bean plant.

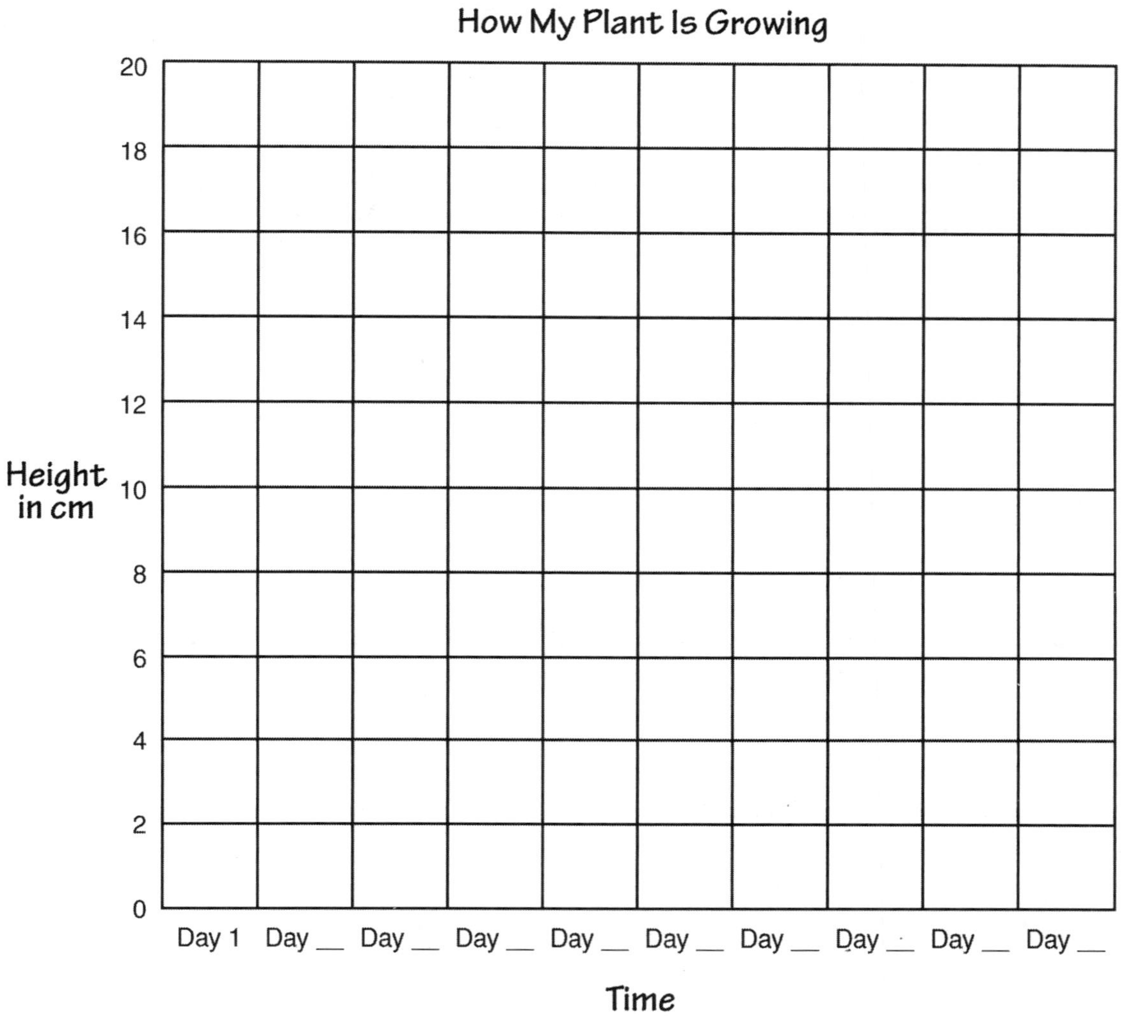


Do you notice a pattern in the height of your bean plant? Describe any patterns you see.

___

___

___

___

**Name:** ____________________________________

# Basic Needs

Look at the pictures on page 14 of the student book. What do the animals and plants shown need to survive? Record your answers in the table below.

| What Animals Need to Survive | What Plants Need to Survive |
| --- | --- |
| | |

Do plants and animals need any of the same things? Record your information in the diagram below.

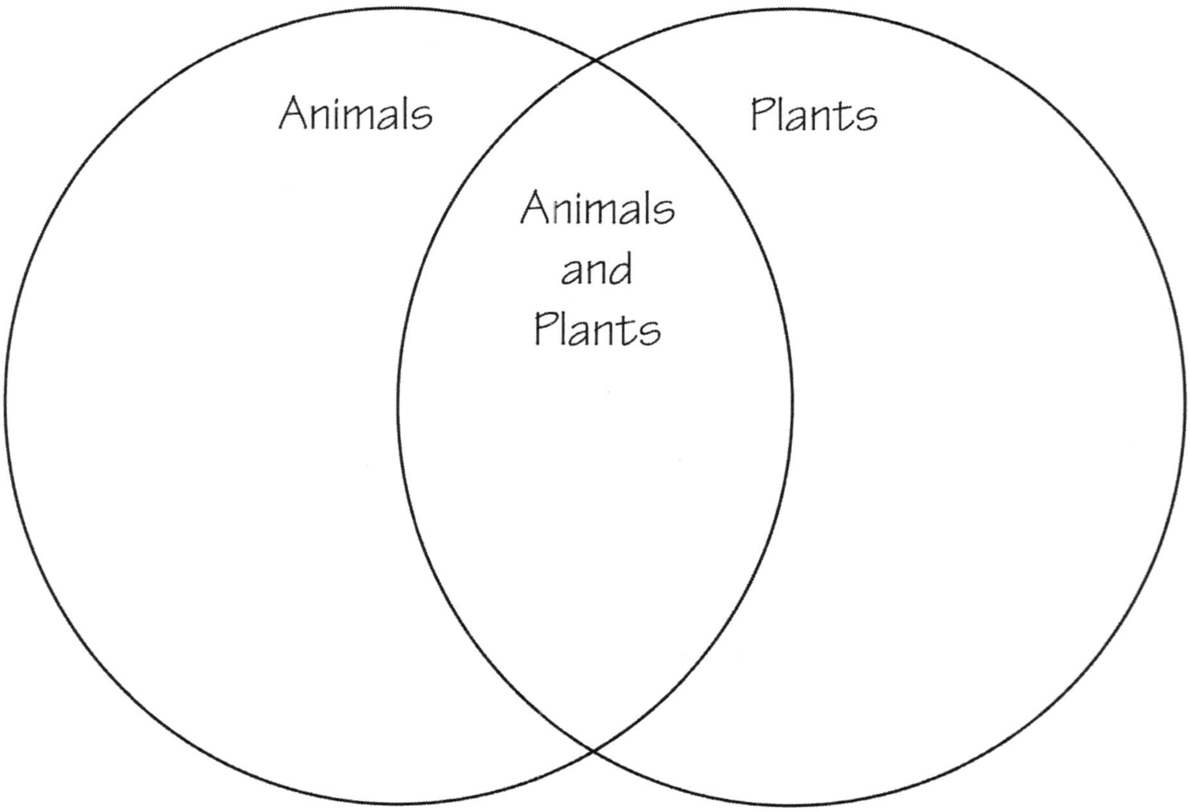

Name: ______________________________

# Helping Plants Get Water

What do you think will happen if you water one plant but not the other? Record your prediction.

_______________________________________________________________

_______________________________________________________________

For the next two weeks, check both plants every two days. Record the date and draw pictures in the boxes below to record how each plant is changing.

| | |
|---|---|
| W | |
| Date: ____________ Height: ______ | Date: ____________ Height: ______ |
| W | |
| Date: ____________ Height: ______ | Date: ____________ Height: ______ |

| | |
|---|---|
| W | |
| Date: ________________ Height: ________ | Date: ________________ Height: ________ |
| W | |
| Date: ________________ Height: ________ | Date: ________________ Height: ________ |
| W | |
| Date: ________________ Height: ________ | Date: ________________ Height: ________ |

| | |
|---|---|
| W | |
| Date: ________________ Height: ________ | Date: ________________ Height: ________ |
| W | |
| Date: ________________ Height: ________ | Date: ________________ Height: ________ |

Name: ________________________________

# Design a Watering Device

Can you think of a device for watering indoor plants? In this activity, you and a partner will design and build a watering device that will make it easier for you to care for a plant.

Your device must:
- keep a plant watered without you touching it
- attach to the edge of a plant pot so it will not get lost

## What You Need

- a variety of items, such as craft sticks, string, foam cups, and empty plastic containers
- glue
- tape
- scissors
- plant
- water

**SAFETY CAUTION!**

Remember to work safely when using scissors.

## What You Will Do

1. With your partner, brainstorm ideas for how to build your watering device. What does your device have to do? Think about how plants obtain water when planning your device.
2. Decide on the best design and sketch a picture of it on the back of this page or a separate page.
3. Build your watering device.
4. Does your device do what it is supposed to do? Test it by using it to water a plant.
5. Use your test results to make any needed changes.

## What Did You Find Out?

1. What challenges did you face as you made your device? Explain how you met them.

______________________________________________

______________________________________________

______________________________________________

______________________________________________

Name: ______________________________

# Life Cycles

**1.** What are the four stages of a pumpkin's life cycle? In the circle below, sketch the stages. Use the photos on page 19 of the student book to help you.

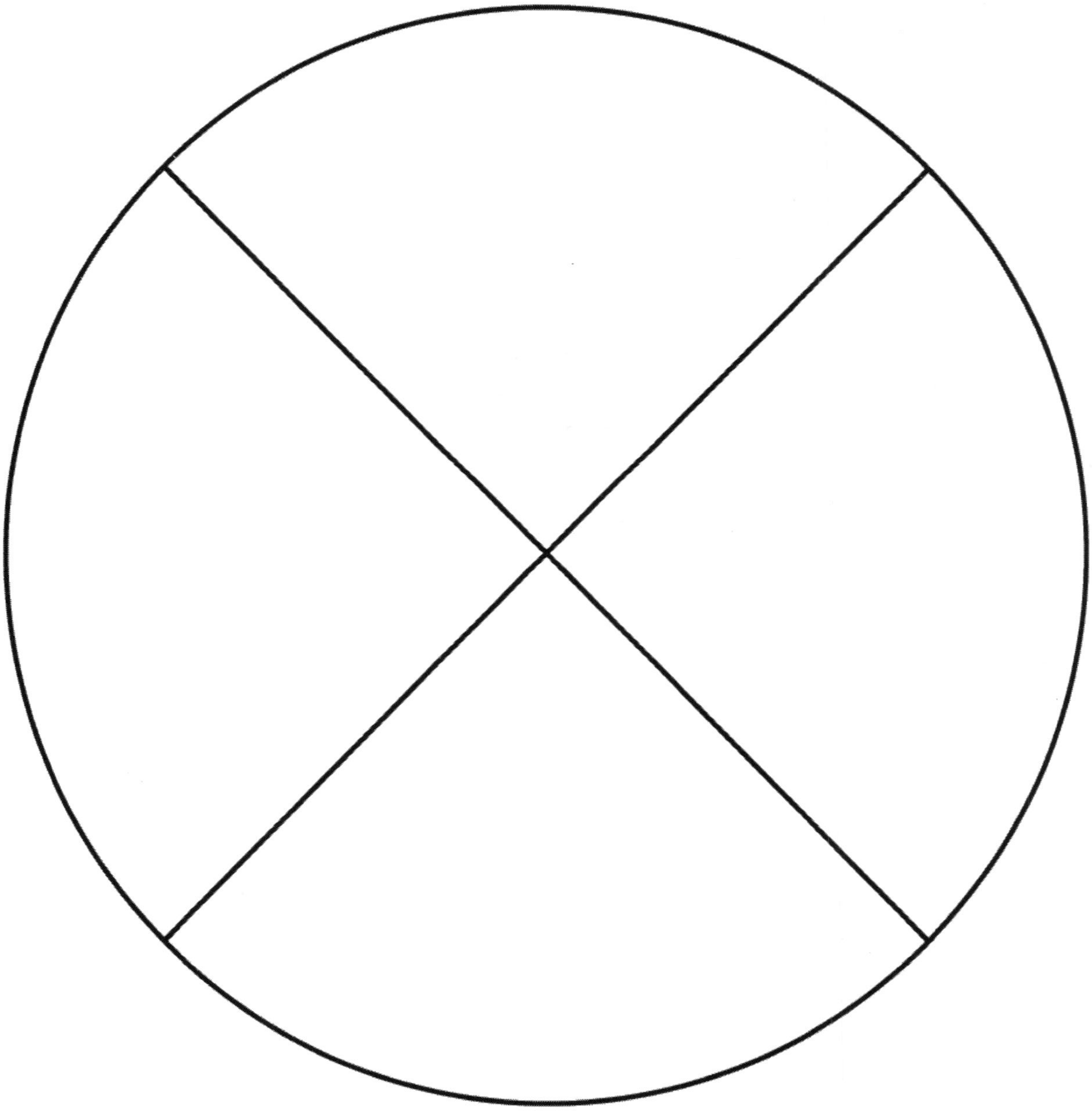

**2.** How are the life cycles of an oak tree and a pumpkin the same? How are they different?

_______________________________________________

_______________________________________________

3. Decide on a plant you and your partner are familiar with, such as a dandelion. What stages of its life cycle have you seen? In the circle below, draw pictures of these stages.

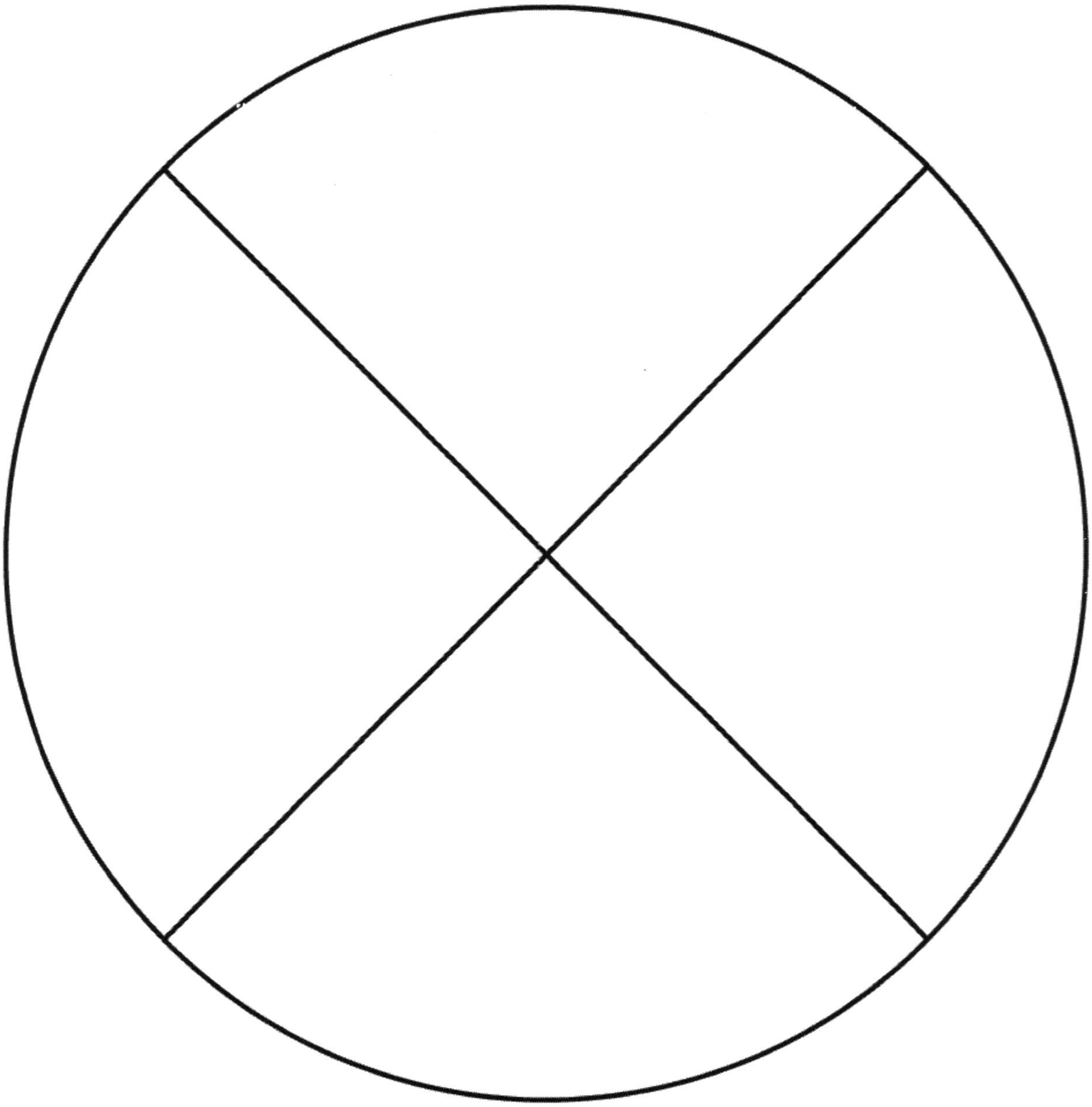

Name: ______________________________

# Drying and Roasting Pumpkin Seeds

Drying and roasting pumpkin seeds are two processes that can make pumpkin seeds into a tasty treat that you can eat.

## What You Need

- newspaper
- pumpkin
- knife
- spoon
- bowl
- sink and tap
- colander
- paper towels
- cookie sheet (optional)
- oven (optional)

**SAFETY CAUTION!**
Do not use the oven by yourself. An adult must be with you.

## What You Will Do

1. Cover your work surface with newspaper. Set a pumpkin on the newspaper.
2. Ask your teacher to help you cut open the pumpkin.
3. Scoop out the pumpkin seeds and put them in a bowl.
4. Wash the seeds with water carefully and remove all the fleshy bits of the pumpkin.
5. Pour the seeds into a colander to drain off the water.
6. To dry the seeds, place a paper towel in a sunny spot. Spread the seeds on the paper towel so they are flat and only one layer thick. Wait 24 hours. To dry the seeds in an oven, place the seeds on a cookie sheet and put the sheet in an oven heated to 135°C. Wait one to two hours. But stir your seeds every 15 to 20 minutes until they are golden brown, so they do not burn.
7. To roast your dried pumpkin seeds, place them on a cookie sheet so they are flat and only one layer thick. Preheat an oven to 120°C. Roast the seeds in the oven for 15 to 20 minutes.
8. Remove the seeds from the oven and let them cool.

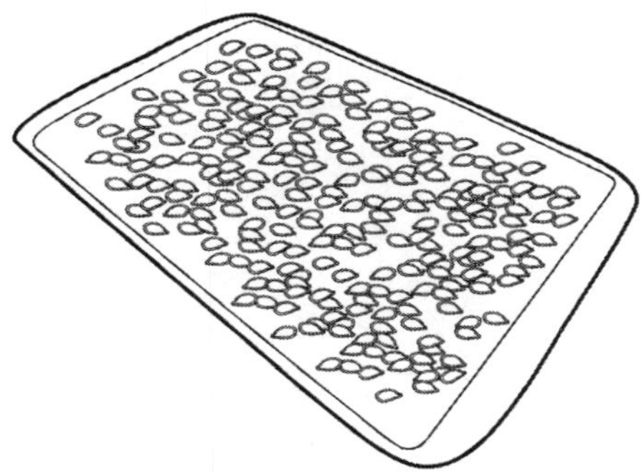

## What Did You Find Out?

1. What do you think might make seeds a nutritious food for people to eat?

______________________________

______________________________

**Name:** ______________________________

# Grouping Plants

Record the way you sorted the leaves and the flowers in the table below.

| Name of Group | Plants I Put in the Group | Why I Put Each Plant in the Group |
|---|---|---|
| | | |

**Name:** ________________________________

# How Do Animals Help Plants?

Carefully observe the burr or cattail. In the box below, draw a picture of what you see.

In the box below, draw a picture of what is inside the burr or cattail.

How do you think animals help the plant that produces the burr or cattail? (**Hint:** How could animals help carry the seeds to other places?)

______________________________________________

______________________________________________

______________________________________________

______________________________________________

Name: ______________________________

# How Can Wind and Water Spread Seeds?

**What You Need**

- grass seeds
- pumpkin seeds
- pinecone
- dry bean
- walnut, pecan, or hazelnut in its shell
- table fan (optional)
- bucket of water

**What You Will Do**

1. In the first column of the table below, write the names of the seeds you are using.

| Seed | What I Think Will Spread the Seed Better | What Happened When I Blew on the Seed | What Happened When I Put the Seed in Water |
|---|---|---|---|
| | | | |
| | | | |
| | | | |
| | | | |
| | | | |

2. Do you think water or wind will spread each seed better? Record your predictions in the second column of the table.

3. Set all the seeds on a tabletop. Blow on them or use a fan (set on low) to blow on them. Record what happens to each seed in the third column of the table.

4. Place all the seeds in the bucket of water. Record what happens to each seed in the fourth column of the table.

**What Did You Find Out?**

1. Based on what you have observed, which seeds do you think are most likely to be spread by wind? By water? Explain your reasoning.

Name: ______________________________

# My Field Trip Notes

Record your observations in the table below. Use the back of this sheet if you need more space.

| Plant | Where I Saw the Plant | Why I Think the Plant Is There |
|---|---|---|
| | | |
| | | |
| | | |
| | | |
| | | |
| | | |
| | | |

Name: ______________________________

# What Crops Grow in Saskatchewan?

Wheat grows in Saskatchewan. What foods have wheat? List the foods below.

______________________________________________________________________

______________________________________________________________________

______________________________________________________________________

______________________________________________________________________

With your group, choose an area in another part of the world. Research what trees, shrubs, grasses, and crops grow there. Record your findings in the web below.

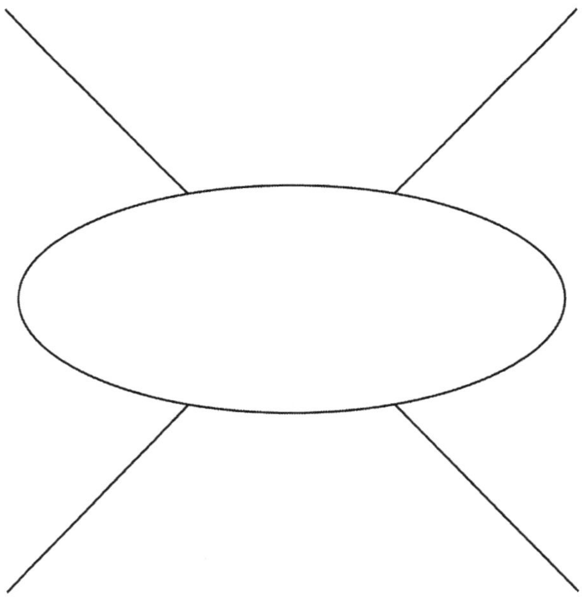

**Name:** ______________________________

# Plants Are Food for the World

Look at the photos on page 30 of the student book. In the table below, record where each family lives and any plants, parts of plants, and foods made from plants that you can identify in the food they eat.

| Place Where Family Lives | Plants, Plant Parts, and Foods That Come from Plants |
|---|---|
| | |
| | |
| | |

Which family eats the most food from plants? ______________________________

Which family eats the least food from plants? ______________________________

Choose one place from your table above. Research what types of trees, grasses, and other plants grow there and how the plants are used. Record your findings below.

| Plants That Grow in ____________ | How People Use the Plants |
| --- | --- |
| | |

Name: ______________________________

# Nature's Renewal

With your group, choose one of the topics below to research. Circle the topic you choose.

- How do forest or prairie fires help plants?
- How do forest or prairie fires harm plants?

Record your findings in the table below.

| **How?**<br>(How is a forest or prairie fire helpful/harmful to plants?) | **When?**<br>(When is a forest or prairie fire helpful/harmful to plants?) |
| --- | --- |
| | |

Name: ______________________________

# How Can People Affect Plants?

Watch what happens to the plants. In the boxes below, record what happens to each plant.

| Day | Plant Watered with Clean Water | Plant Watered with Water With Road Salt |
|---|---|---|
| 1 | | |
| 2 | | |
| 3 | | |
| 4 | | |
| 5 | | |
| 6 | | |
| 7 | | |
| 8 | | |
| 9 | | |
| 10 | | |
| 11 | | |
| 12 | | |
| 13 | | |
| 14 | | |

**Name:** ______________________________

# How Can People Help Plants?

Make a list of ways people can help plants:

___________________________________________________________________

___________________________________________________________________

___________________________________________________________________

___________________________________________________________________

With your group, choose one of these actions:
- Harvesting crops
- Fertilizing crops
- Protecting some areas where plants grow

List all the positive and negative ways the action uses plants and/or protects plants. Decide if the positive ways are greater than the negative ways. Be prepared to defend your position.

**Positive Ways**

___________________________________________________________________

___________________________________________________________________

___________________________________________________________________

___________________________________________________________________

**Negative Ways**

___________________________________________________________________

___________________________________________________________________

___________________________________________________________________

___________________________________________________________________

Name: ______________________ Due Date: ______________

# Design Project Planner: Create a Garden

You will design a vegetable or flower garden. You will build a model of your garden to show how you will help the plants grow.

Your design must:
- give seeds what they need to sprout
- include how you will care for the plants

1. Decide whether your garden will be a vegetable or flower garden. Circle your choice below:

   - Vegetable garden
   - Flower garden

2. What will you grow in your garden? List as many plants as you can:

______________________________________________

______________________________________________

______________________________________________

______________________________________________

3. How will you place the plants in your garden? Brainstorm as many ways as you can. Record your ideas on the back of this sheet.

4. Decide which way is best. Draw a picture to record it:

5. What can you use to build a model of your garden? Record your ideas:

**Materials and Equipment**

_______________________________________________

_______________________________________________

_______________________________________________

_______________________________________________

6. Ask your teacher to approve your design and list of materials.

7. Build a model of your garden. Check that your model does what it is supposed to do. Does it give seeds all the things that they need to sprout? Does it show how you will care for the plants?

8. Do you need to make any changes to your design after you have checked it?

9. Make any needed changes. Describe the changes and explain why you made them:

_______________________________________________

_______________________________________________

_______________________________________________

_______________________________________________

**Assessment Checklist**

**I made sure that I**

- ❑ put my garden in a place where plants will grow
- ❑ created a garden that helps plants grow
- ❑ built a model that does what it is supposed to do

Name: ______________________________

# Design Project Rubric: Create a Garden

| | 1 Star ★ | 2 Stars ★★ | 3 Stars ★★★ | 4 Stars ★★★★ |
|---|---|---|---|---|
| **Designing and planning your garden** | You needed help to plan and design your garden to give seeds the things they need to grow. | Your garden design gives seeds some of the things they need to grow. | Your garden design gives seeds most of the things they need to grow. | Your garden design gives seeds all the things they need to grow. |
| **Building a model of your garden** | You needed help to build a model that shows how you will care for the plants in your garden. | You built a model that shows some of the ways you will care for the plants in your garden. | You built a model that shows most of the ways you will care for the plants in your garden. | You built a model that shows all of the ways you will care for the plants in your garden. |
| **Using materials and equipment safely** | You had to be reminded to use the materials and equipment safely. | You used the materials and equipment safely some of the time. | You used the materials and equipment safely most of the time. | You used the materials and equipment safely all of the time. |
| **Working with group members** | You needed help to cooperate and work with your group members. | You worked cooperatively and usefully with group members some of the time. | You worked cooperatively and usefully with group members most of the time. | You worked cooperatively and usefully with group members all of the time. |
| **Group presentation** | You needed help to explain and demonstrate your garden design. | You could explain and demonstrate some of your garden design clearly. | You could explain and demonstrate most of your garden design clearly. | You could explain and demonstrate your garden design very clearly. |

Name: ___________________________

# Show What You Know

1. Name the parts of the plant shown on page 42 of the student book. Beside each name, write what the part does for the plant.

   a) ___________________________

   b) ___________________________

   c) ___________________________

   d) ___________________________

   e) ___________________________

2. Sort the foods in the list below into groups. Choose two features to sort them.

| | |
|---|---|
| lettuce | cauliflower |
| tomato | apple |
| cucumber | broccoli |
| spinach | carrot |

3. Describe what seeds need to sprout.

___________________________

___________________________

___________________________

4. Compare your basic needs with a plant's basic needs. Use the Venn diagram below. Label each part of the diagram.

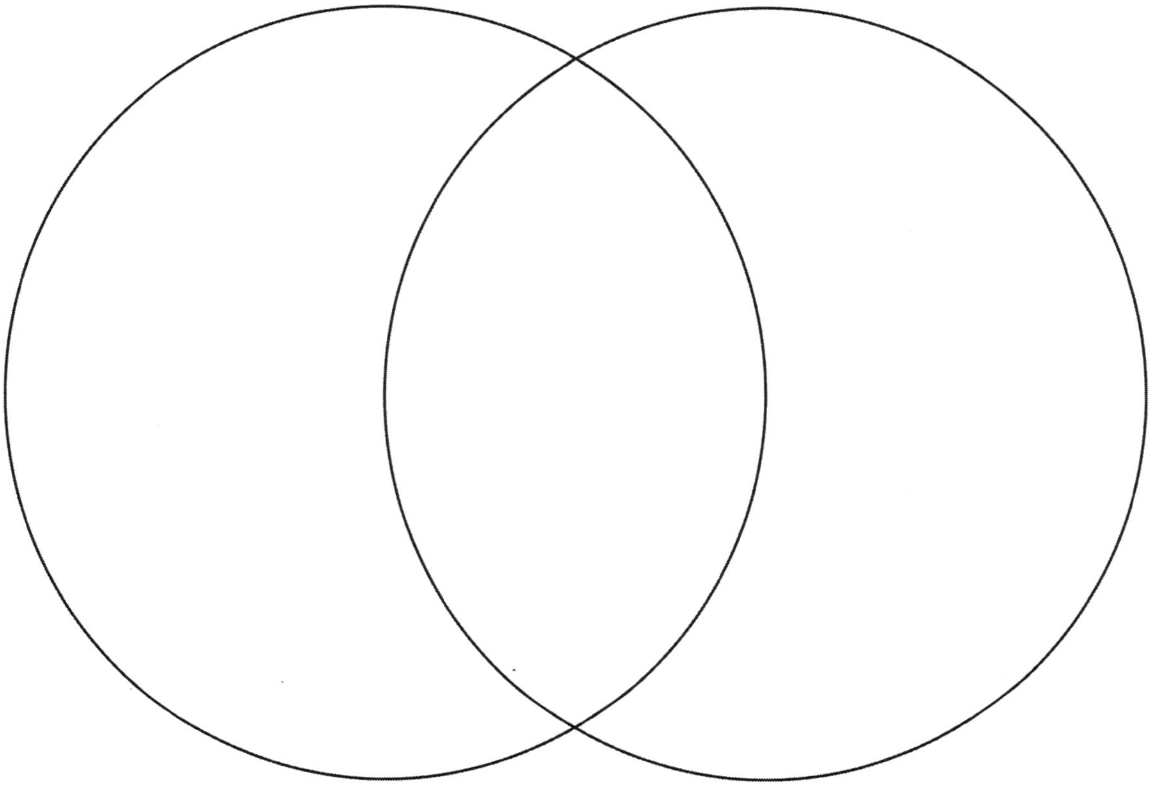

5. Give three examples of plant products you use that are not food.

6. Give one example of how animals help plants.

7. Give three examples of how plants help people.

8. Describe the main reason that most First Nations and Métis people respect plants and animals.

______________________________________________

______________________________________________

______________________________________________

9. Draw pictures to show the life cycle of a plant. Identify features that stay the same and those that change during the life cycle.

10. Say the wheat crops in Saskatchewan were not harvested this year because of wet and cold weather. How might this affect the diets of people around the world?

______________________________________________

______________________________________________

______________________________________________

11. Which four plants are sacred to many First Nations and Métis people? Research to find out. Then present your findings to the class.

12. Imagine you are camping with your family and you notice that some people have gone to bed and left their campfire burning. Explain the danger to plants.

13. Say the plant you have been growing is looking wilted and the leaves are dry. What could you do to make it healthy again?

**Looking Back**

14. Give one reason why you think learning about plants is important.

15. Did anything you learned about plants surprise you? Explain your answer.

# Answers to Unit 1 Line Masters

## LM 1-5: Paper Making

1. Students' answers may vary but could include ripping paper into smaller pieces and using less water so the new paper might take less time to dry.

## LM 1-8: Coloured Flowers

1. The flower turned the same colour as the food colouring. Students should recognize that as the plant took in water the water travelled up the stem to the flower.

2. To make one flower turn two colours, students can do a technique known as "Split Ends." Help students to split the stem of the flower in half vertically by cutting it with a sharp knife. Then students can put one half of the stem in water coloured with food colouring of one colour and the other half in water coloured with food colouring of another colour.

## LM 1-13: Design a Watering Device

1. Students' answers may vary but could include finding it difficult to design a device that will stay intact when dipped in water or that will make it easier to care for a plant than existing devices.

## LM 1-15: Drying and Roasting Pumpkin Seeds

1. Students' answers may vary but could include that seeds may have nutrients or food that is required to develop into new plants.

## LM 1-18: How Can Wind and Water Spread Seeds?

1. Students should recognize that small and lightweight seeds are moved more easily by wind and water than large and heavy seeds. Large and heavy seeds are not easily moved by wind if at all. Moving water, such as river water, can move large and heavy seeds.

UNIT 2

# Structures and Materials

## Table of Contents

## Table of Contents *(continued)*

## Unit Indicators Correlation Chart

| Indicator | Lesson References | Assessment Opportunities |
|---|---|---|
| By the end of grade 3, students will be able to: | | |
| **SM3.1 Investigate properties of materials and methods of joinery used in structures.** | | |
| a. Identify problems to be solved related to the properties of materials in structures. | Lesson 8<br><br>Lesson 11<br>Design Project<br>Show What You Know | Work On It, p. 64<br>Communicate, p. 65, q. 1<br>Communicate, p. 71, q. 3<br>Work On It, p. 77<br>Show What You Know, p. 81, q. 10, 11, 12, 13 |
| b. Examine the properties of materials used in natural and human-built structures. | Lesson 1<br>Lesson 11 | Work On It, p. 48<br>Communicate, p. 71, q. 3 |
| c. Compare the properties of materials used historically and currently to construct structures such as houses, bridges, towers, and roads throughout the world. | Lesson 7<br>Lesson 9 | Communicate, p. 61, q. 1, 2<br>Work On It, p. 67<br>Communicate, p. 67, q. 1, 2, 3 |
| d. Sort materials for use in constructing structures according to one or more physical properties such as strength, texture, colour, flexibility, and durability. | Lesson 2<br>Lesson 4 | Communicate, p. 51, q. 1, 2<br>Communicate, p. 55, q. 1, 2, 3, 4 |
| e. Analyze how various similar and dissimilar materials can be joined and identify the most appropriate methods for joining specific materials for an identified use. | Lesson 8 | Work On It, p. 64<br>Communicate, p. 65, q. 1, 2 |
| f. Use appropriate tools to safely cut, shape, make holes, sew, and assemble materials. | Lesson 3<br>Lesson 8<br>Lesson 10<br>Lesson 12<br>Lesson 13<br>Design Project | Work On It, p. 52<br>Work On It, p. 64<br>Work On It, p. 68<br>Work On It, p. 72<br>Work On It, p. 74<br>Work On It, p. 77 |
| g. Develop and carry out a plan, including making predictions, identifying variables, and recording relevant observations, to test the strength of various materials. | Lesson 2<br>Lesson 10<br><br>Design Project | Work On It, p. 50<br>Work On It, p. 68<br>Communicate, p. 69, q. 1<br>Work On It, p. 77 |
| h. Assess the suitability of various materials for constructing structures, including methods of strengthening those materials. | Lesson 4<br><br>Show What You Know | Work On It, p. 54<br>Communicate, p. 55, q. 1, 2, 3, 4<br>Show What You Know, p. 81, q. 6, 7, 11, 12 |
| i. Examine the suitability of using recycled materials to construct structures. | Lesson 11<br><br>Lesson 12<br><br>Show What You Know | Work On It, p. 71<br>Communicate, p. 71, q. 1, 2<br>Work On It, p. 72<br>Communicate, p. 73, q. 1, 2, 3, 4<br>Show What You Know, p. 81, q. 4, 13 |

| Indicator | Lesson References | Assessment Opportunities |
|---|---|---|
| **SM3.2 Assess the function and characteristics of strong, stable, and balanced natural and human-built structures.** | | |
| a. Analyze the purpose or function of various natural and human-built structures. | Lesson 11<br>Lesson 13 | Communicate, p. 71, q. 1, 3<br>Communicate, p. 75, q. 3 |
| b. Examine how some human-built structures are modelled on shapes and structures found in nature. | Lesson 1<br><br>Lesson 3<br>Lesson 13<br>Show What You Know | Work On It, p. 48<br>Communicate p. 49, q. 1, 2, 3<br>Communicate, p. 53, q. 2<br>Work On It, p. 74<br>Show What You know, p. 81, q. 9 |
| c. Assess how 2-D shapes and 3-D objects provide strength, stability, and balance to natural and human-built structures. | Lesson 3<br><br>Lesson 4<br>Lesson 5<br>Lesson 13<br>Show What You Know | Work On It, p. 52<br>Communicate, p. 53, q. 1, 2, 3<br>Communicate, p. 55, q. 2<br>Work On It, p. 56<br>Communicate, p. 75, q. 1, 2<br>Show What You Know, p. 80, q. 1, 2 |
| d. Compare the characteristics of solid, frame, and shell structures. | Lesson 7 | Work On It, p. 61<br>Communicate, p. 61, q. 1, 2 |
| e. Classify natural and human-built structures as solid, frame, or shell structures. | Lesson 7<br><br>Show What You Know | Work On It, p. 61<br>Communicate, p. 61, q. 3<br>Show What You Know, p. 80, q. 3 |
| f. Compare the characteristics of different types of shelter constructed by people throughout the world, past and present. | Lesson 9 | Work On It, p. 67<br>Communicate, p. 67, q. 1, 2, 3 |
| g. Examine the characteristics and significance of historical structures such as Stonehenge, the Parthenon, Petra, the Great Wall of China, Angkor Wat, Machu Picchu, the Taj Mahal, the Pyramids, and Easter Island moai. | Lesson 9 | Work On It, p. 67<br>Communicate, p. 67, q. 1 |
| h. Analyze how various shapes contribute to balance and stability in humans and various animals. | Lesson 6<br><br>Show What You Know | Work On It, p. 59<br>Communicate, p. 59, q. 1, 2, 3, 4<br>Show What You Know, p. 81, q. 8 |
| i. Develop and carry out a plan to construct a simple structure such as a tower, bridge, tipi, or bird feeder that meets teacher- or student-specified criteria related to strength, stability, and function. | Lesson 5<br>Lesson 10<br><br>Lesson 12<br>Lesson 13<br>Design Project | Work On It, p. 56<br>Work On It, p. 68<br>Communicate, p. 69, q. 1, 2, 3<br>Work On It, p. 72<br>Work On It, p. 74<br>Work On It, p. 77 |

## Unit Indicators Correlation Chart *(continued)*

| Indicator | Lesson References | Assessment Opportunities |
|---|---|---|
| j. Estimate measurements in order to select appropriate quantities of required materials for constructing a structure. | Lesson 5<br>Lesson 10<br>Lesson 13<br>Design Project | Work On It, p. 56<br>Work On It, p. 68<br>Work On It, p. 74<br>Work On It, p. 77 |
| k. Follow safety procedures and rules while constructing structures and explain the need for such procedures and rules. | Lesson 2<br>Lesson 5<br>Lesson 10<br>Lesson 12<br>Lesson 13<br>Design Project | Work On It, p. 50<br>Work On It, p. 56<br>Work On It, p. 68<br>Work On It, p. 72<br>Work On It, p. 74<br>Work On It, p. 77 |
| l. Illustrate the construction process for a simple structure, including descriptions of the components of the structure, using labelled drawings, written and oral explanations, and demonstrations. | Lesson 2<br>Lesson 5<br><br>Lesson 10<br>Design Project | Work On It, p. 50<br>Work On It, p. 56<br>Communicate, p. 57, q. 3<br>Communicate, p. 69, q. 1, 2<br>Work On It, p. 77 |
| m. Assess the strength, stability, and balance of personally constructed structures and make changes to improve the structure as deemed necessary. | Lesson 3<br>Lesson 5<br><br>Lesson 10<br>Lesson 13 | Work On It, p. 52<br>Work On It, p. 56<br>Communicate, p. 57, q. 1, 2, 4<br>Work On It, p. 68<br>Work On It, p. 74<br>Communicate, p. 75, q. 1, 2 |
| n. Identify materials or parts of a structure that failed and hypothesize why they failed. | Lesson 2<br>Lesson 5<br>Lesson 8<br>Lesson 10 | Communicate, p. 51, q. 2, 3<br>Communicate, p. 57, q. 4<br>Work On It, p. 64<br>Communicate, p. 69, q. 3 |
| o. Assess natural and human-built structures to determine if they are effective, safe, make efficient use of materials, meet user's needs, and minimize impact on the environment. | Lesson 11<br>Lesson 13 | Communicate, p. 71, q. 1, 3<br>Communicate, p. 75, q. 2 |
| p. Research jobs and hobbies which contribute to the design, building, and maintenance of natural and human-built structures. | Ask … | Research, p. 63 |

## Lesson Planning Chart

Note that estimates of class times are based on 40 min per period.

| Lesson | Type of Activity | Time (number of classes) | Materials Required (for each group) | Line Masters |
|---|---|---|---|---|
| **Unit Opener** | | 0.5 | one deck of cards<br>paper<br>pencils | LM 2-1<br>LM 2-2 |
| **Launch:** Finding Structures | confirmation inquiry | 1 | paper<br>pencils | LM 2-3 |
| **1.** Copying Nature | structured inquiry | 1 | shape pictures<br>scissors<br>paper<br>pencils | LM 2-4 |
| **2.** Which Material Is the Strongest? | guided inquiry | 2 | straws<br>toothpicks<br>tape<br>string<br>wooden blocks<br>cloth<br>block of clay<br>spaghetti<br>small paper cup<br>ruler<br>scissors<br>pennies or marbles<br>paper<br>pencils | LM 2-5 |
| **3.** Which Shape Is the Strongest? | guided inquiry | 1 | 7 Bristol board strips (10 cm by 2 cm)<br>paper punch<br>7 paper fasteners<br>scissors<br>paper<br>pencils | LM 2-6 |
| **4.** How Can We Strengthen Structures? | structured inquiry | 1 | no materials needed | LM 2-7 |
| **5.** Making Paper Towers Strong | guided inquiry | 2 | photocopy paper (1 sheet for each test)<br>ruler<br>2 cardboard squares (15 cm by 15 cm)<br>rolls of pennies<br>paper<br>pencils | LM 2-8 |
| **6.** Nature's Balancing Act | guided inquiry | 2 | beanbag or small pillow<br>paper<br>pencils | LM 2-9 |

# Lesson Planning Chart *(continued)*

| Lesson | Type of Activity | Time (number of classes) | Materials Required (for each group) | Line Masters |
|---|---|---|---|---|
| **7.** Is It a Solid, Frame, or Shell Structure? | structured inquiry | 2 | pictures of structures<br>magazines or catalogues<br>scissors<br>paper<br>pencils | LM 2-10 |
| **Ask ...** Why is it important to understand structures? | guided inquiry | 3 | reference books<br>computer with Internet access<br>paper<br>pencils | |
| **8.** How Are Materials Joined Together? | guided inquiry | 2–3 | file folder<br>ruler<br>scissors<br>glue<br>tape<br>stapler<br>paper fasteners<br>paper clips<br>paper<br>pencils | LM 2-11<br>LM 2-12 |
| **9.** What Makes a Structure Last? | guided inquiry | 1 | pictures of structures<br>paper<br>pencils | LM 2-13 |
| **10.** Earthquake-Proof Structures | structured inquiry | 2 | Bristol board (15 cm by 20 cm)<br>ruler<br>scissors<br>glue<br>tape<br>paper fasteners<br>stapler<br>paper<br>pencils<br>box lid<br>marbles<br>lightweight cardboard (20 cm by 30 cm)<br>modelling clay | LM 2-14 |
| **11.** Looking at Materials | guided inquiry | 1 | paper<br>pencils | LM 2-15 |
| **12.** Reusing and Recycling Materials | confirmation inquiry | 2 | clean milk or juice cartons or plastic water bottles<br>scissors<br>nails<br>craft sticks or twigs<br>wire or string<br>birdseed | LM 2-16 |

## Lesson Planning Chart *(continued)*

| Lesson | Type of Activity | Time (number of classes) | Materials Required (for each group) | Line Masters |
|---|---|---|---|---|
| **13.** Well Built or Not? | guided inquiry | 2 | 15 twigs or bamboo skewers (25 to 30 cm long)<br>coarse string or twine (40 cm long)<br>scrap Bristol board<br>scissors<br>3 brown paper lunch bags<br>ruler<br>tape or glue<br>paper<br>pencils | LM 2-17<br>LM 2-18 |
| **Design Project:** Build a Bridge | open inquiry | 3 | paper<br>pencils<br>2 stacks of books (15 cm tall)<br>ruler<br>50 pennies<br>materials left over from the unit or provided by students | LM 2-19<br>LM 2-20<br>LM 2-21 |

traditional **KNOWLEDGE**

## First Nations Cultural References

The following references provide information on First Nations topics. The information may not be specific to Saskatchewan First Nations and should not be generalized to all First Nations.

- Wanuskewin Heritage Park: www.wanuskewin.com
- Games of the Arctic: www.virtualmuseum.ca/Exhibitions/Traditions/English/inuit_games.html
- Wonderville: Build a Tipi: www.learnalberta.ca/content/wonbt/html/index.html?launch=true

## Suggested Websites

Please note that website URLs constantly change and the addresses given below may become out of date. In this case, please use the website title and a search engine to find the appropriate website.

- The Building Big Educators' Guide presents a flexible collection of fun, simple hands-on activities: www.pbs.org/wgbh/buildingbig/educator/act_index.html
- Quick Tips in Design: Part 5: Shape: www.atpm.com/9.11/design.shtml
- Bridge Building: The Basics: http://42explore.com/bridge.htm
- Grade Three Science: Topic B: Building with a Variety of Materials: http://ake.epsb.ca/bridges/curriculum.htm
- Recycle card game: http://edweb.sdsu.edu/courses/edtec670/Cardboard/Card/R/recycle.html
- Breaking Stuff On Purpose—How Strong is a Chocolate Bar?: www.wpsu.org/nano/media/Breaking_HS_Lab_v102.pdf
- CBC 4 Kids: Why don't hens break their eggs when they sit on them?: http://resources.yesican-science.ca/lpdd/g03/demos/eggs.html
- Seismic Sleuths: Earthquakes: www.fema.gov/library/viewRecord.do?id=3558
- Shell, Frame, and Solid Structures: http://goulbournms.ocdsb.ca/design%20and%20tech/structures7.pdf
- Let's Do Science: Grade Three—Testing Materials and Designs: http://letsdoscience.com/content_pdf/Grade3TestingMaterials.pdf
- Assignment Discovery Online Curriculum: Constructing Earthquake-Proof Buildings: http://school.discoveryeducation.com/lessonplans/pdf/earthquakeproof/earthquakeproof.pdf
- Nova Super Bridge—Build a Bridge: www.pbs.org/wgbh/nova/bridge/build.html
- Science Games for Kids—Properties of Materials: www.sciencekids.co.nz/gamesactivities/materialproperties.html
- Links to Grade 3 Materials and Structures: www.stam.mb.ca/stam_grade3_links.html#Materials%20and%20Structures

- Teacher background for Stability and Manoeuvrability of Terrestrial Vertebrates: http://icb.oxfordjournals.org/content/42/1/158.full
- Discovery Education—Stable and Unstable Structures: www.discoveryeducation.com/teachers/free-lesson-plans/stable-and-unstable-structures.cfm
- Recycling Lesson Plans: www.theteachersguide.com/Recyclinglessonplans.htm
- World's Tallest Buildings: www.infoplease.com/ipa/A0001338.html
- Craik Ecovillage: www.craikecovillage.com
- EcoArk Saskatchewan: www.ecoarksaskatchewan.com/about.html
- Recycle Saskatchewan: www.recyclesaskatchewan.ca/for-sk-schools/structures-materials.html

## Suggested Field Trips

- EcoArk Saskatchewan welcomes classes for tours and supplies workshops when it has an instructor volunteer available.
- Wanuskewin Heritage Park, Tipi Lodging: *"Ever thought what it would be like to sleep in a tipi? Book your tipi village experience and sleep in a tipi and participate in the programs that are offered."*

## Suggested Guest Speakers

- Innovators in the Schools *"Innovators are experts in many fields of science, math, and technology who will share their education and employment experiences with your students. Choose from professionals working in a variety of fields throughout the province."* To find out more about these Innovators, check the website: www.sasksciencecentre.com/edprograms/innovators.html
- Local contractors, lumber yards, or building centres
- Local architects or engineering firms, road contractors

traditional ***KNOWLEDGE***

- You might invite an Elder or Knowledge Keeper into the classroom to discuss tipis or to set up a tipi. Several divisions across Saskatchewan may be able to arrange this visit. Please refer to the "Protocol for Contacting Elders and Traditional Knowledge Keepers" in the Program Overview of this Teacher's Resource.

## Suggested Additional Student Resources

- *Build It! Structures, Systems and You* by Adrienne Mason and illustrated by Claudia Davila (Kids Can Press, 2006)
- *The Three Little Pigs*—A good review of materials and their relative strengths.
- ZOOMsci Activities—A great website for kids to explore by themselves. This site includes interactive activities and suggestions for hands-on exploration:
  http://pbskids.org/zoom/activities/sci/#structures
- Structures Around the World. Students see different structures and are given instructions for building a straw tower:
  www.exploratorium.edu/structures/
  www.exploratorium.edu/scale/straws.html
- Structures— *YES Mag* is a great addition to your library. It can also be found online:
  www.yesmag.bc.ca/focus/structures/structures.html

## Materials and Equipment Needed for Unit 2

(based on 30 students)

|  |  |
|---|---|
| **Unit Opener (p. 44)** | |
| **Materials**<br>• paper<br>• pencils | **Equipment**<br>• 10 decks of cards |
| **Launch: Finding Structures (p. 46)** | |
| **Materials**<br>• paper<br>• pencils | **Equipment**<br>• no equipment needed |
| **1. Copying Nature (p. 48)** | |
| **Materials**<br>• 15 pages of shape pictures<br>• paper<br>• pencils | **Equipment**<br>• 15 pairs of scissors |
| **2. Which Material Is the Strongest? (p. 50)** | |
| **Materials**<br>• straws<br>• toothpicks<br>• tape<br>• string<br>• wooden blocks<br>• cloth<br>• block of clay<br>• spaghetti<br>• 15 small paper cups<br>• paper<br>• pencils | **Equipment**<br>• 15 rulers<br>• 15 pairs of scissors<br>• pennies or marbles |
| **3. Which Shape Is the Strongest? (p. 52)** | |
| **Materials**<br>• 105 Bristol board strips (10 cm by 2 cm)<br>• paper<br>• pencils | **Equipment**<br>• paper punches<br>• 105 paper fasteners<br>• 15 pairs of scissors |
| **4. How Can We Strengthen Structures? (p. 54)** | |
| **Materials**<br>• no materials needed | **Equipment**<br>• no equipment needed |
| **5. Making Paper Towers Strong (p. 56)** | |
| **Materials**<br>• photocopy paper<br>• 30 cardboard squares (15 cm by 15 cm)<br>• paper<br>• pencils | **Equipment**<br>• 15 rulers<br>• 60 rolls of pennies |

## Materials and Equipment

*(continued)*

| 6. Nature's Balancing Act (p. 58) | |
|---|---|
| **Materials**<br>• paper<br>• pencils | **Equipment**<br>• 15 beanbags or small pillows |
| **7. Is It a Solid, Frame, or Shell Structure? (p. 60)** | |
| **Materials**<br>• 30 pages of pictures of structures<br>• 30 magazines or catalogues<br>• paper<br>• pencils | **Equipment**<br>• 30 pairs of scissors |
| **8. How Are Materials Joined Together? (p. 64)** | |
| **Materials**<br>• 15 file folders<br>• glue<br>• tape<br>• staplers<br>• 15 paper fasteners<br>• 15 paper clips<br>• paper<br>• pencils | **Equipment**<br>• 15 rulers<br>• 15 pairs of scissors |
| **9. What Makes a Structure Last? (p. 66)** | |
| **Materials**<br>• paper<br>• pencils | **Equipment**<br>• 30 pages with pictures of structures |
| **10. Earthquake-Proof Structures (p. 68)** | |
| **Materials**<br>• 15 Bristol boards (15 cm by 20 cm)<br>• glue<br>• tape<br>• paper fasteners<br>• paper<br>• pencils<br>• modelling clay | **Equipment**<br>• 15 rulers<br>• 15 pairs of scissors<br>• staplers<br>• 15 box lids<br>• marbles<br>• 15 lightweight cardboards (about 20 cm by 30 cm) |
| **11. Looking at Materials (p. 70)** | |
| **Materials**<br>• paper<br>• pencils | **Equipment**<br>• no equipment needed |

## Materials and Equipment

***(continued)***

| 12. Reusing and Recycling Materials (p. 72) | |
|---|---|
| **Materials**<br>• 30 clean milk or juice cartons or plastic water bottles<br>• 30 craft sticks or twigs<br>• wire or string<br>• 30 nails (7.5 cm)<br>• birdseed | **Equipment**<br>• 30 pairs of scissors |
| **13. Well Built or Not? (p. 74)** | |
| **Materials**<br>• 3 bags of 100 bamboo skewers (25 to 30 cm long)<br>• 600 cm coarse string or twine<br>• 15 scrap Bristol boards<br>• 45 brown paper lunch bags<br>• tape or glue<br>• paper<br>• pencils | **Equipment**<br>• 15 pairs of scissors<br>• 15 rulers |
| **Design Project: Build a Bridge (p. 76)** | |
| **Materials**<br>• materials left over from the unit or provided by students<br>• paper<br>• pencils | **Equipment**<br>• 30 stacks of books (15 cm tall)<br>• 15 rulers<br>• 750 pennies |

## Materials and Equipment

*(continued)*

| Overall Unit Requirements | |
|---|---|
| **Materials**<br>• 400–500 straws<br>• 3 or 4 boxes of toothpicks<br>• 3 rolls tape<br>• one ball of string<br>• 60 wooden blocks<br>• cloth<br>• modelling clay<br>• 1 pkg. spaghetti<br>• 15 small paper cups<br>• 5 sheets Bristol board<br>• 30 magazines and catalogues<br>• 15 file folders<br>• 10 sheets light weight Bristol board<br>• 6 sheets light weight cardboard<br>• 30 clean milk or juice cartons or plastic water bottles<br>• 30 craft sticks or twigs<br>• thirty 30-cm pieces of wire<br>• 30 nails (7.5 cm)<br>• 30 kg birdseed<br>• 2 large bottles of glue<br>• 3 bags of 100 bamboo skewers<br>• one ball of coarse twine<br>• 45 brown paper lunch bags<br>• paper<br>• pencils<br>• 15 pages of shape pictures<br>• 30 pages of pictures of structures<br>• 120 paper fasteners<br>• 2 boxes of paper clips | **Equipment**<br>• 30 pairs of scissors<br>• 30 rulers<br>• 60 rolls of pennies<br>• 15 box lids<br>• 6000–7000 marbles<br>• 10 decks of cards<br>• paper punches<br>• staplers<br>• 15 beanbags or small pillows<br>• 30 stacks of books |

# UNIT 2 Unit Opener



| Time |
|---|
| 20 min |
| **Line Masters** |
| • LM 2-1<br>• LM 2-2 |

The Big Ideas on page 44 of the student book introduce students to the idea that structures have jobs and the materials used in the construction of those structures depend on the job being done. Students may be fascinated with natural structures and may find it difficult to make connections to the human-built structures they see every day. Examining both types of structures by using different filters such as materials, fasteners, and shapes will allow them to find the links that exist. Because the unit deals with humans and nature, it is a natural fit for making connections between what nature provides, in the way of materials and shapes, and the traditions of First Nations and Métis peoples. These shapes from the past are echoed in the structures of today and can be seen in the photo of the trestle bridge at Outlook, Saskatchewan.

You may want to start a discussion about the unit by having students come up with a list of broad inquiry questions that they may have about the unit content. These questions should be answered by the end of the unit.

- What is a structure?
- What are different types of structures?
- What are structures made of?
- Who builds structures?
- Where are structures found?
- Does nature make structures?
- Why are structures important?
- How are structures the same?
- How do you know what structure will work best?
- Is everything a structure?

## Assessing Prior Knowledge

- Divide the class into groups of five or six students.
- On the board, large sheet of paper, or flip chart write, *What I know, What I want to know,* and *What I learned.*
- Explain that you are interested in facts, or things that students know to be true, about structures and their materials. Examples may include the following: Structures are all around; the school is a structure; there are lots of shapes; structures are made of hard materials.
- Ask students if they agree with the statements. If they agree the statement is true, write it in the *What I know* column.
- If they do not agree, reword the statement as a question and include it in the *What I want to know* column of your KWL chart. An example may be: What are structures made of?
- You can add to and edit this chart as you progress through the unit.

## Introduce the Unit

- Explain to students that they are about to study a unit in which they will be learning about structures, how structures are shaped, and what materials are used to make structures.
- Have students discuss what they think structures are.
- Invite students to think not only of human-built structures, but to consider objects found in nature, such as spider webs.
- Explain to students that the shapes of structures give them strength and stability.
- You can encourage students to see that they probably already know something about structures and materials. When students build with building toys, they are investigating shapes and the effect shapes have on stability.
- Once you have determined students' prior knowledge, you may want to hand out LM 2-1 Unit 2 Summary and LM 2-2 Unit 2 Vocabulary to help students record their understanding of the unit and vocabulary terms.

## Introduce the Design Project

- Engage students' interest in structures and materials by emphasizing a real-life application.
- Inform students that at the end of this unit, they will be asked to design and build a bridge.
- The bridge must be a stable structure that can span a distance of 25 cm. This bridge must be able to hold a load of at least 50 pennies.
- The students' task will be to work in small groups and produce a plan for this bridge.
- Explain to students that they will design and build the bridge, test their bridge, and then improve their design based on their test results.
- Remind students to take notes throughout the unit that might relate to their Design Project.

**Time**

20 min

**Skills**

- comparing
- observing
- experimenting
- communicating

**Grouping**

groups of three

**Materials and Equipment**

- one deck of cards
- paper
- pencils

**Line Masters**

- none

### Looking Forward

- Work surfaces need to be flat. Slanted desk tops will make it difficult to set up the card houses.
- Slippery tile floor also makes it challenging to build card houses. Working on a carpeted or textured surface works well.

**3.** Triangular shapes stand up best without falling.

LAUNCH

# Finding Structures

Page 46

**Time**

40 min

**Vocabulary**

- structure

**Line Masters**

- LM 2-3

**traditional KNOWLEDGE**

## Get Started ▶

- Use a Think-Pair-Share format to prepare an initial list of examples of structures found in the picture on page 47 of the student book. Ask students to work independently to come up with their own ideas and then pair up with a classmate to compare lists before sharing with the class. You may want to hand out LM 2-3 Finding Structures to help students record their answers.
- While students are sharing their lists with the class, write a list on the board or have students write the suggestions they did not have on their line master.
- The materials available for building structures were different depending on where a person lived. Many First Nations and Métis peoples lived in sod houses because they lived in locations where other types of building materials were scarce.

**Time**

30 min

**Learning Context**

inquiry

**Level of Inquiry**

confirmation

**Skills**

- observing
- interpreting
- comparing

**Grouping**

individuals or pairs

**Materials and Equipment**

- paper
- pencils

**Line Masters**

- LM 2-3

## Work On It

### Purpose

To have students identify types of structures from the picture—human-built structures and structures found in nature, and to describe how these structures are similar and how they are different

### Activity Notes

- Remind students that both humans and nature make structures.
- Encourage students to consider shapes of structures and how they are similar or different.
- Ask students to complete LM 2-3 Finding Structures, by recording the structures' similarities and differences.

1. The structures in the picture are towers (Regina's twin towers), office buildings, a trestle bridge, the Wanuskewin Heritage Park sign, a grain elevator, an oil derrick, a bird feeder, a beaver dam, a wasp nest, a spider web, a house, barns, a car, tractors, and trucks.
2. Students' answers may vary but could include a reference to the materials they are made of or the shape of the structures.
3. Students' answers may vary but could include a reference to the location or the use of the structure.
4. Students' answers may vary but could include the bridge (built by humans) and the beaver dam (built by beavers).

## Communicate

1. Students' questions may vary but could include
   - What are stable structures made of?
   - Are rocks and trees structures?
   - Can nature make structures?

## DI Differentiating Instruction

### *For EAL/ELL*

Encourage students to record their observations using diagrams and sketches.

### *For Enrichment*

Have students list structures found in the classroom. Discuss how these structures are stable. Ask students to describe how simple structures, such as chairs and desks, are safe and appropriate to the user.

### *For Reteaching*

Ask students to point to the structures that confuse them. Trace the outline of the structure to show them the overall shape. This will give students prior knowledge, which will be useful later in the unit.

## Assessment *for* Learning

| What to Look for in Student Work | What to Do |
| --- | --- |
| Students can identify both human-built and natural structures. | • Have students move into pairs to discuss why they consider something a structure. |

# 1 Copying Nature



| Time |
| --- |
| 40 min |
| **Line Masters** |
| • LM 2-4 |

## Indicator Assessment Chart

| Indicator | Assessment Opportunities |
| --- | --- |
| **SM3.1 b.** Examine the properties of materials used in natural and human-built structures (e.g., beaver lodge, bird nest, wasps' nest, honeycomb, ant hill, tipi, house, marionette, circus float, umbrella, ladder, bridge, earthlodge, quinzhee, drink can, hockey puck, playground equipment, and toys). | • Work On It, p. 48 |
| **SM3.2 b.** Examine how some human-built structures are modelled on shapes and structures found in nature. | • Work On It, p. 48<br>• Communicate p. 49, q. 1, 2, 3 |

## Lesson Goal

To find and identify shapes in structures

### Background Information

Triangles, circles, arches, and other shapes are found in nature. These shapes lend strength to natural structures like leaves, trees, and eggs. When force is applied to these shapes, the force is distributed over the entire shape as in leaves and eggs, or over the entire footprint, as in pyramidal-shaped structures.

## Curriculum Connections

In this lesson, students have the opportunity to develop skills and concepts in these areas:

***Mathematics***

SS3.3 e. Identify and determine the length of the dimensions of a personally relevant 2-D shape or 3-D object.
SS3.3 p. Sort a set of 2-D shapes into groups with equal perimeters.

***Social Studies***

DR3.1 a. Demonstrate understanding that the surface of Earth can be represented through maps, aerial photographs, and satellite images.

***Visual Arts***

CP3.8 f. Recognize circles, squares, triangles, and rectangles as geometric shapes and apply this knowledge to art work.
CP3.8 g. Recognize cubes, cylinders, and spheres as geometric forms and apply this knowledge to art work.

CP3.8 h. Identify formal and informal patterns in own surroundings and art works.

## Misconceptions

Students sometimes have difficulty identifying the relationship between the type of material and its use in a structure. They may think using more material will increase the structure's strength, or that the bigger the structure, the stronger it will be.

## Get Started ▶

- After students have read the first three paragraphs from the student book, ask them which three words seem to be very important. Elicit the words *structures*, *materials*, and *shapes*. Have students reread the first paragraph to find what structure means, and then the second paragraph to determine what materials and shape refer to.
- After reading the Get Started section aloud and looking at the photos, ask students, *What have you found out so far about structures and materials?* Encourage students to explain how they learned what they did by saying, *From looking at the photos and reading the information, I guess a structure is something that has a shape and is used for a purpose. Materials are the things used to make the structure.*

| Time |
| --- |
| 30 min |
| **Learning Context** |
| inquiry |
| **Level of Inquiry** |
| structured |
| **Skills** |
| • classifying<br>• comparing<br>• communicating |
| **Grouping** |
| pairs or individuals |
| **Materials and Equipment** |
| • shape pictures<br>• scissors<br>• paper<br>• pencils |
| **Line Masters** |
| • LM 2-4 |

**SAFETY CAUTION!**
Remember to work safely when using scissors.

## Work On It

### Purpose

To have students identify shapes in natural and human-built structures

### Activity Notes

- Discuss the difference between a natural structure and a human-built structure.
- Hand out copies of LM 2-4 Copying Nature to students. It is important that students cut the shapes cleanly, so they can identify the shapes in the picture.
- Students will find that certain shapes repeat themselves. Add any questions students generate to your KWL chart.
- Students will begin to recognize the shapes most commonly found in nature. They will be able to make connections between natural shapes and the shapes found in human-built structures.

**2.** Students should recognize that triangles and curves are found in nature and that triangles are often used in human-built structures.

**4.** Natural structures include the ant hill, trees, and clouds. The natural shapes include curves and triangles. Human-built structures include the bike rack, picnic table, cup, sign post, swing set, basketball hoop, basketball, power line, and sun shelter. The human-built shapes include triangles, rectangles, rhombus, and spheres.

**5.** Triangles — more than 20; Spheres — 1; Rectangles — more than 5.

## Additional Activity

Show students an empty 2 L soda bottle and an empty glass bottle. Ask students the following questions.

- Are these bottles structures?
- What were these bottles originally used for?
- What could these bottles be used for now?

Ask students if they chose those uses based on the material the bottles were made from, or based on their shapes. Discuss their choice.

## Communicate

Communicate questions can be used as formative guides for learning or as summative pieces.

1. Students will probably notice the repetition of a triangular shape.
2. Students should identify arcs or circles as the second shape. Some students may identify straight lines, but should be helped to understand that straight lines are not shapes but are used to make shapes.
3. Students will say that they see triangles or squares. You may want to show students that a square can be divided into two triangles.

## DI Differentiating Instruction

### *For Enrichment*

Have pictures of a city and pictures of a natural area on hand. Ask students to identify shapes without the use of the shape template.

### *For Reteaching*

Use two triangles and a circle cut in half to help students find the shapes in the picture.

## Assessment *for* Learning

| What to Look for in Student Work | What to Do |
| --- | --- |
| Students can identify the shapes most commonly found in nature and those most commonly found in human-built structures. | • Have students share their findings with a partner, then with the class. |
| Students can see the connections between natural structures and human-built structures. | • Have students make a list of the connections between natural structures and human-built structures in their notebooks. |

# 2 Which Material Is the Strongest? *Page 50*

| Time |
| --- |
| 80 min |
| **Vocabulary** |
| • load |
| **Line Masters** |
| • LM 2-5 |

## Indicator Assessment Chart

| Indicator | Assessment Opportunities |
| --- | --- |
| **SM3.1 d.** Sort materials for use in constructing structures according to one or more physical properties such as strength, texture, colour, flexibility, and durability. | • Communicate, p. 51, q. 1, 2 |
| **SM3.1 g.** Develop and carry out a plan, including making predictions, identifying variables, and recording relevant observations, to test the strength of various materials (e.g., straws, toothpicks, masking tape, string, cotton balls, wooden blocks, Styrofoam, cloth, clay, and spaghetti). | • Work On It, p. 50 |
| **SM3.2 k.** Follow safety procedures and rules while constructing structures and explain the need for such procedures and rules. | • Work On It, p. 50 |
| **SM3.2 l.** Illustrate the construction process for a simple structure, including descriptions of the components of the structure, using labelled drawings, written and oral explanations, and demonstrations. | • Work On It, p. 50 |
| **SM3.2 n.** Identify materials or parts of a structure that failed and hypothesize why they failed. | • Communicate, p. 51, q. 2, 3 |

## Lesson Goal

To investigate the strength of materials

### Background Information

Sometimes the materials used to build a structure lead to its destruction. Sometimes the method of fastening is the culprit and sometimes it is the design itself that is flawed. A great example to show and discuss with students is the Tacoma Narrows Bridge, an engineering disaster.

*continued→*

The bridge was nicknamed "Gallopin' Gertie" because construction workers noticed the deck of the bridge moved up and down when it was windy. The bridge was opened in July 1940, but collapsed four months later. Video footage of the disaster can be found at http://commons.wikimedia.org/wiki/File:Tacoma_Narrows_Bridge_destruction.ogg.

## Curriculum Connections

In this lesson, students have the opportunity to develop skills and concepts in these areas:

### *Mathematics*

SS3.3 j. Create a picture of a 2-D shape with specified length and width (or length and height) and explain whether the 2-D shape was constructed using estimates or actual lengths.
SS3.4 c. Observe and describe the 2-D shapes found on a 3-D object.
SS3.4 d. Construct a skeleton of a given 3-D object and describe how the skeleton relates to the 3-D object.
SS3.4 e. Determine the number of faces, edges, and vertices of a given 3-D object and explain the reasoning and strategies.

### *Social Studies*

IN3.3 c. Identify products produced locally and sold elsewhere.

## Misconceptions

Students sometimes have difficulty identifying the relationship between the shape of a structure and strength. They may think using more material will increase the strength, or that the bigger the structure, the stronger it will be. Adding more material may increase the mass of the structure, making it less able to withstand a load.

## Get Started ▶

- Begin a class discussion on the types of materials used to build a structure that would support a weight, such as a book.
- Ask students if they would consider using marshmallows in the structure. Ask them if they would consider using pencils. Ask students why they would choose pencils over marshmallows.
- Ask students the questions, *What if you could use both? Would using both make the structure stronger?*

**Time**

30–40 min

**Learning Context**

problem solving

**Level of Inquiry**

guided

**Skills**

- observing
- interpreting
- experimenting
- communicating
- controlling variables
- predicting

**Grouping**

pairs or small groups

**Materials and Equipment**

- straws
- toothpicks
- tape
- string
- wooden blocks
- cloth
- block of clay
- spaghetti
- small paper cup
- ruler
- scissors
- pennies or marbles
- paper
- pencils

**Line Masters**

- LM 2-5

**SAFETY CAUTION!**

Remember to work safely when using scissors.

## Work On It

### Purpose

To have students investigate the strength of different materials and to investigate which material will hold the most weight

### Activity Notes

- In this Work On It, making predictions and planning are the most important parts of the activity.
- Offering a variety of resources will stimulate student imaginations, but be sure to display those resources in an open way, outside of their original packaging. Displaying materials in their original packaging may cause students to only think of the original use for the material.
- Ensure that all students have access to the materials. Discourage hoarding.
- You may want to hand out LM 2-5 Which Material Is the Strongest? to help students record their answers.
- Students will learn that different materials are suitable for different tasks. When materials are combined, their characteristics can be enhanced.

1. Students' answers may vary but will probably reflect the materials found most commonly in human-built structures. Students will look toward the material they feel has the most strength.
2. Students' answers may vary but will most likely mimic the photo in the student book.
3. Students should recognize that not all materials available are suitable for their test. Only those materials required in their plan should be listed.

## Additional Activity

Have students revise their plan after their original trial. Then, if time and material availability permit, have students create and test their new structure.

## Communicate

1. Students' answers may vary but must reflect the results they found in their investigation. Students will notice that rigid materials worked better for spanning a distance or supporting a load.
2. Students should notice a similarity in their results. Some materials, such as straws and string, were quite useful.
3. Some students may have suspended their cup of pennies from a string. This would have focussed the load over a small area. Others may have set the cup of pennies on top of their structure, spreading the load over a slightly larger area.

## DI Differentiating Instruction

### *For EAL/ELL*

Have students draw a picture diary of their experiment. Have students explain their pictures to students from other groups.

### *For Enrichment*

Have students design a structure that does not use straws or spaghetti. Challenge them to make a suspended structure.

## Assessment *for* Learning

| What to Look for in Student Work | What to Do |
|---|---|
| Students should be able to sort materials for use in constructing their structure and identify materials that would not be suitable for their structure. | • Check to be sure students do not include all available materials in their materials list. |
| Students should be able to work co-operatively to develop and carry out a plan for their structure. | • Encourage discussion between group members. Explaining their ideas will allow students to develop a viable plan. |
| Taking care in the building and testing of their structure will show an understanding of safety. | • Set a test site separate from the work site. Having all students use the same area for testing should help students illustrate their understanding. |
| Students' answers to the Communicate questions will give you a profile of how well they understand the importance of materials in the construction of a structure. | • Have students include a list of suitable materials they could have used along with their original materials list. |

# 3 Which Shape Is the Strongest? *Page 52*

| Time |
|---|
| 40 min |

| Line Masters |
|---|
| • LM 2-6 |

## Indicator Assessment Chart

| Indicator | Assessment Opportunities |
|---|---|
| **SM3.1 f.** Use appropriate tools (e.g., hammer, nail, glue, and scissors) to safely cut, shape, make holes, sew, and assemble materials. | • Work On It, p. 52 |
| **SM3.2 b.** Examine how some human-built structures are modelled on shapes and structures found in nature. | • Communicate, p. 53, q. 2 |
| **SM3.2 c.** Assess how 2-D shapes (e.g., rectangle, triangle, circle, square, hexagon, and octagon) and 3-D objects (e.g., dome, arch, and cylinders) provide strength, stability, and balance to natural and human-built structures. | • Work On It, p. 52<br>• Communicate, p. 53, q. 1, 2, 3 |
| **SM3.2 m.** Assess the strength, stability, and balance of personally constructed structures and make changes to improve the structure as deemed necessary. | • Work On It, p. 52 |

## Lesson Goal

To investigate the strength of shapes

## Background Information

The geometry of shapes gives the materials in a structure the ability to withstand the forces being applied to it. The shape must direct the forces to the part of the structure that is most capable of withstanding the force. Generally, the larger the areas for forces to be carried, the more stable the shape. A triangle is a great example of this as it is a rigid shape. When a structure is rigid, it is able to support a greater load than one that is not rigid. Adding extra cross-pieces or cross-members to shapes, other than triangles, adds to their rigidity.
A triangle will not push out of shape. Truss bridges are excellent examples of incorporating triangle shapes to improve the strength of a structure.

traditional ***KNOWLEDGE***

Taking cues from nature, First Nations and Métis peoples used the idea of successful shapes when building structures. A broken tree caught by two other trees formed a lintel, which could support the weight of snow. The shape of a spruce tree shed rain and snow, so that the tree did not collect extra weight on its branches.

## Curriculum Connections

In this lesson, students have the opportunity to develop skills and concepts in these areas:

### *Mathematics*

SS3.3 j. Create a picture of a 2-D shape with specified length and width (or length and height) and explain whether the 2-D shape was constructed using estimates or actual lengths.
SS3.4 c. Observe and describe the 2-D shapes found on a 3-D object.
SS3.4 d. Construct a skeleton of a given 3-D object and describe how the skeleton relates to the 3-D object.
SS3.4 e. Determine the number of faces, edges, and vertices of a given 3-D object and explain the reasoning and strategies.

### *Social Studies*

DR3.3 a. Research the view of land as held by Indigenous peoples in communities studied.
DR3.3 b. Identify ways in which people in communities studied interact with the land (e.g., meeting needs and wants, how land is protected or neglected).

### *Visual Arts*

CP3.8 f. Recognize circles, squares, triangles, and rectangles as geometric shapes and apply this knowledge to art work.
CP3.8 g. Recognize cubes, cylinders, and spheres as geometric forms and apply this knowledge to art work.
CP3.8 h. Identify formal and informal patterns in own surroundings and art works.

## Misconceptions

The relationships between the physical dimensions of a structure and its strength often confuse students. They may relate strength to size, thinking the bigger the structure is, the stronger it will be. They may also think the heavier it is, the stronger it will be. Something as simple as blowing a bubble or blowing up a balloon should allow you to have an open discussion that shows students that size does not equal strength.

## Get Started ▶

- Students learn that they can improve the strength and stability of a structure with triangle shapes. They discover that a triangle shape is strong and rigid, and will not twist or bend out of shape when pushed.

| Time |
| --- |
| 30 min |
| **Learning Context** |
| inquiry |
| **Level of Inquiry** |
| guided |
| **Skills** |
| • making models<br>• observing<br>• communicating<br>• inferring |
| **Grouping** |
| pairs |
| **Materials and Equipment** |
| • 7 Bristol board strips (10 cm by 2 cm)<br>• paper punch<br>• 7 paper fasteners<br>• scissors<br>• paper<br>• pencils |
| **Line Masters** |
| • LM 2-6 |

## Work On It

### Purpose

To have students investigate the strength of two-dimensional shapes of a square and a triangle

### Activity Notes

- Read the question aloud as a group.
- Invite students to think of a square and a triangle. Ask them to predict which shape they think will be the strongest and have them record their answers in their notebook or on LM 2-6 Which Shape Is the Strongest?
- In answer to question 1, students may decide that the square is the strongest because in their experience, a flat surface such as a desk top or table top can hold a large weight. They may not take into account corners, which can be seen as a point of collapse. Students with an advanced understanding will choose the triangle because it can withstand the application of force from any angle.
- Organize students into pairs for step 2. Give each pair of students 7 Bristol board strips. Remind students that after they have completed steps 3 and 4, they are to draw each shape in their notebook.
- After testing their shapes, have students reread Get Started and discuss their results in relation to a force such as wind, earthquakes, or waves.
- Students will develop the understanding that directional application of force determines the strength and shape of a structure.

## Communicate

These questions can be assigned to pairs or individuals.

1. The triangle should be the strongest.
2. Students' answers may vary but should reflect natural shapes, particularly triangles.
3. Through their investigation, students should discover that the triangle is the most rigid shape, as it does not push out of shape when the corners are pushed. The results of each group should be the same.

### BUILD ON WHAT YOU KNOW

Ask students to turn to page 44 of their student book. Discuss the shapes they see in the photo of the bridge. Have students think about the bridge they will build. Encourage them to sketch their ideas in their notebook.

## DI Differentiating Instruction

### *For Enrichment*

Have students make 3-D shapes and test them for rigidity.

### *For Reteaching*

Students may not have the same understanding of geometric shapes. Have pairs of students play a game of Go Fish to consolidate their knowledge of the names of various shapes. Provide three of each shape shown, taken from your classroom mathematics materials or on cards cut from cardboard. Each student should have a set of six of the nine objects or cards in a paper bag or small box, so that one player cannot see which shapes the other player has. Leftover shapes go into another bag, to be dipped into when the answer to the question *Do you have a (rhombus)?* is no.

## Assessment *for* Learning

| What to Look for in Student Work | What to Do |
|---|---|
| After completing this activity, students should be able to tell you that one way to improve the strength and stability of a frame structure is to use triangle shapes. | • As students are creating their different shapes and testing them, use this opportunity to work with individuals. Have students describe to you what they have found. Having them communicate their thoughts as they work will help them clarify their findings, and help you to assess how well they are able to communicate results of investigations. |

# 4 How Can We Strengthen Structures?

Page 54

**Time**

40 min

**Line Masters**

- LM 2-7

## Indicator Assessment Chart

| Indicator | Assessment Opportunities |
|---|---|
| **SM3.1 d.** Sort materials for use in constructing structures according to one or more physical properties such as strength, texture, colour, flexibility, and durability. | • Communicate, p. 55, q. 1, 2, 3, 4 |
| **SM3.1 h.** Assess the suitability of various materials for constructing structures, including methods of strengthening those materials (e.g., adding more layers, tying or gluing together, triangulation, cross-bracing, and changing the shape of the materials). | • Work On It, p. 54<br>• Communicate, p. 55, q. 1, 2, 3, 4 |
| **SM3.2 c.** Assess how 2-D shapes (e.g., rectangle, triangle, circle, square, hexagon, and octagon) and 3-D objects (e.g., dome, arch, and cylinders) provide strength, stability, and balance to natural and human-built structures. | • Communicate, p. 55, q. 2 |

## Lesson Goal

To investigate ways to strengthen structures

### Background Information

Structures made to withstand a load incorporate a number of important features in their design. One is the use of the rigid shape of a triangle to give added strength. The more rigid the framework of a structure, the larger the load it will hold. Triangle shapes, for strength, can be seen in the gusset plates, which are glued to two pieces of wood where they join. The triangle shape found in roof trusses also contributes to the strength of a roof. A second way of increasing strength and stability in structures is by adding width and mass, frequently at the base. A third way is through layering. Heavy plywood, made from layers of timber, incorporates mass and is an excellent example of layering in building materials. Layering in construction can also be found in walls and in roofs, although this is in part for insulation.

## Curriculum Connections

In this lesson, students have the opportunity to develop skills and concepts in these areas:

***Mathematics***

SS3.2 i. Generalize statements about the mass of a specific amount of matter when reformed into different shapes or sizes (e.g., use clay to make an object, measure the mass of the object, reform the clay into another object and measure the mass of the two objects; an empty balloon versus a full balloon; or water versus ice).
SS3.5 c. Observe, describe the characteristics of, and sort polygons found in situations relevant to self, family, or community (including First Nations and Métis), into irregular and regular polygons (e.g., the bottom of a kamatiq, the screen of a TV, the bottom of a curling broom, and an arrowhead).
P3.1 a. Identify and observe situations relevant to self, family, and community that contain an increasing or decreasing pattern, identify the starting value of the pattern, and describe the rule for the pattern and how the pattern would continue.

## Misconceptions

Students may think that layering materials without affixing them to each other will make a structure strong. It will be necessary to explain to them that the materials must move together, supporting each other to make the structure rigid and strong.

| **Time** |
|---|
| 30 min |
| **Learning Context** |
| inquiry |
| **Level of Inquiry** |
| structured |
| **Skills** |
| • observing<br>• communicating<br>• inferring |
| **Grouping** |
| pairs or small groups |
| **Materials and Equipment** |
| none |
| **Line Masters** |
| • LM 2-7 |

## Get Started ▶

- Students are made aware that the strength in structures is due to bulk (or mass), the number of layers in the materials, or the number of layers of materials, and the shapes used (triangle shapes). They will be encouraged to observe this in their own environment.

## Work On It

### Purpose

To have students investigate ways that structures are strengthened

### Activity Notes

- After reading the first sentence of the Work On It activity, ask students, *What do these photos tell you about adding strength to structures?*
- Remind students of what they observed in Lesson 2: Which Material Is the Strongest?
- Discuss how width and mass at the base of a structure make it stronger and more stable.
- Have students read the last two paragraphs of the Work On It activity and look at the photos. Ask students, *What does it mean when we talk about layers? What has been done with these materials to help strengthen the structure?*

## Communicate

All of these questions can be answered individually or in small groups. You may want to hand out LM 2-7 How Can We Strengthen Structures? to help students record their answers.

1. Students' answers may vary but could include extra metal welded to the base of swing sets or bike racks, basketball hoops, etc.
2. Students' answers may vary but could include the triangle shape that a chart stand makes looking at it from the side, or the shapes in the beams of a climbing apparatus in a playground.
3. Students' answers may vary but could include desk tops, broom handles, or doors. They may find play equipment that uses laminated wood or plastic.
4. Students' answers may vary but could include the shapes in hydro-electric towers and water towers, the pillars holding awnings on front porches, or the pillars in the front of some schools or public buildings. They may begin a discussion of new buildings under construction.

### BUILD ON WHAT YOU KNOW

Students should return to their cardboard strip shapes of the squares and triangles from Lesson 3. Provide students with another cardboard strip. Discuss how this cardboard strip could be used to strengthen the weak cardboard square. Use the information from Lessons 6 and 7 to determine how to make a square a stronger shape. Students will observe that by placing the strip diagonally as a cross member, their square becomes two rigid triangles that cannot be pushed out of shape.

## DI Differentiating Instruction

### *For Enrichment*

Discuss with students the terms "construction," "engineering," and "architecture." Invite students to investigate and identify hobbies and jobs related to these fields.

### *For Reteaching*

Students can cut out pictures of structures constructed of layered materials from old magazines and glue the pictures onto index cards. Students can sort the cards to show the different ways structures have been made stronger.

## Assessment *for* Learning

| What to Look for in Student Work | What to Do |
|---|---|
| Students should show an understanding of the relationship between the science of adding strength to materials and the use of those materials in everyday structures. | • Questions 1–4 of the Communicate section allow you to assess how well students are able to record relevant observations and make connections between science ideas and everyday practices. |

# 5 Making Paper Towers Strong

Page 56

| Time |
|---|
| 80 min |
| **Line Masters** |
| • LM 2-8 |

## Indicator Assessment Chart

| Indicator | Assessment Opportunities |
|---|---|
| **SM3.2 c.** Assess how 2-D shapes (e.g., rectangle, triangle, circle, square, hexagon, and octagon) and 3-D objects (e.g., dome, arch, and cylinders) provide strength, stability, and balance to natural and human-built structures. | • Work On It, p. 56 |
| **SM3.2 i.** Develop and carry out a plan to construct a simple structure such as a tower, bridge, tipi, or bird feeder that meets teacher-or student-specified criteria related to strength, stability, and function. | • Work On It, p. 56 |
| **SM3.2 j.** Estimate measurements in order to select appropriate quantities of required materials for constructing a structure. | • Work On It, p. 56 |
| **SM3.2 k.** Follow safety procedures and rules while constructing structures and explain the need for such procedures and rules. | • Work On It, p. 56 |
| **SM3.2 l.** Illustrate the construction process for a simple structure, including descriptions of the components of the structure, using labelled drawings, written and oral explanations, and demonstrations. | • Work On It, p. 56<br>• Communicate, p. 57, q. 3 |
| **SM3.2 m.** Assess the strength, stability, and balance of personally constructed structures and make changes to improve the structure as deemed necessary. | • Work On It, p. 56<br>• Communicate, p. 57, q. 1, 2, 4 |
| **SM3.2 n.** Identify materials or parts of a structure that failed and hypothesize why they failed. | • Communicate, p. 57, q. 4 |

## Lesson Goal

To design and build a strong tower

## Background Information

Materials that may seem weak can be strengthened by folding, bending, or altering them in different ways. This means that light and inexpensive construction materials may be incorporated into structures to help make them stronger or more stable. A structure is any supporting framework that is built to hold a load.

## Curriculum Connections

In this lesson, students have the opportunity to develop skills and concepts in these areas:

### *Mathematics*

SS3.5 c. Observe, describe the characteristics of, and sort polygons found in situations relevant to self, family, or community (including First Nations and Métis), into irregular and regular polygons (e.g., the bottom of a kamatiq, the screen of a TV, the bottom of a curling broom, and an arrowhead).
P3.1 a. Identify and observe situations relevant to self, family, and community that contain an increasing or decreasing pattern, identify the starting value of the pattern, and describe the rule for the pattern and how the pattern would continue.
P3.1 c. Observe various patterns (increasing or decreasing) found on a hundred chart, such as horizontal, vertical, and diagonal patterns, and describe the pattern rule.
SS3.4 a. Observe and describe the faces, edges, and vertices of given 3-D objects, including cubes, spheres, cones, cylinders, pyramids, and prisms (e.g., drum, tipi, South American Pyramids, and other objects from the natural environment).

### *Social Studies*

RW3.3 a. Recognize that technology includes more than electronics (i.e., paper, forging steel, manufacturing, vehicles, making cloth, products created for construction).
RW3.3 b. Give examples of technologies in communities studied (e.g., communications, transportation, housing, food acquisition, preparation and storage, construction, manufacturing), and categorize the influences of the application of the technology as positive or negative.

## Misconceptions

Students may believe that extra layers of the same type of material create strength. It should be pointed out that laminated materials differ from layer to layer. A piece of plywood or a skate board, as seen in the student book, shows this difference in the layering of material.

**Get Started ▶**

- The class is invited to talk about the kinds of structures in their neighbourhood. Students are led to discover that structures are not always what they seem. Materials can be altered or changed to make structures stronger and more stable, so that they can hold a load.

| Time |
| --- |
| 60 min |
| **Learning Context** |
| inquiry |
| **Level of Inquiry** |
| guided |
| **Skills** |
| • observing<br>• comparing |
| **Grouping** |
| pairs or groups |
| **Materials and Equipment** |
| • photocopy paper (1 sheet for each test)<br>• ruler<br>• 2 cardboard squares (15 cm by 15 cm)<br>• rolls of pennies<br>• paper<br>• pencils |
| **Line Masters** |
| • LM 2-8 |

**SAFETY CAUTION!**

Remember to work on the floor when you are testing if the tower can hold the pennies.

## Work On It

### Purpose

To have students design and build strong paper towers

### Activity Notes

- Help students to read the procedure carefully before beginning the activity and to focus on the correct steps. Ask students questions such as, *Why do we need a ruler for this activity?* (The paper tower has to be a certain height.) *Why do we need the two cardboard squares?* (The squares are for the base and the top of the tower.) *What do the rolls of pennies do?* (The mass acts as a load.)
- Make sure students understand that they are to make each paper tower with only one piece of paper, and no tape or glue.
- Instruct each pair of students to brainstorm different ways of folding the paper to make a tower. Each student should have at least one or two opportunities to try the suggestions.
- Discuss ways students can record their successful paper towers, for example, a bird's eye view of a circle, square, or sheet folded like an accordion. Students should record the results of each paper tower test before starting a new test. You may want to hand out LM 2-8 Making Paper Towers Strong for students to draw their paper towers on.
- Students will see that making simple changes to a material, such as adding corrugations to cardboard, can increase its strength.
- Students will discover that folds, bends, or curves can help to prevent materials from buckling, thus making a stronger structure. They will use rolls of pennies to test paper towers that they have made.
- Students will observe that by altering one piece of paper, they can increase its strength.
- Students should be led to understand that when they increase the strength of the paper tower, they are increasing its stability.

## Communicate

Meet in large groups to discuss the results of the investigation.

1. Students' answers may vary depending on how they folded or altered their papers to hold the rolls of pennies. Students should be given the opportunity to present their recordings and show their models of towers that did not buckle under the mass of the pennies.
2. Students' answers may vary depending on how they folded or altered their papers to make what they consider the strongest tower.
3. Students should be given time to discuss with their group which tower they considered to be the most stable and balanced. Drawings will vary depending on the agreement within the group.
4. Students' answers may vary but could include folding the paper, which gave it more strength.

## DI Differentiating Instruction

### *For EAL/ELL*

Ask students what they think *strong* means. Ask students for examples of things that are strong. Compare the things they suggest with structures, such as a tower. Help them find similar examples from their own life.

### *For Enrichment*

Challenge students to create a set of questions that they would like to ask an engineer. After they have completed their lists, they could write a letter to an engineer, inviting that person to visit their classroom.

### *For Reteaching*

Tell students that it is important to choose the best material possible when building a structure. Students can investigate creating towers that will support a mass of penny rolls using common materials such as toothpicks, plastic straws, or cardboard. Ask students, *Did any of the materials need to be changed to become stronger?*

## Assessment *for* Learning

| What to Look for in Student Work | What to Do |
| --- | --- |
| Students should plan, prepare, and test their tower. From their observations, they should be able to make modifications that show increased understanding of the principle being studied. | • As students work, observe to see whether they test each type of structure to make sure that it will support a given mass and record their results. |

# 6 Nature's Balancing Act

*Page 58*

| Time |
| --- |
| 80 min |
| **Line Masters** |
| • LM 2-9 |

## Indicator Assessment Chart

| Indicator | Assessment Opportunities |
| --- | --- |
| **SM3.2 h.** Analyze how various shapes contribute to balance and stability in humans and various animals. | • Work On It, p. 59<br>• Communicate, p. 59, q. 1, 2, 3, 4 |

## Lesson Goal

To explore how shape helps humans and animals balance and stay stable

## Background Information

If an animal is standing still, all the forces acting on its body are in equilibrium. If the animal shifts its weight, and it does not fall over, the equilibrium is considered stable. What really defines this concept is the polygon that is formed with the animal's points of support on the ground. If you drew a vertical line through the centre of mass of the animal, the line would have to fall within the polygon. If you tilt the animal's body, the vertical line would fall outside the polygon and the animal would fall over. Three is usually the minimum number of contact points needed for an animal to be stable, but a biped can be stable standing on one or two feet because each foot contacts the ground over a finite area. So, for a standing human, our polygon of support is essentially a straight line.

traditional ***KNOWLEDGE***

Many traditional games and competitions relied on understanding balance. Many Métis people competed against First Nations people and voyageurs in skills such as snowshoe races, jumping, throwing a weight, and races carrying heavy packs weighing hundreds of kilograms.

For more information, go to the Virtual Museum of Canada: www.virtualmuseum.ca/Exhibitions/Traditions/English/metis_games_02.html.

## Curriculum Connections

In this lesson, students have the opportunity to develop skills and concepts in these areas:

***Mathematics***

SS3.4 c. Observe and describe the 2-D shapes found on a 3-D object.

***Dance***

CP3.1 c. Create a wide variety of movements to a given stimuli.

CP3.1 d. Generate a range of alternatives for representing movement ideas and solving movement problems.
CP3.1 e. Reflect on which movements worked best and adjust own work accordingly.
CP3.2 a. Generate movements in order to represent own movement ideas.
CP3.2 b. Apply knowledge of body zones including right side, left side, front, back, upper half, and lower half to own movements.
CP3.2 c. Apply a wide variety of actions including the five basic jumps of leap, hop, jump (from two feet to land on two feet), sissone (from two feet to land on one foot), and assemble (from one foot to land on two feet).
CP3.2 d. Apply a variety of dynamics including moving with the extremes of speed (fast and slow), duration (short and long), and varying forces (strong and light).
CP3.2 e. Demonstrate that energy is on a continuum of a little to a lot and apply to own movement explorations and dances.
CP3.2 f. Demonstrate ways of grouping speed and duration to form rhythmic patterns.

***Visual Arts***

CP3.8 a. Observe visual details, and include details to enhance depictions of animals, people, and objects.

## Misconceptions

Students may think that it is easy for four-legged animals to stand on two legs. As the lesson continues, point out the difficulty the animal experiences due to centre-of-balance issues. To keep its balance, the animal needs to arch its back in a direction it does not usually bend.

**Get Started ▶**

- Before reading the page, ask students to think of all the animals they have seen in the last week/month. After you have drawn up a list, read the first paragraph with students.
- Return to the list and identify how many points of contact each animal has.
- Have students choose an animal and using dots, map the points of contact it has with the ground. Have students connect the dots to form an outline.
- If students have chosen an animal with two points of contact, have them draw a straight line that connects the two dots.

**Time**

60 min

**Learning Context**

inquiry

**Level of Inquiry**

guided

**Skills**

- inferring
- observing
- experimenting

**Grouping**

pairs or groups of 3

**Materials and Equipment**

- beanbag or small pillow
- paper
- pencils

**Line Masters**

- LM 2-9

**SAFETY CAUTION!**

Take care when moving backward or moving quickly. Make sure you move in the same direction as the rest of the class.

## Work On It

### Purpose

To have students explore the balance points of different animals

### Activity Notes

- Guide students to walk in the following ways:

**Bear Walk**

- Hands and feet on the ground with your rear end in the air.
- Move left hand and left foot forward, and then right hand and right foot.
- Repeat movement around a given area.

**Dog Walk**

- On your hands and knees.
- Move left hand and right knee forward, and then right hand and left knee.
- Repeat movement around a given area.

**Penguin Walk**

- Standing upright with hands at your side and your feet close together.
- Waddle back and forth moving one foot at a time.

**Rabbit Hop**

- Hands should be tucked up like a little bunny while standing up.
- Create little jumps around the room, as if you were doing a hop with both feet at the same time.

- Have one student in the group be the animal and have the other student place the beanbag where he or she thinks the balance point is.
- You may want to hand out LM 2-9 Nature's Balancing Act to help students record their observations.
- Students will begin to associate the idea of balance point with a broad stance. The connection to the base of a music stand or tripod and the stance of an animal should reinforce the idea that a stable structure is wider at its base than at its top.

## Communicate

1. Students will indicate that either the beanbag fell off, if it was not placed on the point of balance, or that it stayed on, if it was placed on the point of balance.
2. Students will say that the shape is different for each animal. They should recognize that there is a difference depending on how many points of contact the animal has with the ground. Students should recognize that the majority of the animal's body stays within the shape they drew. You may want to review the idea of a straight line for two-legged animals.
3. Students may decide that all animal walks are stable. This would be an appropriate response. Others may pick an individual animal based on their results, but their results will only be as valid as their practice. Not all students will get the same results.
4. Students will pick "feet apart." Point out that this forms a triangle.

## DI Differentiating Instruction

### *For Enrichment*

Students may want to try walking like other animals.

**Limp Dog Walk**

- With both hands on the ground and holding one knee off the ground, try to have students move.

**Crab Walk**

- With your pelvis facing the sky, start walking on your hands and feet.
- Keep your buttocks off the ground as you perform the movement.
- Move right hand and left foot, and then left hand and right foot.
- Repeat movement around a given area.

**Seal Walk**

- On the floor, keep your lower body limp and an upright position with your upper body with arms extended.
- Move one hand at a time dragging your legs behind you as you move around in a given area.

**Duck Walk**

- Start in a squat position.
- Walk around moving one foot at a time and your hands in your armpits flapping like a duck.

**Frog Jump**

- Start in a squat position with your hands slightly in front of your body on the floor.
- Kick off with your legs making your body move forward.
- Your hands should touch the ground first and then your legs come behind you and on the ground.

## Assessment *for* Learning

| What to Look for in Student Work | What to Do |
|---|---|
| Students should be able to identify the points of balance for the animal walks they completed. They should be able to relate this to the points of contact with the ground. | • Have students observe other students as they complete this activity. Have a class discussion and observe students' responses. |

# 7 Is It a Solid, Frame, or Shell Structure?

Page 60

**Time**

80 min

**Vocabulary**

- solid structures
- frame structures
- shell structures

**Line Masters**

- LM 2-10

## Indicator Assessment Chart

| Indicator | Assessment Opportunities |
|---|---|
| **SM3.1 c.** Compare the properties of materials used historically and currently to construct structures such as houses, bridges, towers, and roads throughout the world. | • Communicate, p. 61, q. 1, 2 |
| **SM3.2 d.** Compare the characteristics of solid (e.g., sand castle, mountain, and dam), frame (e.g., partition wall, hockey net, and spider web), and shell (e.g., igloo, bike helmet, balloon, and drink can) structures. | • Work On It, p. 61<br>• Communicate, p. 61, q. 1, 2 |
| **SM3.2 e.** Classify natural and human-built structures as solid, frame, or shell structures. | • Work On It, p. 61<br>• Communicate, p. 61, q. 3 |

## Lesson Goal

To investigate and sort different types of structures

### Background Information

Each type of structure has its strong points and its inherent weaknesses. Solid structures are great for supporting loads, but the space they take up is not useable. Frame structures have a skeleton made of strong materials such as steel, wood, bone, or manufactured material such as carbon fibre. The parts of a frame structure transfer forces from the outside of the structure to the different parts of a frame. In a house, some internal walls are "load-bearing" because they share the job of supporting the load with the outside walls. In this way, frame structures can carry immense loads and, if one of the load bearing walls is slightly imperfect, the structure usually does not suffer.

Shell structures can span large areas without needing walls on the inside. With a shell structure, the entire load is carried over the curve of the surface but if there is a tiny imperfection in the covering, the structure could fail catastrophically. Also most materials strong enough to withstand an impact and prevent an imperfection are difficult to mould into a shell shape. Methods of joinery must be very specific or the dome shape will pull itself apart at the joint or collapse on itself.

**traditional KNOWLEDGE**

Many examples of frame structures are found in First Nations and Métis life. A lacrosse stick, the ribs of a canoe, a fishing weir, a travois, and a backpack are all examples of frame structures.

## Curriculum Connections

In this lesson, students have the opportunity to develop skills and concepts in these areas:

### *Mathematics*

SS3.3 a. Observe and describe situations relevant to self, family, and community that involve measuring lengths, including perimeter, in cm or m.
SS3.4 a. Observe and describe the faces, edges, and vertices of given 3-D objects, including cubes, spheres, cones, cylinders, pyramids, and prisms (e.g., drum, tipi, South American Pyramids, and other objects from the natural environment).
SS3.4 g. Sort a set of 3-D objects according to the faces, edges, or vertices and explain the sorting rule used.
P3.1 a. Identify and observe situations relevant to self, family, and community that contain an increasing or decreasing pattern, identify the starting value of the pattern, and describe the rule for the pattern and how the pattern would continue.
P3.1 c. Observe various patterns (increasing or decreasing) found on a hundred chart, such as horizontal, vertical, and diagonal patterns, and describe the pattern rule.
SS3.5 c. Observe, describe the characteristics of, and sort polygons found in situations relevant to self, family, or community (including First Nations and Métis), into irregular and regular polygons (e.g., the bottom of a kamatiq, the screen of a TV, the bottom of a curling broom, and an arrowhead).
SS3.5 d. Analyze irregular and regular polygons in different orientations in terms of the characteristics of the polygons (such as number or measurement of sides and angles).

### *Social Studies*

DR3.2 c. Describe the impact of environmental factors and events on ways of life in communities studied (e.g., climate, vegetation, natural resources, landforms, floods, droughts, storms).
DR3.3 a. Research the view of land as held by Indigenous peoples in communities studied.
DR3.3 b. Identify ways in which people in communities studied interact with the land (e.g., meeting needs and wants, how land is protected or neglected).
RW3.3 a. Recognize that technology includes more than electronics (i.e., paper, forging steel, manufacturing, vehicles, making cloth, products created for construction).
RW3.3 b. Give examples of technologies in communities studied (e.g., communications, transportation, housing, food acquisition, preparation and storage, construction, manufacturing), and categorize the influences of the application of the technology as positive or negative.

### *Visual Arts*

CP3.7 a. Generate questions that arise from the investigation of a topic or area of interest to initiate inquiry (e.g., How have different artists represented turtles in visual art works and book illustrations?).
CP3.8 b. Apply understanding of contour lines to form the outline of an object.
CP3.8 f. Recognize circles, squares, triangles, and rectangles as geometric shapes and apply this knowledge to art work.
CP3.8 h. Identify formal and informal patterns in own surroundings and art works.

## Focus on Literacy

### *Before Reading/Writing: Previewing Text and Building Upon Prior Knowledge*

Tell students, *Writers use a variety of text features, or physical characteristics on a page, to help us make meaning of what we are reading. Some of these features recur or are used consistently throughout the student book so that we become very familiar with them. When we look at page 60, we see a number of text features that we have seen before; for example, the lesson number and title, the goal of the lesson, photos with captions, and bold words. We know if a writer bolds some words they must be important. The bold words on this page seem familiar, but we know that familiar words are sometimes used in a different way in science.*

Ask students to share what they already know about the words "solid," "frame," and "shell." Have students give examples of something that would fit the definition of each of these words. Students can now read the Get Started paragraph and the captions that go with the photos to confirm their thinking.

Next, draw students' attention to the three bold terms found in the paragraph at the bottom of page 60: "solid structures," "frame structures," and "shell structures." Review with students what they have learned about structures thus far in this unit, for example, on page 45, structures need to be strong, stable, and steady; on page 46, structures hold weight; and on page 48, structures carry out jobs. Ask students to turn to a partner and share how adding the word "structure" to the words "solid," "frame," and "shell" changes the meaning. Discuss some student responses before reading this paragraph to confirm students' thinking.

### *After Reading/Writing: Creating a Possible Product*

Tell students, *In order to remember new vocabulary better, it is sometimes useful to create a graphic organizer that revisits the new word in a variety of different ways. A Frayer Model is an organizer that can help us do this.* Show students how the Frayer Model below is set up in four quadrants and allows them to record important information. Give students time to complete a Frayer Model for each of the three types of structures focussed on in this lesson.

Remind students they could look through the rest of the unit for more examples and non-examples of each type of structure.

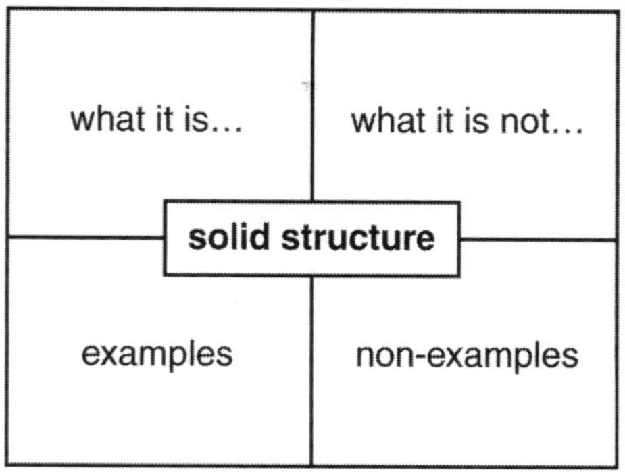


## Misconceptions

Students might have difficulty seeing beyond the covering of a building to identify the load-bearing frame structure inside. Compare the frame of a building to the skeleton inside each student. A skeleton is also a frame structure that students know exists even though it is difficult to see.

## Get Started ▶

- Have students read the first paragraph of Get Started and look at the accompanying photos of solid, frame, and shell structures. Ask students, *What is the difference between a solid structure and a frame structure? What is the difference between a frame structure and a shell structure? Do the structures have different jobs?* As students suggest various responses, encourage the use of the structure names.
- Have students read the second paragraph and look again at the accompanying photos. Have them identify the materials that make up the solid structures, the frame of the frame structures, and the shell of the shell structures.

## Work On It

### Purpose

To have students investigate and sort solid, frame, and shell structures

### Activity Notes

- Do the first step of the procedure together as a class. You may want to hand out LM 2-10 Is It a Solid, Frame, or Shell Structure? to help students record their answers.
- Preselect pages from magazines or catalogues to make sure students have a selection of each type of structure.
- Show students pictures of a human and a human skeleton. Tell them their skeleton is the frame for their body. Show a picture of a house and ask students, *How is a house like a human?* Encourage students to recognize that our bones are like two-by-four pieces of lumber and although you cannot see inside a human or inside walls, both a human and a house are frame structures.

**Time**

60 min

**Learning Context**

inquiry

**Level of Inquiry**

structured

**Skills**

- classifying
- observing
- communicating

**Grouping**

individuals or pairs

**Materials and Equipment**

- pictures of structures
- magazines or catalogues
- scissors
- paper
- pencils

**Line Masters**

- LM 2-10

**SAFETY CAUTION!**

Remember to work safely when using scissors.

## Communicate

These questions can be answered by individuals or in a class discussion.

1. Students' answers will vary depending on the pictures supplied. Students should notice that frame structures have inside and outside walls, that shell structures have no inside walls, and that solid structures have no empty space inside.
2. Students' answers may vary but should include a reference to the type of structure and its characteristics.
3. Solid structures are not hollow. They are the same throughout and usually made of one material. Frame structures are made of firm parts that are fastened together. Shell structures have hard outer cases that hold the structure together.

## DI Differentiating Instruction

### *For EAL/ELL*

Have students glue or tape the pictures onto separate pages entitled Frame, Shell, and Solid rather than write the name of the structure. Review the pictures, placing a name beside each one.

### *For Reteaching*

Have students make flash cards by gluing the pictures onto index cards. On the other side of each card, have them write the type of structure. Students could practise with their own set, then switch sets with another student. Students may also work in pairs or small groups.

## Assessment *for* Learning

| What to Look for in Student Work | What to Do |
|---|---|
| Students may have difficulty differentiating between a shell structure and a frame structure. | • After completing the Work On It, have a class discussion and observe students' responses. Use additional examples to increase students' knowledge. On your KWL chart, add items such as a bike rack is a frame structure and a yurt and a beaver hut are shell structures. |

# Ask … Why is it important to understand structures?

Page 62

| Time |
| --- |
| 120 min |
| **Line Masters** |
| • none |

## Indicator Assessment Chart

| Indicator | Assessment Opportunities |
| --- | --- |
| **SM3.2 p.** Research jobs and hobbies which contribute to the design, building, and maintenance of natural and human-built structures. | • Research, p. 63 |

## A Builder

- Have students research Habitat for Humanity.
- Help them generate a list of questions they would like answered, such as
  - Who gets to live in the houses?
  - Where are the houses built?
  - Who supplies the materials for the houses?
  - How can we help?

## A Recycler

- Challenge your students to start their own classroom or school recycling/reusing project.
- With students' help, make a list of things they could collect for recycling or offer for reuse.
- Students could also make a list of things they could do to reduce their impact on the environment. Some suggestions you could offer to get them started include:
  - make sure lights, computers, and televisions are turned off when rooms are empty
  - turn down the heat at night or when no one is home
  - walk to school and other places more often
  - bring garbage-free lunches to school more often

traditional ***KNOWLEDGE***

## An Elder's Helper

- Be wary of the spiritual significance that the tipi lodge has for First Nations people. We must acknowledge the importance of spirituality in First Nations cultures. The belief in spirit is deeply embedded into all facets of First Nations life, including areas that we might consider mundane, such as the building and construction of the tipi itself. As a result, emphasize the importance that spirituality plays, regardless of your own beliefs.
- If you wish to instruct the class about the tipi teachings, it would be best to consult a Knowledge Keeper or an Elder. The tipi teachings are a sacred woman's teaching and it might not be appropriate for anyone else to lead such teachings.

- Several divisions across Saskatchewan may be able to arrange to have Elders and Knowledge Keepers come into the classroom to discuss or to set up a tipi. Please refer to the "Protocol for Contacting Elders and Traditional Knowledge Keepers" in the Program Overview of this Teacher's Resource.
- Be wary not to generalize. Not all First Nations groups used tipis for shelter. In the far north, the Dené, for example, used a different kind of lodge. Tipis varied from region to region and from Nation to Nation though they are similarly made.
- Tipis were common dwellings for many Plains First Nations groups. A frame structure, the tipi consisted of 15 poles made from lodge pole pine or tamarack, which were found locally. The use of local fauna and flora is considered place-based knowledge. Many centuries ago when buffalo were abundant, First Nations people used buffalo hide sewn together by sinew or strips of hide with bone needles to fashion the covering. Both the wood and hide were taken only after tobacco was offered to thank Creator for their use. As many as a dozen hides or more were needed to create the covering. By the late 1800s when the millions of buffalo had been nearly eradicated, First Nations people traded with European traders for canvas and metal needles.
- The tipi is a conical structure made of interlocking poles. A tripod is erected and lashed together near the top with a long rope. In this profile, Riley Joseph uses four poles to create the tripod. The poles are carefully chosen and are very long and straight. After the poles are lifted up, a helper gathers up the long rope and pole after pole is laid onto the tripod in clockwise fashion. After each pole is interlocked with the tripod, the helper walks around the tipi's base and lashes the rope tightly around the tripod so that each pole is then bound to the tripod. The diameter of the lodge depends on the stride of the woman who sets up the lodge. In this fashion, because the woman's strides will be about the same each time, the diameter of specific lodges will be roughly equal. After the twelfth pole is laid, the tripod is tied and staked to the ground. The covering is rolled up from each end and tied firmly to the last pole. Then the pole and the hide covering are hoisted up between the crown of poles. The covering is unfurled like a flag and adjusted. When the builder is satisfied, the front of the tipi is laced up with stakes through holes that were made into the covering. Heavy rocks or stakes are used to hold the edges of the tipi covering down. In some Plains cultures, the tipi opens to the east, while the tipi in other groups might face a different direction.
- Tipi construction is similar among most First Nations groups, though there are differences. For instance, the Dakota, Lakota, and Nakota tipis tend to stretch longer toward the rear of the lodge, and thus the covering of hide is not conical. Most Cree and Saulteaux lodges were conical in shape. Most Nations use 15 poles, of which 13 form the lodge itself and act as the chimney flaps. A pair of poles can be maneuvered to close and open the top of the tipi, acting like flues to regulate the exit of smoke.

- Some Elders believed that tipis were never adorned unless very specific protocols were followed and expressed permission was given. Protocols are a series of crucial, sometimes ritualistic steps that are determined by a community through their religious leaders, such as Elders, medicine people, or shamans. For example, one could only paint on the tipi if one had a powerful vision. Elders then interpreted those dreams and visions and permission was only then granted.
- Associated tipi teachings are considered to be sacred. In the past, women were the keepers of the tipi teachings. In Cree culture, each of the 15 poles represents a sacred value, such as kinship and honesty. The tipi represents the female spirit and woman's place in First Nations societies. For more information regarding tipi teachings, please refer to the site: www.fourdirectionsteachings.com/transcripts/cree.html.
- Here are some key questions you might want to ask students:
  - How is a tipi an example of a frame structure?
  - Why might hides and lodge pole pines be used?
  - Why might tipis built in one area of the province differ from tipis built in another area?

## Focus on Literacy

### *Before Reading/Writing: Generating Questions to Self-monitor*

Tell students, *Writers sometimes try to anticipate the questions readers will have as they are reading about something new. They use their own knowledge, experiences, and what they would want to know about a topic to guide them as they write.*

Pages 62 and 63 present an "Ask ..." feature where the writer answers the key question, *Why is it important to understand structures? While we read, we will want to keep this question in mind to see if it is answered, but we may also have other questions of our own. Asking our own questions will help us set a purpose for reading and keep us more involved with the text.*

Model for students how they can use some of the text features on these pages to develop some other questions they would like answered. For example, when looking at the photo of the tires, I might wonder, *Could tires be used as they are to build a home?* Provide time for students to develop a few questions of their own based on a preview of text features on these pages. Compile a list of students' questions on the board or chart paper for students to refer back to after reading.

### *During Reading/Writing: Self-questioning, Self-monitoring, Self-correcting*

As students are reading, have them track which questions get answered and record a brief response to those questions.

### *After Reading/Writing: Self-questioning, Self-monitoring, Self-correcting*

As a class, check off any questions on the class list that were answered. Discuss with students whether using the strategy of asking questions helped them better understand the text.

Were students more interested in reading the text because they wanted to find out answers to their questions?

Review any questions that remain unanswered and discuss whether they were poorly constructed or would require further research.

## Research

Students may choose to research the job of an architect, of a construction worker, or of a recycling facility manager, as mentioned in the student book. They may choose other jobs related to structures and materials, such as a woodworker who builds furniture, a house builder, or an engineer.

Students should focus their research on how the job relates with structures and materials. If they need help focussing their research, you could give them an example of a structure and ask them what jobs might be involved in building it and what the people in those jobs would need to understand about structures and materials. For example, a house might be designed by an architect and built by a construction worker.

You may need to guide students to appropriate websites or books to help them find the information they need.

## Assessment *for* Learning

| What to Look for in Student Work | What to Do |
|---|---|
| Students should be able to identify jobs, hobbies, or volunteer work associated with natural and human-built structures. | • Ask students to explain the difference between natural and human-built structures.<br>• Have students present their research findings to the class in a round-table discussion. |
| Students should be able to recognize the items in their life that can be reused, recycled, or reduced. | • Plan a class or school recycling program that targets 3 or 4 items students can successfully reduce or recycle.<br>• Plan a class garage sale, where students bring items they no longer need or use, such as binders, pencil crayons, T-shirts, etc. Proceeds of the sale go to Habitat for Humanity or another local charity. |
| Students should be aware of the cultural significance of nature for First Nations and Métis peoples. | • Invite or visit with a First Nations Elder. Ask for his or her assistance in showing students the significance of the tipi tradition. |

# 8 How Are Materials Joined Together?

*Page 64*

| Time |
|---|
| 80–120 min |
| **Vocabulary** |
| • fasteners |
| **Line Masters** |
| • LM 2-11<br>• LM 2-12 |

## Indicator Assessment Chart

| Indicator | Assessment Opportunities |
|---|---|
| **SM3.1 a.** Identify problems to be solved related to the properties of materials in structures (e.g., What is the purpose of the structure? What materials are appropriate for constructing the structure? What are appropriate methods of joinery?). | • Work On It, p. 64<br>• Communicate, p. 65, q. 1 |
| **SM3.1 e.** Analyze how various similar and dissimilar materials can be joined (e.g., gluing, nailing, screwing, stapling, taping, Velcroing, and tying) and identify the most appropriate methods for joining specific materials for an identified use. | • Work On It, p. 64<br>• Communicate, p. 65, q. 1, 2 |
| **SM3.1 f.** Use appropriate tools (e.g., hammer, nail, glue, and scissors) to safely cut, shape, make holes, sew, and assemble materials. | • Work On It, p. 64 |
| **SM3.2 n.** Identify materials or parts of a structure that failed and hypothesize why they failed. | • Work On It, p. 64 |

## Lesson Goal

To explore how materials can be joined together

## Background Information

Adhesives, such as glue and tape, actually work because of two different forces: one between the molecules of the adhesive and one between the adhesive and the material being glued. The force between the molecules of the adhesive is called a cohesive force. This force is really the internal strength of the adhesive, the adhesive's ability to stick to itself. The other force is adhesion, which is the actual bonding of one material to another. Strong glue will have good adhesion and cohesion.

Some glues need special preparations, such as a rough surface, or moisture. Instant glues such as Krazy Glue® are not good for gluing paper because they need a bit of moisture to cause chemical bonds to form. This is why you can stick your fingers together with just a tiny bit of the glue.

## Curriculum Connections

In this lesson, students have the opportunity to develop skills and concepts in these areas:

### *Mathematics*

SS3.4 a. Observe and describe the faces, edges, and vertices of given 3-D objects, including cubes, spheres, cones, cylinders, pyramids, and prisms (e.g., drum, tipi, South American Pyramids, and other objects from the natural environment).

P3.1 a. Identify and observe situations relevant to self, family, and community that contain an increasing or decreasing pattern, identify the starting value of the pattern, and describe the rule for the pattern and how the pattern would continue.

### *Social Studies*

RW3.3 a. Recognize that technology includes more than electronics (i.e., paper, forging steel, manufacturing, vehicles, making cloth, products created for construction).

RW3.3 b. Give examples of technologies in communities studied (e.g., communications, transportation, housing, food acquisition, preparation and storage, construction, manufacturing), and categorize the influences of the application of the technology as positive or negative.

## Focus on Literacy

### *Before Reading/Writing: Activating and Building Upon Prior Knowledge and Experiences*

The strategy of "Concept Attainment" is based on the inquiry process. It helps students clarify ideas and ensures that they understand the attributes or characteristics of a concept or topic. This strategy will be used to introduce the topic of "fasteners" in this lesson. Students will sort relevant information, identify relationships, and extend their thinking beyond a simple definition of the word through the use of this strategy.

Begin by preparing cards with the following sets of words:

- Yes, paper clip, Velcro™, zipper, nail, string, staples, tape, glue, ...
- No, cardboard, wood, bricks, glass, rock, crayons, paint, ...

Set up a T-chart on the board. Leave the area at the top of the T-chart blank for the topic. Students will be deducing what the "mystery" topic is based on the examples that you will provide. Post the two subheadings, "Yes" on the top left-hand side of the T-chart, and "No" on the top right-hand side of the T-chart.

Tell students, *I have a mystery topic in mind and I am going to give you an opportunity to figure out what that mystery topic is based on some examples I present to you.*

Present the first card by saying, *This is a Yes.* Place it in the appropriate column on the board, e.g., nails. Present the next card by saying, *This is a No.* Place it in the appropriate column, e.g., glass.

Continue this process until you have three examples in each column. Ask students to turn to a partner and discuss what all the items in the "Yes" column have in common. Present two more examples and ask students whether each item belongs in the "Yes" or "No" column. At this point, some students may know what the topic/concept is.

Do not let students reveal the topic yet; instead ask them to show what they know by offering another example for each column. Have one or two more students offer other examples.

At this point, have one student reveal the topic/concept: "fasteners" or "things that hold/join something together."

Now that prior knowledge has been built, begin reading the text on page 64 drawing special attention to the word "fasteners," its definition, and other examples.

## Misconceptions

Students may think that all forms of glue work the same way. They are not yet aware that when gluing materials together, the type of glue used depends on the job the material must do. For example, water-soluble glue would not be used to patch a canoe.

## Get Started ▶

- Review the word "fasteners" with the class. Read the paragraph in Get Started aloud.
- Challenge students to come up with as many different types of fasteners as they can think of.
- Create groups within the fastener types based on what they are good for fastening. Zippers may be good for fastening cloth, but they are not good for fastening glass.

**!**

Natural glues are found in many substances. The casein found in milk is a good example. You can make milk glue with your students. Just search the Internet using search words such as "casein," milk as glue," or "glue from milk." You can also include search words such as "experiment" or "recipe" to find more specific websites.

**traditional *KNOWLEDGE***

First Nations peoples made natural glues from animal bones. This type of traditional glue is often called hide glue. It is widely produced by many cultures and is not endemic to just Saskatchewan Plains people. The Inuit make a similar mixture. The glue was made from boiling down the joints and bones of animals. Once the mixture was boiled, an acid was added. The resulting mixture was allowed to simmer. The glue had to be boiled very carefully. If the mixture became too hot, the glue lost its adhesive strength and could burn. First Nations people boiled their mixtures by heating stones in a fire. Then the stones were removed carefully with deer antlers and placed into the hide glue mixture that sat in a leather bag or pot made from hides. Heated stones would raise the temperature of the mixture and had to be removed when they cooled. New rocks would be placed inside to continue the heating process.

See the following sites for further information:
www1.umn.edu/ships/culture/inuit.htm
www.kakwa.ca

Some key questions to consider:
- How might First Nations people have discovered hide glue?
- Why might this glue have been useful?
- Where did they use this glue?

| Time |
| --- |
| 60–90 min |
| **Learning Context** |
| inquiry |
| **Level of Inquiry** |
| guided |
| **Skills** |
| • observing<br>• experimenting<br>• comparing |
| **Grouping** |
| pairs |
| **Materials and Equipment** |
| • file folder<br>• ruler<br>• scissors<br>• glue<br>• tape<br>• stapler<br>• paper fasteners<br>• paper clips<br>• paper<br>• pencils |
| **Line Masters** |
| • LM 2-11 |

**SAFETY CAUTION!**

Remember to work safely when using scissors.

## Work On It

### Purpose

To have students investigate how well different fasteners hold paper together

### Activity Notes

- Review the fastener options available to students. For those who choose glue, drying time is necessary and may result in next-day testing. This may be included as a negative aspect of glue as a fastener.
- Use a follow-the-teacher method for completing steps one and two of What You Will Do.
- Remind students to make their list of positive and negative points after each fastener is tested. You may want to hand out LM 2-11 How Are Materials Joined Together? to help students record their observations.
- Students will be able to identify how materials are joined together and relate this to an increase in the strength of the structure.

## Communicate

1. Students' answers may vary. Students should recognize the importance of choosing a fastener based on the job that the fastener will need to do.
2. Students' answers may vary but could include desks made of steel with welds as fasteners; jackets made of cloth with zippers, Velcro™, or snaps as fasteners; desks made of wood with screws, nuts and bolts, or glue as fasteners; doors joined to walls with hinges as fasteners.

### BUILD ON WHAT YOU KNOW

Work as a class to create a list of fasteners that could be used for building bridges and a list of fasteners that should not be used for building bridges. Add this information to your KWL chart.

## DI Differentiating Instruction

### *For Enrichment*

- Ask students to consider the following questions for each fastener they tested: *How did the paper rip when each bond broke? Did the material fail or did the bond fail? Why do you think that?*
- For extra practice, you may want to hand out LM 2-12 Connecting Materials.

## Assessment *for* Learning

| What to Look for in Student Work | What to Do |
|---|---|
| Students can distinguish between materials and fasteners. They can identify which fasteners are suitable for certain tasks and certain materials. | • After testing is complete, compile a class list consisting of positive and negative points for each fastener tested. |

# 9 What Makes a Structure Last? Page 66

| Time |
|---|
| 40 min |
| **Line Masters** |
| • LM 2-13 |

## Indicator Assessment Chart

| Indicator | Assessment Opportunities |
|---|---|
| **SM3.1 c.** Compare the properties of materials used historically and currently to construct structures such as houses, bridges, towers, and roads throughout the world. | • Work On It, p. 67<br>• Communicate, p. 67, q. 1, 2, 3 |
| **SM3.2 f.** Compare the characteristics of different types of shelter (e.g., tent, igloo, hut, boat, castle, tipi, yurt, and house) constructed by people throughout the world, past and present. | • Work On It, p. 67<br>• Communicate, p. 67, q. 1, 2, 3 |
| **SM3.2 g.** Examine the characteristics and significance of historical structures such as Stonehenge, the Parthenon, Petra, the Great Wall of China, Angkor Wat, Machu Picchu, the Taj Mahal, the Pyramids, and Easter Island moai. | • Work On It, p. 67<br>• Communicate, p. 67, q. 1 |

## Lesson Goal

To find out what makes a structure last

### Background Information

Temporary structures are often the first structures to go up at a construction site. They may be used to keep water or soil out of the excavation, where something is being built, or they may be bunk houses for workers. These structures are usually easy to take down or move and do not usually sit on permanent foundations. Permanent structures take much longer to build and their construction must comply with many codes.

traditional ***KNOWLEDGE***

Not all First Nations and Métis people lived in temporary structures leading a semi-nomadic lifestyle. Some people lived in permanent sod houses, residing in the same area for generations.

## Curriculum Connections

In this lesson, students have the opportunity to develop skills and concepts in these areas:

### *Mathematics*

SS3.4 a. Observe and describe the faces, edges, and vertices of given 3-D objects, including cubes, spheres, cones, cylinders, pyramids, and prisms (e.g., drum, tipi, South American Pyramids, and other objects from the natural environment).

P3.1 a. Identify and observe situations relevant to self, family, and community that contain an increasing or decreasing pattern, identify the starting value of the pattern, and describe the rule for the pattern and how the pattern would continue.

SS3.5 c. Observe, describe the characteristics of, and sort polygons found in situations relevant to self, family, or community (including First Nations and Métis), into irregular and regular polygons (e.g., the bottom of a kamatiq, the screen of a TV, the bottom of a curling broom, and an arrowhead).

### *Social Studies*

IN3.1 a. Describe characteristics of daily life in communities studied, and compare the ways in which the needs are met by individuals in diverse communities (e.g., housing, tools, work, use of the land, games, education).

IN3.1 b. Give examples of how culture is reflected in daily life in various communities, and examine why these cultural elements are important (e.g., language, stories, cultural traditions, religious traditions, recreation, art, architecture, clothing).

## Get Started ▶

- Read Get Started with your students. Have them look carefully at the photos of the Taj Mahal and Angkor Wat. Prepare a T-chart on the board with the labels "Similarities" and "Differences." Ask students how the structures are the same. Make a list of similarities on the T-chart. Then ask students how the structures are different. Add these ideas to the T-chart.
- Ask students, *What material was used to build these structures?* Guide them to the idea that stone is a major part of the construction. Ask, *Why do you think they used stone?* Help students understand that such buildings were usually constructed of materials that were available in the area or could be easily transported to the build site.
- Direct students to the descriptions of the buildings. Add to the chart any new similarities and differences that they may find.
- Have students trace the outline of the building with their finger. Ask, *What shapes do you see?* Record similarities such as "they have curved/dome/shell structure shape" on your chart.

| Time |
| --- |
| 30 min |
| **Learning Context** |
| cultural perspectives |
| **Level of Inquiry** |
| guided |
| **Skills** |
| • classifying<br>• comparing<br>• communicating<br>• predicting |
| **Grouping** |
| individuals |
| **Materials and Equipment** |
| • pictures of structures<br>• paper<br>• pencils |
| **Line Masters** |
| • LM 2-13 |

## Work On It

### Purpose

To have students determine which structures will last and which will not last

### Activity Notes

- Choose pictures of structures from all over the world. Allow students to switch pictures when they have classified the original set they were given.
- Although this is listed as an individual assignment, allow students to discuss their ideas with their neighbours.
- If the name of a structure is not known, have students write a description that will identify the structure.
- Have students compare their work with others to verify their choice of permanent or temporary. You may want to hand out LM 2-13 What Makes a Structure Last? to help students record their answers.
- Students will recognize that the structural and material requirements for temporary structures are different than for permanent structures.

## Communicate

After students have shared their work with their neighbours, have them share their results with the class. Add new information from this lesson to the KWL chart.

1. Students' answers may vary but should include mention of rigid materials, such as stone (rock), concrete, steel, wood, and maybe glass. The materials listed will be ones that do not break down or decompose easily.
2. Students should notice that temporary structures are usually made from materials that are easily replaced, such as grass or hide.
3. Rock was not readily available in Saskatchewan, and without metal tools to shape the rock, a structure would be difficult to build. First Nations and Métis people and settlers therefore used the materials available to them in the environment, which were cloth, wood, and sod. Many First Nations people were migratory and travelled the same migratory paths as their food sources. Structures built from rock are not easily transportable.

## DI Differentiating Instruction

### *For Enrichment*

Have students work in teams to separate the pictures into two piles. Have them discuss why the structures were placed in each pile. Then ask them, *Which buildings would last the longest?* and *Did you place these buildings in the same pile?* If not, have students create a pile of long-lasting and not so long-lasting structures. Refer to the long-lasting pile as permanent structures and to the not so long-lasting pile as temporary structures.

## Assessment *for* Learning

| What to Look for in Student Work | What to Do |
|---|---|
| Students should be able to identify and describe characteristics of permanent and temporary structures. | • Provide pictures that clearly show characteristics of temporary structures and ones that show characteristics of permanent structures. |

# 10 Earthquake-Proof Structures

Page 68

| Time |
|---|
| 80 min |
| **Line Masters** |
| • LM 2-14 |

## Indicator Assessment Chart

| Indicator | Assessment Opportunities |
|---|---|
| **SM3.1 f.** Use appropriate tools (e.g., hammer, nail, glue, and scissors) to safely cut, shape, make holes, sew, and assemble materials. | • Work On It, p. 68 |
| **SM3.1 g.** Develop and carry out a plan, including making predictions, identifying variables, and recording relevant observations, to test the strength of various materials (e.g., straws, toothpicks, masking tape, string, cotton balls, wooden blocks, Styrofoam, cloth, clay, and spaghetti). | • Work On It, p. 68<br>• Communicate, p. 69, q. 1 |
| **SM3.2 i.** Develop and carry out a plan to construct a simple structure such as a tower, bridge, tipi, or bird feeder that meets teacher-or student-specified criteria related to strength, stability, and function. | • Work On It, p. 68<br>• Communicate, p. 69, q. 1, 2, 3 |
| **SM3.2 j.** Estimate measurements in order to select appropriate quantities of required materials for constructing a structure. | • Work On It, p. 68 |
| **SM3.2 k.** Follow safety procedures and rules while constructing structures and explain the need for such procedures and rules. | • Work On It, p. 68 |
| **SM3.2 l.** Illustrate the construction process for a simple structure, including descriptions of the components of the structure, using labelled drawings, written and oral explanations, and demonstrations. | • Communicate, p. 69, q. 1, 2 |
| **SM3.2 m.** Assess the strength, stability, and balance of personally constructed structures and make changes to improve the structure as deemed necessary. | • Work On It, p. 68 |
| **SM3.2 n.** Identify materials or parts of a structure that failed and hypothesize why they failed. | • Communicate, p. 69, q. 3 |

## Lesson Goal

To design and build a lasting structure

### Background Information

The construction of the domed roof on the Hagia Sophia in Istanbul, Turkey turned out to be a real geometric headache. The question: How do you build a massive circular roof and support it with a square base? Fortunately, the architects of the Hagia Sophia, Isidore of Miletus and Anthemius of Tralles, were professors of geometry at the University of Constantinople. Anthemius decided to build four massive columns at the corner of each square. On top of the columns were four arches filled with masonry to create curved triangular shapes called pendentives. The pendentives and the tops of the arches combined to form a strong base for the dome. The entire domed structure took 10 000 workers 5 years, 10 months, and 4 days to complete. Because the dome had suffered earthquake damage in the past, the outside walls needed to be reinforced. The original walls were made of bricks and mortar, but the mortar was too thick so the walls were not strong. The repair work helped the walls survive the earthquake of 1999. The quake struck in the middle of the night, lasted for 37 seconds, and killed more than 17 000 people. Most died in their beds as their homes collapsed. Better construction would have saved many lives.

traditional ***KNOWLEDGE***

Saskatchewan sits in the centre of a continent with the northeast portion containing some of the most stable rock in the world: the Canadian Shield. Although earthquakes in Saskatchewan are not common, they do still occur. First Nations and Métis people probably did not recognize these quakes, as the quakes would have felt like a stampeding herd of animals.

## Curriculum Connections

In this lesson, students have the opportunity to develop skills and concepts in these areas:

***Mathematics***

SS3.3 a. Observe and describe situations relevant to self, family, and community that involve measuring lengths, including perimeter, in cm or m.

SS3.3 c. Create models to generalize a numerical relationship between cm and m (i.e., 100 cm is equivalent to 1 metre).

SS3.3 e. Identify and determine the length of the dimensions of a personally relevant 2-D shape or 3-D object.

SS3.3 j. Create a picture of a 2-D shape with specified length and width (or length and height) and explain whether the 2-D shape was constructed using estimates or actual lengths.

SS3.3 m. Construct or draw more than one 2-D shape for the same given perimeter (cm, m).
SS3.4 d. Construct a skeleton of a given 3-D object and describe how the skeleton relates to the 3-D object.
P3.1 a. Identify and observe situations relevant to self, family, and community that contain an increasing or decreasing pattern, identify the starting value of the pattern, and describe the rule for the pattern and how the pattern would continue.

***Social Studies***

DR3.2 a. Identify the influences that geography has on societies (e.g., location of settlements, transportation of goods and people, types of industry such as farming, ranching, forestry, mining, tourism, and manufacturing).
DR3.2 c. Describe the impact of environmental factors and events on ways of life in communities studied (e.g., climate, vegetation, natural resources, landforms, floods, droughts, storms).
RW3.1 c. Describe ways in which communities help ensure basic human needs are met (e.g., food and water, shelter, clothing, education, safety).
RW3.3 a. Recognize that technology includes more than electronics (i.e., paper, forging steel, manufacturing, vehicles, making cloth, products created for construction).
RW3.3 b. Give examples of technologies in communities studied (e.g., communications, transportation, housing, food acquisition, preparation and storage, construction, manufacturing), and categorize the influences of the application of the technology as positive or negative.

## Misconceptions

Students may not understand the immense size of the dome on the structure. To help them understand, point out the windows in your school. Have students count the windows, then tell them that the dome of the Hagia Sophia has 40 windows around its base.

**Get Started ▶**

- Have students read the first two paragraphs and then carefully examine the photos on the page.
- Ask students, *What materials were used to build the Hagia Sophia? What materials were used to build the apartment buildings? What kinds of fasteners were used in their construction?* Students may suggest that stones and mortar are better than wood and nails. Suggest that materials used must reflect what they are being used for.
- Point out the minarets in the photo of the Hagia Sophia. Have students look at the base of the minarets. Relate the area covered by the base to a footprint. Ask them, *Is the top of the tower (minaret) bigger than its base?*
- Remind students about Lesson 6: Nature's Balancing Act. Review their answers to Communicate question 4, then ask, *Do you think a larger base makes the tower more stable?*

! You'll come across many websites for the Hagia Sophia, as it is an incredible engineering marvel. Students might be interested to know its past. A good place to start is at http://encyclopedia.kids.net.au/page/ha/Hagia_Sophia.

**Time**

60 min

**Learning Context**

problem solving

**Level of Inquiry**

structured

**Skills**

- making models
- experimenting
- comparing
- measuring
- controlling variables

**Grouping**

pairs or individuals

**Materials and Equipment**

- Bristol board (15 cm by 20 cm)
- ruler
- scissors
- glue
- tape
- paper fasteners
- stapler
- paper
- pencils
- box lid
- marbles
- lightweight cardboard (about 20 cm by 30 cm)
- modelling clay

**Line Masters**

- LM 2-14

**SAFETY CAUTION!**

Remember to work safely when using scissors. Remember to follow safety procedures and rules while building your tower.

## Work On It

### Purpose

To have students design and build an earthquake-proof tower and to test it on a shake table

### Activity Notes

- This activity can be completed individually if sufficient materials are available, but working in pairs allows students to discuss their design ideas for the tower.
- Give students plenty of time to decide on their design. Move among students, listening to their ideas. Ask students questions only during this time. *What are those lines for?* is better than *You need cross supports.*
- While students are working, build the shake table they will be using for their tests.
- Allow students to test as many times as they want within the timeline of the class. Testing allows them to see any flaws in their plan.
- If students change their design, have them adjust their sketch to include the changes they made. Tell students that a person should be able to build the tower just by reading their instructions. You can compare this to a recipe.
- Have students record in their notebook the steps needed to build their tower. A diagram of the tower with labels indicating what each part is/does should also be recorded in their notebook or on LM 2-14 Earthquake-Proof Structures. You may want to give them words such as "load," "cross-ties," "base," "floor," and "beam" to use as labels.
- Students will gain experience in the construction of a stable structure. They will understand that cross-ties create stability in structures such as roof trusses, bridges, and barn doors as well as in the construction of towers.

## Communicate

The answers to these questions will help students with their final Design Project.

1. Students' answers may vary. Answers should look like the instructions for making their tower.
2. Students' answers may vary but should include words like "cross-ties," "load," and "base."
3. Students' answers may vary but could include the joints, which may not be dry; the cross-ties, which may suffer failure due to placement or joint dryness; or the beams, which may have been weakened by a poor cut, a bend, or a tear.

## DI Differentiating Instruction

### *For EAL/ELL*

Rather than writing the construction steps, students can draw the instructions for making the tower.

### *For Enrichment*

Allow students to add materials to their tower in an effort to increase its strength and stability. If students have an effective design, have them try moving the marbles in a circular fashion to see if the tower can withstand forces from other directions.

### *For Reteaching*

Review Lessons 5 and 6 before designing another tower.

## Assessment *for* Learning

| What to Look for in Student Work | What to Do |
|---|---|
| Students should be able to design, build, and test a tower to determine whether the design or construction is "earthquake-proof." | • Review the Communicate questions with the class. Spend time discussing question 3, focussing questions on materials and fasteners. |

# 11 Looking at Materials

Page 70

**Time**

40 min

**Vocabulary**

- recyclable
- renewable
- reusable

**Line Masters**

- LM 2-15

## Indicator Assessment Chart

| Indicator | Assessment Opportunities |
|---|---|
| **SM3.1 a.** Identify problems to be solved related to the properties of materials in structures (e.g., What is the purpose of the structure? What materials are appropriate for constructing the structure? What are appropriate methods of joinery?). | • Communicate, p. 71, q. 3 |
| **SM3.1 b.** Examine the properties of materials used in natural and human-built structures (e.g., beaver lodge, bird nest, wasps' nest, honeycomb, ant hill, tipi, house, marionette, circus float, umbrella, ladder, bridge, earthlodge, quinzhee, drink can, hockey puck, playground equipment, and toys). | • Communicate, p. 71, q. 3 |
| **SM3.1 i.** Examine the suitability of using recycled materials to construct structures (e.g., tires as highway surfacing, and reclaimed lumber or straw bales for houses). | • Work On It, p. 71<br>• Communicate, p. 71, q. 1, 2 |
| **SM3.2 a.** Analyze the purpose or function of various natural and human-built structures. | • Communicate, p. 71, q. 1, 3 |
| **SM3.2 o.** Assess natural and human-built structures to determine if they are effective, safe, make efficient use of materials, meet user's needs, and minimize impact on the environment. | • Communicate, p. 71, q. 1, 3 |

## Lesson Goal

To find out what materials are recyclable, renewable, and reusable

### Background Information

Most people know about the three Rs: reduce, reuse, and recycle, but not as many know about the fourth R because it changes depending on where you live. Some say the fourth R is rebuy, which refers to buying recycled products; recover, which refers to using technology that can recover waste materials and energy that cannot be reused, recycled, or reduced; or repair, which extends the life of things. Among the main three Rs, the best choice is reduce, as this will prevent waste from being generated. Reusing is giving a second chance to items rather than letting them visit the landfill, but recycle is the only one that involves the further use of energy and resources.

*continued→*

traditional ***KNOWLEDGE***

In Saskatchewan, people can recycle beverage containers, waste electronics, used oil materials, scrap tires, and paint.

In fact, you can recycle anything from antifreeze to wood and trees. See www.saskwastereduction.ca/dbase.php, for a complete list.

Traditional knowledge is about people and their relationship with the land. How to make best use of materials from the land is the type of knowledge that is passed down over time by watching and listening. Traditional teachings are usually shared in the winter months when there is snow on the ground. When the snow goes away, the teachings are practical and learning is done by doing.

## Curriculum Connections

In this lesson, students have the opportunity to develop skills and concepts in these areas:

### *Mathematics*

SS3.2 i. Generalize statements about the mass of a specific amount of matter when reformed into different shapes or sizes (e.g., use clay to make an object, measure the mass of the object, reform the clay into another object and measure the mass of the two objects; an empty balloon versus a full balloon; or water versus ice).

P3.1 a. Identify and observe situations relevant to self, family, and community that contain an increasing or decreasing pattern, identify the starting value of the pattern, and describe the rule for the pattern and how the pattern would continue.

### *Social Studies*

IN3.1 a. Describe characteristics of daily life in communities studied, and compare the ways in which the needs are met by individuals in diverse communities (e.g., housing, tools, work, use of the land, games, education).

IN3.3 a. Research the origins of products and items used by students in the local classroom.

IN3.3 c. Identify products produced locally and sold elsewhere.

DR3.3 a. Research the view of land as held by Indigenous peoples in communities studied.

DR3.3 b. Identify ways in which people in communities studied interact with the land (e.g., meeting needs and wants, how land is protected or neglected).

RW3.1 c. Describe ways in which communities help ensure basic human needs are met (e.g., food and water, shelter, clothing, education, safety).

RW3.2 b. Define the term natural resources, and differentiate between renewable and non-renewable resources.

RW3.3 a. Recognize that technology includes more than electronics (i.e., paper, forging steel, manufacturing, vehicles, making cloth, products created for construction).

RW3.3 b. Give examples of technologies in communities studied (e.g., communications, transportation, housing, food acquisition, preparation and storage, construction, manufacturing), and categorize the influences of the application of the technology as positive or negative.

## Focus on Literacy

### *During Reading/Writing: Using Common Prefixes and Suffixes*

Post a picture of the "reduce, reuse, recycle" symbol. Ask students if they are familiar with what this symbol stands for. Write these three words on the board or chart paper. Have students identify the common part in all three of these words, "re." Remind them that this small word part is called a "prefix" and circle it in each word. Invite students to offer other words they know that begin with this prefix (reread, react, reappear, retell, redo, recover ...). Have students turn to a partner and discuss what the prefix "re" means (again), and what it does to the root word in each case.

Tell students, *In Lesson 11, we will look at a number of structures that are made from both natural and human-made materials, some of which can be reused, recycled, or possibly renewed.*

Draw students' attention to the bold words on page 71: recyclable, renewable, reusable. Ask students to identify any common word parts in these three words, i.e., "re-, -able." Focus on "able" this time. Remind students that when a small word part comes at the end of a word it is called a "suffix." Have students turn to a partner and discuss what the suffix "able" means (capable of) and what each of the bold words means as a whole. Have students share their definitions and brainstorm other words that end with the suffix, "able" (usable, adjustable, affordable, controllable, correctable, disposable, ...).

Tell students, *Science has a lot of special vocabulary that will be unfamiliar to us or used in a different way than we are used to. Writers often provide the definition of a word right in the sentence or use the word in context to give you a sense of what it means. When we come across new words, we now have another strategy we can use to help us determine its meaning: breaking it into its common word parts.*

## Misconceptions

Students may think recycling is the most important part of the responsible use of materials. Unfortunately, recycling materials takes energy as well as other resources. This makes it the least valuable of reduce, reuse, recycle.

| Time |
| --- |
| 30 min |
| **Learning Context** |
| inquiry |
| **Level of Inquiry** |
| guided |
| **Skills** |
| • inferring<br>• comparing<br>• communicating |
| **Grouping** |
| individuals |
| **Materials and Equipment** |
| • paper<br>• pencils |
| **Line Masters** |
| • LM 2-15 |

## Get Started ▶

- Begin by explaining to students that a master builder is recognized as someone who is the best at a particular task. Bees are master cone builders, beavers are master dam builders, and birds are master nest builders.
- Invite students to read Get Started. Have them look at the pictures and decide which structures are made from human-made materials and which are made from natural materials.
- Compile a list with suggestions from the class.
- Add any unknowns to the KWL chart.

## Work On It

### Purpose

To have students determine what types of materials the structures are made of and which materials are recyclable, renewable, and reusable

### Activity Notes

- Begin the Work On It by discussing the data table. Explain each column by adding "What Is" to the beginning of the first three columns and "Is It" to the beginning of the last three columns.
- Use the beaver dam as an example. It is made from wood and strengthened by branches and mud woven together. It is reusable, probably not recyclable, but definitely renewable.
- Students comparing their decisions with those of other students is an essential part of this lesson. Encourage students to explain their thinking when there is disagreement. Have them add any information they are missing. You may want to hand out LM 2-15 Looking at Materials to help students record their answers.
- Any agreement and unresolved disagreement can be added to the KWL chart.

**!** Craik, Saskatchewan not only has an eco-centre made of straw bales and recycled materials, it also has an eco-village. People from around the world, interested in living an environmentally friendly lifestyle, go to the village to live sustainably with Earth. For more information, visit www.craik.ca/ecovillage.html.

## Communicate

1. Students' answers may vary but should include information from the Get Started portion of the lesson.
2. Students should recognize that renewable material needs time to regenerate. Sometimes this takes many years. Using too much would mean we would run out of material in the short term. Likewise, overuse of non-renewable material would result in a permanent loss of the resource.

3. Students should notice that all three structures are made mainly of natural materials, such as wood. They should also notice that shape and structure are well suited to their use. The dam and wigwam are constructed with little waste and the house would have the most waste. (Students who have experience with beavers may consider the trees they kill as waste and classify this as a high amount of waste.) Environmental effects of a beaver dam might include raised water levels in a river, flooding, or damaged trees. Environmental effects of a house might be change in land characteristics, loss of plant life, and loss of animal life. Environmental effects of a wigwam might be packed soil, packed grasses, damaged trees, and loss of animals.

## DI Differentiating Instruction

### *For Enrichment*

Have students draw pictures of the structures from page 70 of the student book on an enlarged version of the table. Have students place checkmarks in the Reusable, Recyclable, and Renewable portions to reflect what they know about the structures. As a class, discuss the Made From and Strengthened By sections to ensure all students have a common experience.

## Assessment *for* Learning

| What to Look for in Student Work | What to Do |
|---|---|
| Students should be able to identify materials that can be reused or recycled, or if the material is renewable. | • Keep a list of students' responses. Watch for frequent and appropriate use of vocabulary terms. Review the terms frequently for students who need extra help.<br>• Use Communicate question 3 to evaluate understanding. |

# 12 Reusing and Recycling Materials

Page 72

| Time |
| --- |
| 80 min |
| **Vocabulary** |
| • raw materials |
| **Line Masters** |
| • LM 2-16 |

## Indicator Assessment Chart

| Indicator | Assessment Opportunities |
| --- | --- |
| **SM3.1 f.** Use appropriate tools (e.g., hammer, nail, glue, and scissors) to safely cut, shape, make holes, sew, and assemble materials. | • Work On It, p. 72 |
| **SM3.1 i.** Examine the suitability of using recycled materials to construct structures (e.g., tires as highway surfacing, and reclaimed lumber or straw bales for houses). | • Work On It, p. 72<br>• Communicate, p. 73, q. 1, 2, 3, 4 |
| **SM3.2 i.** Develop and carry out a plan to construct a simple structure such as a tower, bridge, tipi, or bird feeder that meets teacher-or student-specified criteria related to strength, stability, and function. | • Work On It, p. 72 |
| **SM3.2 k.** Follow safety procedures and rules while constructing structures and explain the need for such procedures and rules. | • Work On It, p. 72 |

## Lesson Goal

To use materials in ways that respect nature

## Background Information

One person's trash is another person's treasure, and although recycling currently takes centre stage in waste management, reusing and repurposing should not be underestimated. Garage sales and second-hand stores are great places to find items to reuse. This method of redistribution reduces the amount of material going to landfill sites, which makes it good for the environment. Reuse of glass beverage bottles is actually better for the environment than both recycling and the use of throw-away containers. Glass bottles need to be washed, sterilized, and inspected, but recycling plastic involves the use of chemicals and the addition of other materials to strengthen the plastics, and requires more energy than reusing glass bottles to prepare them for their next use.

traditional **KNOWLEDGE**

Reusing and repurposing has long been a tradition for First Nations and Métis peoples. Information on the use of plants, animals, and substances for healing was often place-based and differs from group to group. The method of thanking Mother Earth also differs. If tobacco is not available, the person might use a little of whatever he or she had on hand, such as a bit of food. The important thing is to show gratitude and respect for Mother Earth. This information is passed down from generation to generation, making it part of the culture's traditional knowledge.

The perspective on sustainability, which we might call stewardship, considers the impact of our actions today on future generations. Many great First Nations leaders in Saskatchewan have exemplified this type of thinking. Chief Mistahwasis, for instance, who negotiated on behalf of his people, thought about the legacy his actions would have on his descendents. *What we speak of and do now will last as long as the sun shines and the river runs, we are looking forward to our children's children, for we are old and have but few days to live.* (Mistahwasis, Fort Carlton, August 22, 1876)

This forward thinking not only applied to treaties, but it permeates traditional First Nations understanding and attitudes toward sustainability. The Great Law of the Iroquois contends that actions taken today need careful consideration because their impact will be felt seven generations from now. This First Nations code has inspired and shaped a recent western concept of seven generation sustainability.

**Background information on tobacco**

Tobacco is considered sacred among First Nations and Métis peoples. Traditional tobacco contains a mixture of many sacred plants, including bearberry. The Cree called it *kinikinik.* It is believed that smoke from the sacred plants—tobacco, cedar, sweetgrass, and sage—carries prayers to Creator. Tobacco is used in many important ceremonies including the pipe ceremony. Contrary to Western beliefs, tobacco is a sacred medicine often believed to cleanse.

Tobacco offerings are ways that First Nations people communicate their profound respect and gratitude for a gift or a teaching. First Nations people teach their children to give tobacco as a sign of gratitude. In the community when one needs help from another, especially Elders, protocols must be followed in order to gain that assistance. These protocols always include a tobacco offering.

*continued→*

Tobacco is a means to show gratitude for the spirit of a living being. A tobacco offering expresses appreciation for the gifts that Mother Earth and Creator provide. All First Nations peoples believe that all things, even what western science might consider abiotic, possess a spirit. Therefore, things like rocks and fire have a spirit. A tobacco offering is a way that First Nations people show gratitude to that spirit. Thus, when a tree is cut, an animal is killed, a rock is removed to be used in a ceremony, or a plant is harvested, the spirit in that tree, animal, rock, or plant is thanked with tobacco.

**Teaching notes on tobacco**

Many people view tobacco in a negative light as it is associated with cigarette smoking. In traditional practice, Knowledge Keepers and Elders discourage the use of recreational smoking. Often the tobacco is not smoked at all but left under a tree. When the ceremony is performed, the pipe is shared. Little tobacco smoke is actually consumed.

For teachers, an understanding of the sacred importance of tobacco is necessary to help students understand. Teachers must help elucidate the spiritual nature of tobacco and explain that is the reason why First Nations people use tobacco in their ceremonies. It might be important for teachers to distinguish between the recreational use of tobacco and its traditional usage in ceremonies.

The act of giving thanks is a value that teachers can help students appreciate. Called reciprocity by some First Nations people, this value helps students understand that in order to take from the land, we take only what we need and something must be given back. An attitude of thanksgiving helps promote positive regard for the land. If students appreciate this worldview, they may make better choices such as recycling, reusing, walking, limiting power consumption, and even taking an interest in protecting key local conservation areas. Teachers may wish to further expand this reading. Using a Venn diagram, teachers may wish to compare and contrast western views and First Nations views about tobacco. A diagram may help students understand how First Nations people might view tobacco as sacred in its usage in ceremonies compared to a more negative view of tobacco in western perspectives.

Here are some key questions you may want to ask students.

- How does recreational smoking differ from the use of tobacco in traditional ceremonies?
- In what ways does the First Nations view of giving back to the land helping us to better manage the land?
- Would we be willing to readily exploit natural resources if we believed that trees, rocks, air, and water have spirits? How might that change how we treat the land? Would we be more thankful?

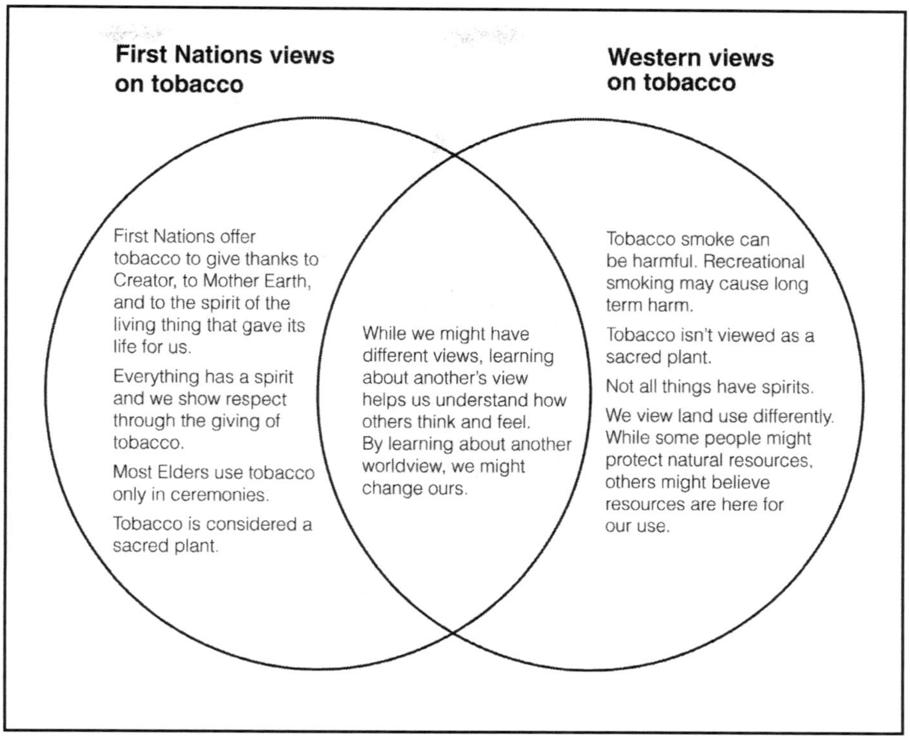


Sources: Elder Mary Lee, Danny Musqua, Velma Goodfeather, the late Simon Kitwayhat, and Knowledge Keeper Delvin Kaniweyakiho
www.aht.ca/approaching-a-traditional-healer-elder-or-medicine-person
www.sgib.ca/index_files/Page3161.htm

## Curriculum Connections

In this lesson, students have the opportunity to develop skills and concepts in these areas:

### *Mathematics*

SS3.2 i. Generalize statements about the mass of a specific amount of matter when reformed into different shapes or sizes (e.g., use clay to make an object, measure the mass of the object, reform the clay into another object and measure the mass of the two objects; an empty balloon versus a full balloon; or water versus ice).

### *Social Studies*

IN3.1 a. Describe characteristics of daily life in communities studied, and compare the ways in which the needs are met by individuals in diverse communities (e.g., housing, tools, work, use of the land, games, education).
IN3.3 a. Research the origins of products and items used by students in the local classroom.
IN3.3 c. Identify products produced locally and sold elsewhere.
DR3.3 a. Research the view of land as held by Indigenous peoples in communities studied.
DR3.3 b. Identify ways in which people in communities studied interact with the land (e.g., meeting needs and wants, how land is protected or neglected).

RW3.1 c. Describe ways in which communities help ensure basic human needs are met (e.g., food and water, shelter, clothing, education, safety).
RW3.2 b. Define the term natural resources, and differentiate between renewable and non-renewable resources.
RW3.3 a. Recognize that technology includes more than electronics (i.e., paper, forging steel, manufacturing, vehicles, making cloth, products created for construction).
RW3.3 b. Give examples of technologies in communities studied (e.g., communications, transportation, housing, food acquisition, preparation and storage, construction, manufacturing), and categorize the influences of the application of the technology as positive or negative.

## Misconceptions

Students may focus on the "raw" part of raw materials. They may believe things need to be cooked before they can be used. Help students understand that in this case "raw" means basic or unused.

## Get Started ▶

- Ask students to make a list of 10 things their family throws away every week, then pair up with one partner to compare lists before sharing with the class.
- While students are sharing their lists with the class, either write a list on the board or ask students to add the items they did not have to their list.
- Go through the list asking, *Can this be reused? recycled?* Mark this beside each item.
- Ask students, *Could this item be made from recycled material? Could this item be replaced by a reusable item?*
- Draw students' attention to Get Started. Read the first paragraph to students. Ask if they understand what a raw material is.
- Point out the photo of potash. Have them read the description, then ask, *Does potash look like fertilizer/soap/glass?* Remind students that raw materials are combined with other materials to make something with new properties. Without the raw material, the new material could not be made.
- Read the second paragraph to students and ask if they think this makes sense. Add to the KWL chart where appropriate.
- Read the third paragraph to students. Explain that giving back to nature could also mean reducing the amount of waste we generate; for example, choosing products and materials that generate very little extra waste, such as a block of cheese rather than individually wrapped pieces.

traditional **KNOWLEDGE**

The concept of seven generations in the Great Law of the Iroquois does not apply to all First Nations groups, though the belief behind it does. Some Elders have suggested that the idea "seven generations" is not part of their cultural lexicon, e.g., the Cree and the Dakota. While all First Nations groups may not use the phrasing "seven generations," they share a similar belief that our actions hold future consequences for our descendents.

The idea of making sure that nature's resources last for seven generations is really about conservation of natural resources. For many First Nations and Métis communities, something as simple as changing the flow of water through an area could change the resources of that area. If a certain plant was traditionally found in that spot, the plant may die out. If only a few people in the community knew what the plant looked like through all seasons, the loss of the plant could mean the loss of that piece of traditional knowledge.

This feature may be used in several ways. First, teachers may wish to use the ideas in the feature to draw out some discussions with students about ecological sustainability. It may be important for teachers to introduce the idea of sustainability. Key questions like "What is sustainability?" and "How does sustainability affect the environment?" may stimulate discussion and hopefully action. Extension activities that might arise include an invitation to envision a world without trees or without clean water, or life without an endangered species, like the burrowing owl or the whooping crane. Students can showcase their ideas through journal entries, an ecologist log, a short story, or a poem. Another powerful activity is to safely sort the trash after students eat their lunch. Using gloves, goggles, and aprons, teachers may sort through the trash to see what is compostable, recyclable, reusable, and what plastics cannot be recycled and might harm the environment.

**Time**

60 min

**Learning Context**

inquiry

**Level of Inquiry**

confirmation

**Skills**

- communicating
- using equipment

**Grouping**

pairs or individuals

**Materials and Equipment**

- clean milk or juice cartons or plastic water bottles
- scissors
- nails
- craft sticks or twigs
- wire or string
- birdseed

**Line Masters**

- LM 2-16

**SAFETY CAUTION!**

Remember to work safely when using sharp objects.

## Work On It

### Purpose

To have students build a bird feeder from reusable and recycled materials found at home or in the classroom

### Activity Notes

- Make sure the cartons or plastic bottles are clean and dry. Wet cartons or bottles will cause the birdseed to mould.
- Students may find it difficult to complete step 1. If possible, have one or two additional adults in the room to help students. Make sure the hole is not cut too high as more seed will be needed to fill the feeder and could result in mouldy feed. If the hole is cut too low, the feeder will need to be refilled constantly.
- The nail should be pushed through the carton or plastic bottle to form a pilot hole for the stick. A 7.5 cm nail works well. If the hole is too big, hot glue can be added to make the fit snug.

## Communicate

These questions could be used for a Think-Pair-Share.

1. Students' answers may vary but could include wood. More creative answers could be an old boot, tin cans, or peanut butter pine cones.
2. Students will probably decide if a material is suitable for recycling by the types of items they have traditionally seen in recycling bins. Others may know of the recycling code on the bottom of plastic containers.
3. Students should recall previous lessons, particularly Lesson 2, which discussed materials and their strength. Students should identify materials they feel are strong enough to do the job.
4. Students' answers may vary depending on the type of structures they are considering. Homes may be built from bales; park benches may be built from recycled plastic; and roads and patio slabs may be built from recycled tires. You may want to hand out LM 2-16 Reusing and Recycling Materials to help students record their answers.

## DI Differentiating Instruction

### *For EAL/ELL*

Make a deck of Go Fish cards with pictures of various structures on them. Ask, *Do you have anything made of plastic?* Have students play the game a few times before they move on to the Communicate questions.

### *For Enrichment*

Challenge students to make a colouring book of structures in Saskatchewan that are made from recyclable and reusable materials. Have them include the original material and structures that could be made from it.

## Assessment *for* Learning

| What to Look for in Student Work | What to Do |
|---|---|
| Students should be able to recognize the types of materials that are suitable for reusing and recycling. | • Students who have difficulty visualizing may benefit from a mind map. Place the resource in the middle of the mind map and have students brainstorm the items that can be made from that product. Have them put a star beside the items they think could be made from recycled material. |

# 13 Well Built or Not?

Page 74

**Time**

80 min

**Vocabulary**

- stability

**Line Masters**

- LM 2-17
- LM 2-18

## Indicator Assessment Chart

| Indicator | Assessment Opportunities |
|---|---|
| **SM3.1 f.** Use appropriate tools (e.g., hammer, nail, glue, and scissors) to safely cut, shape, make holes, sew, and assemble materials. | • Work On It, p. 74 |
| **SM3.2 a.** Analyze the purpose or function of various natural and human-built structures. | • Communicate, p. 75, q. 3 |
| **SM3.2 b.** Examine how some human-built structures are modelled on shapes and structures found in nature. | • Work On It, p. 74 |
| **SM3.2 c.** Assess how 2-D shapes (e.g., rectangle, triangle, circle, square, hexagon, and octagon) and 3-D objects (e.g., dome, arch, and cylinders) provide strength, stability, and balance to natural and human-built structures. | • Communicate, p. 75, q. 1, 2 |
| **SM3.2 i.** Develop and carry out a plan to construct a simple structure such as a tower, bridge, tipi, or bird feeder that meets teacher-or student-specified criteria related to strength, stability, and function. | • Work On It, p. 74 |
| **SM3.2 j.** Estimate measurements in order to select appropriate quantities of required materials for constructing a structure. | • Work On It, p. 74 |
| **SM3.2 k.** Follow safety procedures and rules while constructing structures and explain the need for such procedures and rules. | • Work On It, p. 74 |
| **SM3.2 m.** Assess the strength, stability, and balance of personally constructed structures and make changes to improve the structure as deemed necessary. | • Work On It, p. 74<br>• Communicate, p. 75, q. 1, 2 |
| **SM3.2 o.** Assess natural and human-built structures to determine if they are effective, safe, make efficient use of materials, meet user's needs, and minimize impact on the environment. | • Communicate, p. 75, q. 2 |

## Lesson Goal

To find out how shape can give a structure strength and stability

traditional ***KNOWLEDGE***

## Background Information

Simple temporary structures are quite a common sight in Saskatchewan: a lean-to on a shed, a coverall for a shop, a tent for a vacation at the lake, etc. All temporary structures mimic nature's geometric shapes. The most common shape used by humans is the triangle. Triangles are successful because their base is bigger than their height. The stability of an object or structure is related to its height and its width, particularly at the base. Objects that are short and wide are usually more stable than objects that are tall and narrow.

Although men and boys may help with the setting up of a tipi, it is the women who are usually the keepers of this traditional knowledge. The Cree believe that a tipi is the spirit and body of a woman because she represents the foundation of family and community. The ceremony of constructing a tipi represents the value of women's teachings.

The construction of the tipi is well thought out. Even the door's shape, which reflects the shape of a person, is considered. Since people are not round, the door should not be round. Not all tipis are decorated. Decorations trace the history of the family and hold deep spiritual connections.

For additional information, see the traditional knowledge notes in Riley Joseph's profile and for a deeper understanding, visit www.fourdirectionsteachings.com/transcripts/cree.html.

## Curriculum Connections

In this lesson, students have the opportunity to develop skills and concepts in these areas:

### *Mathematics*

SS3.3 a. Observe and describe situations relevant to self, family, and community that involve measuring lengths, including perimeter, in cm or m.

SS3.3 e. Identify and determine the length of the dimensions of a personally relevant 2-D shape or 3-D object.

P3.1 a. Identify and observe situations relevant to self, family, and community that contain an increasing or decreasing pattern, identify the starting value of the pattern, and describe the rule for the pattern and how the pattern would continue.

P3.1 h. Research (e.g., through Elders, Traditional Knowledge Keepers, naturalists, and media) and present about the role and significance of increasing and decreasing patterns (e.g., making of a star blanket, beading, music, and patterns found in nature) in First Nations and Métis practices, lifestyles, and worldviews.

SS3.5 c. Observe, describe the characteristics of, and sort polygons found in situations relevant to self, family, or community (including First Nations and Métis), into irregular and regular polygons (e.g., the bottom of a kamatiq, the screen of a TV, the bottom of a curling broom, and an arrowhead).

### *Social Studies*

IN3.1 a. Describe characteristics of daily life in communities studied, and compare the ways in which the needs are met by individuals in diverse communities (e.g., housing, tools, work, use of the land, games, education).
IN3.1 b. Give examples of how culture is reflected in daily life in various communities, and examine why these cultural elements are important (e.g., language, stories, cultural traditions, religious traditions, recreation, art, architecture, clothing).
DR3.2 a. Identify the influences that geography has on societies (e.g., location of settlements, transportation of goods and people, types of industry such as farming, ranching, forestry, mining, tourism, and manufacturing).
DR3.2 b. Recognize how environmental and climatic factors are influenced by location (e.g., proximity to water bodies influences precipitation and temperature; mountainous terrain influences soil formation, precipitation, and temperature).
DR3.2 c. Describe the impact of environmental factors and events on ways of life in communities studied (e.g., climate, vegetation, natural resources, landforms, floods, droughts, storms).
RW3.1 c. Describe ways in which communities help ensure basic human needs are met (e.g., food and water, shelter, clothing, education, safety).
RW3.3 a. Recognize that technology includes more than electronics (i.e., paper, forging steel, manufacturing, vehicles, making cloth, products created for construction).

### *Visual Arts*

CP3.7 a. Generate questions that arise from the investigation of a topic or area of interest to initiate inquiry (e.g., How have different artists represented turtles in visual art works and book illustrations?).
CR3.2 a. Demonstrate ways that arts expressions can represent ideas and convey meaning verbally and non-verbally (e.g., music that conveys a mood; dance that conveys ideas about bullying; drama that conveys ideas about compassion; visual art or graphic that conveys a social message).
CH3.1 e. Describe ways that people of various cultures in own and surrounding communities participate in the arts and discuss why they do so.
CH3.2 e. Observe, listen to, and inquire about First Nations and Métis arts and protocols related to arts expressions.

## Misconceptions

Students may think that adding colour to a tipi makes it nicer to look at, but they should be made aware that a decorated tipi shows spiritual connections. In this case, decorations are not art, they are part of religion.

| Time |
| --- |
| 60 min |
| **Learning Context** |
| cultural perspectives |
| **Level of Inquiry** |
| guided |
| **Skills** |
| • making models<br>• inferring<br>• measuring |
| **Grouping** |
| pairs or individuals |
| **Materials and Equipment** |
| • 15 twigs or bamboo skewers (25 to 30 cm long)<br>• coarse string or twine (40 cm long)<br>• scrap Bristol board<br>• scissors<br>• 3 brown paper lunch bags<br>• ruler<br>• tape or glue<br>• paper<br>• pencils |
| **Line Masters** |
| • LM 2-17 |

**SAFETY CAUTION!**

Remember to work safely when using scissors.

## Get Started ▶

- Begin this lesson by asking students if they have visited Wanuskewin Heritage Park, have seen a tipi, or have been to a pow-wow or tipi raising. Ask students who have some experience to tell the others any characteristics they remember about their experience.
- To give all students a common experience, make use of the computer lab and Wonderville: Build a Tipi: www.learnalberta.ca/content/wonbt/html/index.html?launch=true or arrange for an Elder to come to your classroom.
- Ask students to read Get Started. Draw their attention to the photo of the tipi and the yellow outline of a triangle. Ask, *Can you see other triangles in the tipi?*
- Ask, *Why do you think a triangle is strong?* Help students understand the idea of the wider the base, the more stable the structure.
- Have students look back in the student book to find examples of triangle-based structures that are wider at the bottom than at the top. Discuss their findings as a class.

## Work On It

### Purpose

To have students build a tipi to help them learn about shape and stability

### Activity Notes

- Bamboo skewers work well if twigs are not available.
- When tying the string around the first three twigs, do not tie too tightly as the twigs will break. Use only one end of the string, leaving the string long.
- Allow the twigs to slide past each other when standing. Move the poles so the distance between them is about the same. They should form a triangle at their base.
- Add one twig per side till all the remaining twigs are in place. The more organized the twigs, the better the tipi.
- Wrap the leftover string around the twigs where they overlap leaving a bit of string dangling.
- Use LM 2-17 Tipi Cover Template to make a cardboard template for the tipi cover.
- Trace as many continuous triangles as possible on each open lunch bag. You will need 3 sets of 5 connected triangles.
- Folding the edges gives you a surface to glue. This surface will not show as an overlap on the tipi.
- Do not allow your students to decorate their tipis. Decorations are deeply spiritual and should not be taken lightly.

traditional ***KNOWLEDGE***

The Cree people use 15 poles to make the structure of the tipi. For every pole, there is a teaching, so there are 15 teachings that hold up the tipi. Other First Nations use 16 or possibly more poles in their tipis. Some use three starter poles, while some use four. The Cree use three poles, which stand for obedience, respect, and humility. These three poles placed together balance and reinforce each other. The other poles lean on the first three, adding their strength to the structure.

## Communicate

Questions 1 and 2 can serve as a review of concepts learned in the unit.

1. Students should refer to the triangles in the tipi. They should comment on the wide base and the narrow top.
2. Students should recognize the triangle shape, the lightweight materials, and the shell structure, which all contribute to a well-built tipi.
3. Students' answers may reflect other Nations. The beliefs of the Cree Nation can be found at www.fourdirectionsteachings.com/transcripts/cree.html.

## DI Differentiating Instruction

### *For Enrichment*

- Challenge students to predict what would happen if they moved their tipi poles so their tipi was taller? shorter? If resources are available, have them set up a new set of poles and experiment.
- For an additional activity, you may want to hand out LM 2-18 Building a Dog House.

## Assessment *for* Learning

| What to Look for in Student Work | What to Do |
|---|---|
| Students should be able to identify what gives a structure strength and stability. | • In an open area, have students stand straight with their feet together. Have a partner push gently on their side. Have them stand with their feet a shoulder width apart and repeat the test. Changing their base should make a difference as to how difficult it is to push them over. |

DESIGN PROJECT

# Build a Bridge

Page 76

**Time**

120 min

**Learning Context**

problem solving

**Level of Inquiry**

open

**Skills**

- making models
- observing
- experimenting
- comparing
- measuring
- communicating

**Grouping**

pairs or small groups

**Materials and Equipment**

- paper
- pencils
- two stacks of books (15 cm tall)
- ruler
- 50 pennies
- materials left over from the unit or materials provided by students

**Line Masters**

- LM 2-19
- LM 2-20
- LM 2-21

## Curriculum Indicators

| Indicators Met in Design Project |
|---|
| **SM3.1 a.** Identify problems to be solved related to the properties of materials in structures (e.g., What is the purpose of the structure? What materials are appropriate for constructing the structure? What are appropriate methods of joinery?). |
| **SM3.1 f.** Use appropriate tools (e.g., hammer, nail, glue, and scissors) to safely cut, shape, make holes, sew, and assemble materials. |
| **SM3.1 g.** Develop and carry out a plan, including making predictions, identifying variables, and recording relevant observations, to test the strength of various materials (e.g., straws, toothpicks, masking tape, string, cotton balls, wooden blocks, Styrofoam, cloth, clay, and spaghetti). |
| **SM3.2 i.** Develop and carry out a plan to construct a simple structure such as a tower, bridge, tipi, or bird feeder that meets teacher- or student-specified criteria related to strength, stability, and function. |
| **SM3.2 j.** Estimate measurements in order to select appropriate quantities of required materials for constructing a structure. |
| **SM3.2 k.** Follow safety procedures and rules while constructing structures and explain the need for such procedures and rules. |
| **SM3.2 l.** Illustrate the construction process for a simple structure, including descriptions of the components of the structure, using labelled drawings, written and oral explanations, and demonstrations. |

## Background Information

There are five basic types of bridges: arch, beam, cantilever, suspension, and truss. Arch bridges are good for spanning large distances, but cannot stand on their own until the entire arch is complete. The University Bridge and the Broadway Bridge in Saskatoon are arch bridges, but the most famous steel arch bridge is the Sydney Harbour Bridge in Sydney, Australia. Beam bridges, like the Confederation Bridge connecting Prince Edward Island and New Brunswick, also incorporate arches between the beams. Each individual piece of the Confederation Bridge is a beam bridge. The short distance covered by each shows the advantage to a beam bridge. Cantilever bridges are anchored on either bank and consist of two or three beam bridges that meet in the middle. These bridges show a good use of triangles in their construction. The longest cantilever bridge in the world is the Quebec Bridge, which crosses the St. Lawrence River. Suspension bridges are excellent for spanning very large bodies of water. The Golden Gate Bridge in San Francisco is one of the most famous suspension bridges, but it is not the longest. To find the longest bridge, the length of the main span is measured. The Akashi-Kaikyō Bridge in Japan has a central span of 1991 metres. Truss bridges are common in Saskatchewan as they were built by the CN and CP rail lines to bridge rivers and ravines. The Traffic Bridge in Saskatoon and the Outlook Bridge as shown in the student book are great examples of truss bridges.

traditional ***KNOWLEDGE***

In Saskatchewan, permanent river crossings were first established in the 1860s. The first commercial service was established on the South Saskatchewan River at Batoche by Xavier Letendre. Gabriel Dumont started a ferry crossing on the same river at what is now known as Gabriel's Crossing. For more information, go to http://esask.uregina.ca/entry/ferries_and_barges.html.

## Curriculum Connections

In this lesson, students have the opportunity to develop skills and concepts in these areas:

### *Mathematics*

SS3.3 a. Observe and describe situations relevant to self, family, and community that involve measuring lengths, including perimeter, in cm or m.

SS3.5 c. Observe, describe the characteristics of, and sort polygons found in situations relevant to self, family, or community (including First Nations and Métis), into irregular and regular polygons (e.g., the bottom of a kamatiq, the screen of a TV, the bottom of a curling broom, and an arrowhead).

P3.1 a. Identify and observe situations relevant to self, family, and community that contain an increasing or decreasing pattern, identify the starting value of the pattern, and describe the rule for the pattern and how the pattern would continue.

***Social Studies***

RW3.1 c. Describe ways in which communities help ensure basic human needs are met (e.g., food and water, shelter, clothing, education, safety).
RW3.3 a. Recognize that technology includes more than electronics (i.e., paper, forging steel, manufacturing, vehicles, making cloth, products created for construction).

***Visual Arts***

CP3.7 a. Generate questions that arise from the investigation of a topic or area of interest to initiate inquiry (e.g., How have different artists represented turtles in visual art works and book illustrations?).
CP3.8 f. Recognize circles, squares, triangles, and rectangles as geometric shapes and apply this knowledge to art work.

## Get Started ▶

- Students are challenged to apply what they have learned about structures and materials to design, build, and test a bridge that will support a given mass. Share information on the five basic bridge styles with your students. Show as many pictures or diagrams as possible to give students exemplars.
- To stimulate student thinking, ask students questions based on each lesson in the unit. Start with Lesson 1 and ask, *What shapes do you find in natural structures? What shapes do you find in human-made structures?* In Lesson 2, ask students, *What makes a material strong?* In Lesson 3 ask, *Which shape is the strongest?* In Lesson 4 ask, *How can a structure be made stronger?* In Lesson 5 ask, *How did you make your paper tower strong?* In Lesson 6 ask, *What is the most stable shape?* In Lesson 7 ask, *How do shell structures carry their load? How do frame structures carry their load? How do solid structures carry their load?* In Lesson 8 ask, *How can materials be joined together?* In Lesson 9 ask, *Why do some structures last longer than others?* In Lesson 10 ask, *How are long lasting structures built?* In Lesson 11 ask, *What building materials are available?* In Lesson 12 ask, *What raw materials are available?* And in Lesson 13 ask, *How does shape give strength and stability to a structure?*

**SAFETY CAUTION!**
Remember to work safely when using scissors and to follow your classroom safety rules.

## Work On It

### Purpose

To have students design and build a stable bridge between two stacks of books

## Activity Notes

- Students can work in engineering teams to accomplish the task. Show students what materials are available for construction of their bridge. You may want to use leftover materials from other activities in the unit.
- When students are in their teams, have them plan their bridge, draw a diagram, or write a description of their proposed bridge. Have them show you their plan before selecting their materials. Encourage students to incorporate what they learned throughout the unit into their design.
- If students are unsure about how to begin, have them make a list of what all bridges have in common. Point out that all bridges have two anchor points, span a distance, and have a point of balance. Also point out that some bridges use an extra support at this point.
- You may want to hand out LM 2-19 Design a Bridge to help students plan and LM 2-21 Design Project Rubric: Build a Bridge, to assess the Design Project.

## Communicate

1. Student bridge styles will depend on the materials available for construction and their understanding of the principles presented in the unit. If student bridges do not meet the criteria, have students explain how they would change their bridge to meet the criteria.

## DI Differentiating Instruction

### *For EAL/ELL*

Have students plan their bridge based on bridge examples found in the student book. Ask students to draw the bridge they think would work best to carry the penny load.

Show students examples of bridges. Point out topics covered in the unit such as the wide base, laminated materials, balance point, and triangular cross braces. Discuss as a class what goes into a bridge.

### *For Enrichment*

Have students blend bridges together to create a "super bridge" that exceeds the criteria. Challenge students to turn their bridge into a different type of bridge such as a suspension bridge or a truss bridge. You may want to hand out LM 2-20 Connecting Bridges. In this activity, students identify the different types of bridges.

## Assessment *for* Learning

| What to Look for in Student Work | What to Do |
| --- | --- |
| Students should be able to design and build a bridge that reflects an understanding of the concepts learned in the unit. | • Students can demonstrate this knowledge formally within the design and informally throughout the Design Project. Be sure to ask students throughout the project to explain the choices they have made in their designs and how their decisions relate to their understanding of the unit. |

## Unit 2 Summary

*Page 78*

Students may wish to use this unit summary as a study guide. The Unit 2 Summary is available as a line master (LM 2-1 Unit 2 Summary).

## Show What You Know

*Page 80*

After students have completed the assignment, bring the class together to discuss their bridges. Check students' understanding by asking questions about the materials they used in their bridges, the methods they chose to fasten pieces, and the stability of their structures.

You may want to hand out LM 2-22 Show What You Know to help students record their answers.

For additional unit review, you may want to hand out LM 2-23 Unit 2 Review Word Search and LM 2-24 Unit 2 Review Crossword.

1. triangle, square, circle, rhombus
2. The triangle is the most stable because it has a bigger base than top, it covers a large area, and when you push a side, it does not collapse.
3. **a)** solid, **b)** shell, **c)** frame
4. Students' answers may vary but could include: recyclable—almost any plastic container, aluminum, batteries, tires, paint, etc.; reusable—almost any glass beverage container, plastic grocery bag, etc.; renewable—wood products, glass, plant-based products, such as bio diesel, hemp rope, etc.
5. Tobacco offerings show respect to Mother Earth and to the spirit of the plant, animal, or element whose life was taken. First Nations and Métis people are taught that the spirits of all things, even things we consider non-living, are sacred and should be revered because these living spirits gave up their lives so that humans may live. The tobacco or food offering reminds them of this lesson.
6. Students may choose corrugating (sandwiching triangles between two layers) or laminating materials.
7. Fastening materials together, making the base bigger than the top, cross bracing, forming triangles, and adding bulk at the base are examples of how to make structures stronger.
8. The animal's weight must be spread evenly between the points of contact with the ground. For a human, the two points of contact form a straight line. The shape created by the points of contact for a kangaroo, is a triangle and for a dog, is a square.

9. Students' drawings may vary but could include a tipi, which is like a spruce tree, or an ant hill. Students might also compare a wigwam with a nest or a beaver dam. They might consider drawing an Inuit structure and compare it with an egg as an extension. It should be noted that Inuit are not considered First Nations. They have their own cultural identities.
10. Nails, screws, and glue can join wood; glue and staples can join paper; silicon can join glass; and Velcro™, zippers, buttons, and snaps can join cloth.
11. Students' answers may vary but could include wood, concrete, tires, bales, glass bottles, metal, stone, and brick.
12. Students should recognize that not all materials would be used for a skyscraper because they lack the strength when stacked or used in large amounts.
13. Students' answers will vary but should include reference to materials and fasteners.

## Looking Back

Self-evaluation allows students to communicate their learning and their feelings about it. Seeing how students view their learning can give you insight and information on which to base your programming decisions.

Ask students to answer these questions individually, then to share their answers with the class. Some students will likely find some areas of this unit easier than other areas. This exercise may help students identify who can give them assistance to understand difficult concepts.

# Unit 2 Line Masters

## Table of Contents

## Table of Contents *(continued)*

Name: ______________________________

# Unit 2 Summary

| Structures have jobs. | |
|---|---|
| **SUMMARY**<br>□ A structure is something that holds weight.<br>□ A structure must be strong enough to support the weight of a load. | **MY STUDY NOTES** |
| **Humans often build structures shaped like structures found in nature.** | |
| **SUMMARY**<br>□ Nature's structures are made of materials and shapes best suited for the job. | **MY STUDY NOTES** |
| **Materials make structures strong.** | |
| **SUMMARY**<br>□ Structures must be made of strong materials that help them keep their shape.<br>□ Materials can be joined together with fasteners. | **MY STUDY NOTES** |

| Shape makes structures strong and stable. | |
|---|---|
| **SUMMARY**<br>□ The shape of a structure can help it resist forces so it does not fall over. | **MY STUDY NOTES** |

| First Nations and Métis peoples value materials from Mother Earth. | |
|---|---|
| **SUMMARY**<br>□ First Nations and Métis peoples understand that they depend on Mother Earth and must live in balance with Mother Earth.<br>□ First Nations and Métis peoples understand that the resources of an area need to be available for future generations of people. | **MY STUDY NOTES** |

Name: ______________________________

# Unit 2 Vocabulary

Check off each vocabulary term below as you learn it in this unit.

After you check off all the terms, make a concept map using as many terms as you can. Start your concept map with these words in the centre: "structures" and "materials." Use the back of this page or a separate page for your concept map.

- □ fasteners, p. 64
- □ frame structures, p. 60
- □ load, p. 50
- □ raw materials, p. 72
- □ recyclable, p. 71
- □ renewable, p. 71
- □ reusable, p. 71
- □ shell structures, p. 60
- □ solid structures, p. 60
- □ stability, p. 74
- □ structure, p. 46

Name: ______________________________

# Finding Structures

List all the structures that you see in the picture on page 47 of your student book. In what ways are the structures the same? In what ways are the structures different? Record your answers.

| Structure | Similar to __________ because______________. | Different from__________ because______________. |
| --- | --- | --- |
| | | |
| | | |
| | | |
| | | |
| | | |
| | | |
| | | |

| Structure | Similar to ___________ because______________. | Different from__________ because______________. |
|---|---|---|
| | | |
| | | |
| | | |
| | | |
| | | |
| | | |

A structure built by humans is ________________________________________.

A structure built by nature is ________________________________________.

Name: ______________________________

# Copying Nature

Use scissors to cut out the shapes. Remember to work safely!

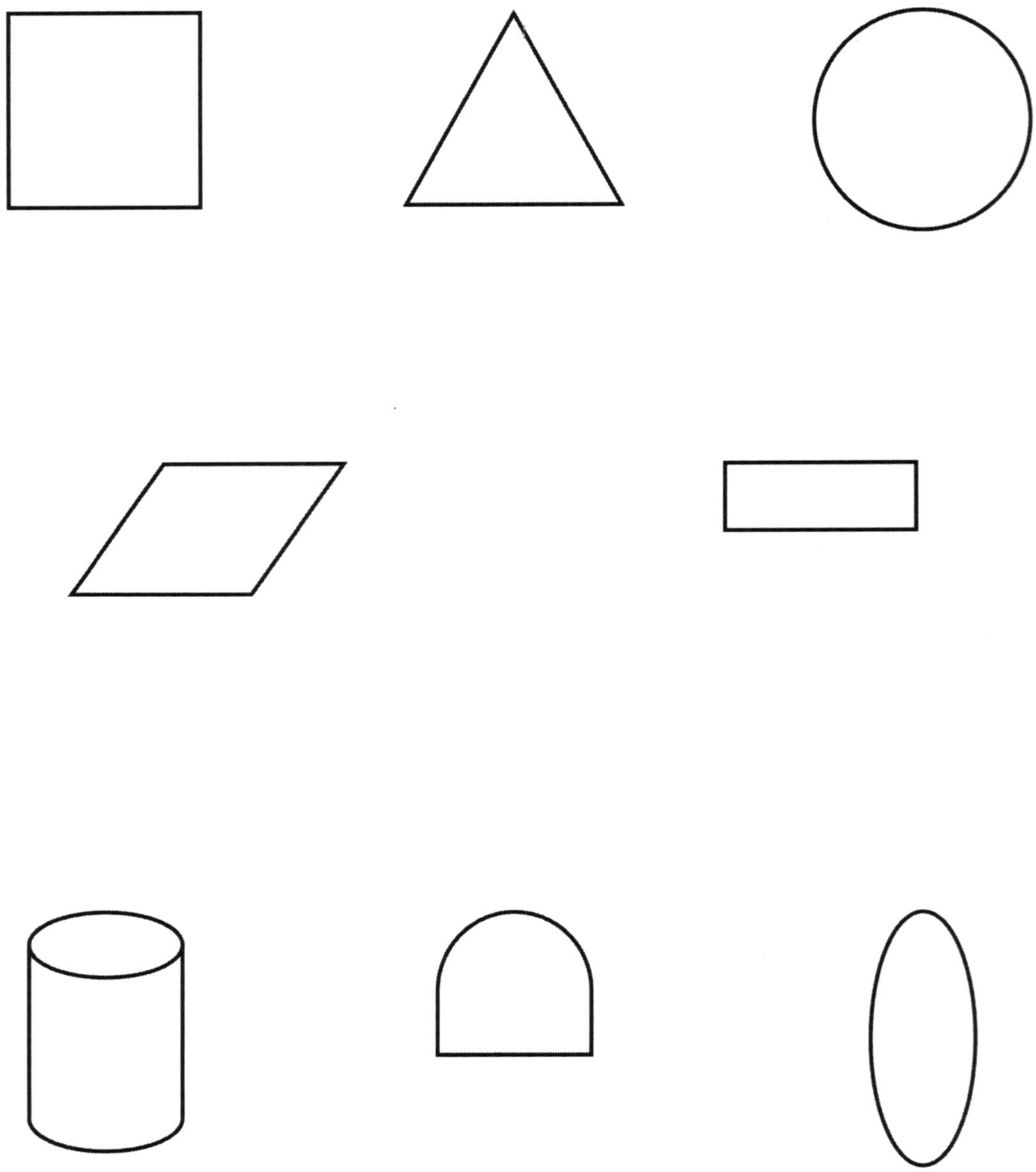

Name: ______________________________

# Which Material Is the Strongest?

| Material | Most Weight Held |
| --- | --- |
| | |

Name: ______________________________

# Which Shape Is the Strongest?

## My Laboratory Notebook

My prediction: Which is stronger, a square or a triangle? I think ____________________

will be stronger because ______________________________________________

______________________________________________________________

______________________________________________________________.

My experiment tells me that ______________________________ is stronger because

______________________________________________________________

______________________________________________________________

______________________________________________________________.

I can use a square and a triangle in the bridge I will build. I can use them for

______________________________________________________________

______________________________________________________________

______________________________________________________________

______________________________________________________________

______________________________________________________________.

Name: ________________________________

# How Can We Strengthen Structures?

Look around your classroom or playground at structures you see. How have these structures been strengthened? Record your answers.

**Structures**

| Strengthened by Adding Bulk | Strengthened by Using Triangles | Strengthened by Adding Layers |
|---|---|---|
| | | |
| | | |
| | | |
| | | |
| | | |
| | | |
| | | |
| | | |
| | | |
| | | |

I can use these ideas to strengthen the materials I will use to build my bridge. I can

______________________________________________________________________

______________________________________________________________________

______________________________________________________________________

______________________________________________________________________.

Name: ________________________________

# Making Paper Towers Strong

Draw a picture of each paper tower. Make a side view drawing or draw the shape from the top.

| **Tower One** | **Tower Two** |
| --- | --- |
| **Tower Three** | **Tower Four** |

Name: ________________________________

# Nature's Balancing Act

Record observations, such as swaying, losing balance, needing to shift weight, and how the beanbag shifts or falls.

| Animals on the Move | | | | | |
|---|---|---|---|---|---|
| | **Human** | **Bear** | **Dog** | **Penguin** | **Rabbit** |
| How many points of contact with the ground? | | | | | |
| Place the beanbag where it won't fall off. This is the most stable point. | **On top of your head** | **On your back close to your tailbone** | **Between your shoulder blades** | **On your neck behind your head** | **On your back between your shoulders** |
| What happens to the beanbag when you are staying still? | | | | | |
| What happens to the beanbag when you are walking backward? | | | | | |
| What happens to the beanbag when you are walking forward? | | | | | |
| What happens to the beanbag when you are running forward? | | | | | |

Name: ______________________________

# Is It a Solid, Frame, or Shell Structure?

| What type of structures do you see? | | |
|---|---|---|
| **Solid Structures** | **Frame Structures** | **Shell Structures** |
| | | |
| **Characteristics of Solid Structures** | **Characteristics of Frame Structures** | **Characteristics of Shell Structures** |
| | | |
| **What type of load might each structure carry?** | | |
| **Solid Structures** | **Frame Structures** | **Shell Structures** |
| | | |

**Solid Structures**

**Frame Structures**

**Shell Structures**

Name: ______________________________

# How Are Materials Joined Together?

How well do fasteners hold paper together?

| Type of Fastener | What Happened? |
|---|---|
| | |
| | |
| | |
| | |
| | |

| Type of Fastener | Positive Points | Negative Points |
|---|---|---|
| | | |
| | | |
| | | |
| | | |
| | | |

How did the paper rip when each bond broke? Did the material or the bond fail? What evidence did you use to make your decision?

______________________________________________

______________________________________________

______________________________________________

______________________________________________

______________________________________________.

Name: ________________________________

# Connecting Materials

Below are two circles with the names of two different building materials in them. Select a type of fastener from the list below and write it in the circle that belongs to the type of material it could be used to fasten. If the fastener can be used for both types of material, write it in the overlapping space between the two circles.

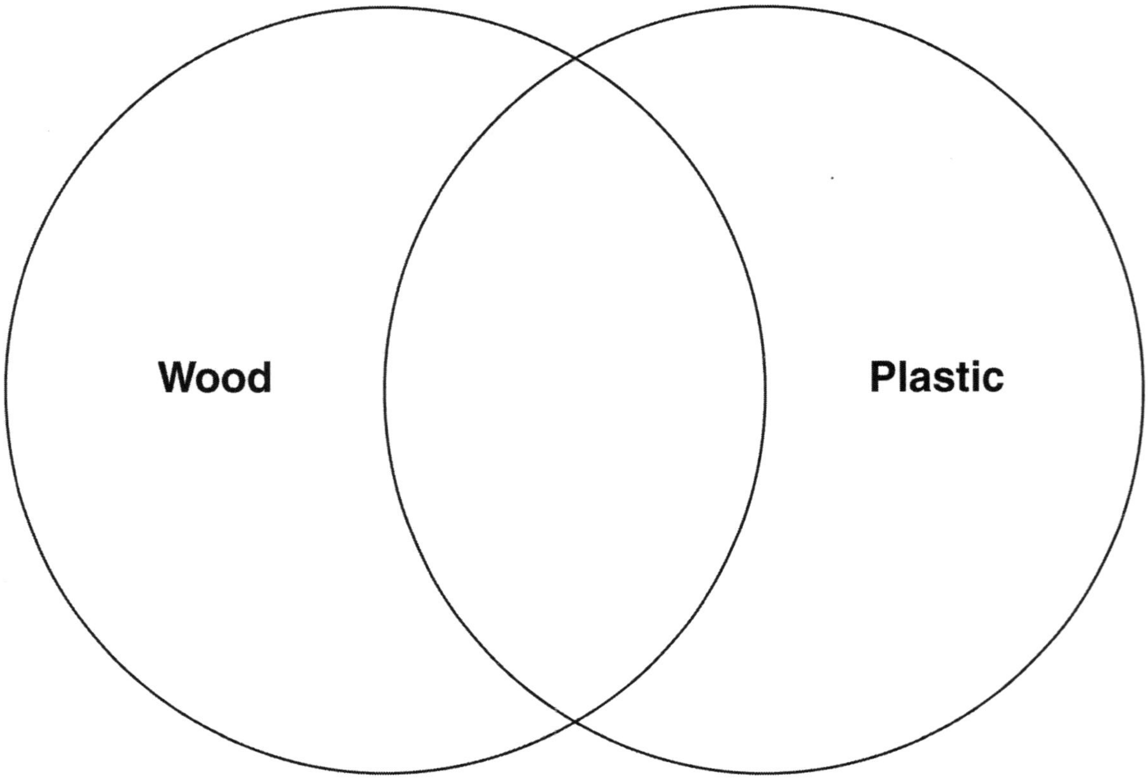


**Fasteners**

glue
nails
screws
staples
tape
Velcro™
string
toothpick
clay
paper fasteners

Name: ______________________________

# What Makes a Structure Last?

| Name of Structure | What Is It Made Of? |
| --- | --- |
| | |
| | |
| | |
| | |
| | |
| | |
| | |

| Permanent | Temporary |
| --- | --- |
| | |
| | |
| | |
| | |
| | |
| | |
| | |

What are many permanent structures made of?

______________________________________________________________

______________________________________________________________.

What do temporary structures have in common?

______________________________________________________________

______________________________________________________________.

Name: ______________________________

# Earthquake-Proof Structures

Draw sketches of your tower. Remember to label the parts of your tower and to write down what each part is for.

## Design Ideas

**First idea** **Next idea**

**Next idea**

**Name:** ______________________________

# Looking at Materials

| Structure | Made From? | Strengthened By? | Reusable? | Recyclable? | Renewable? |
|---|---|---|---|---|---|
| Beaver dam | | | | | |
| Ant hill | | | | | |
| House | | | | | |
| Circus float | | | | | |
| Umbrella | | | | | |
| Ladder | | | | | |
| Wigwam | | | | | |
| Pop can | | | | | |
| Puck | | | | | |

Name: ______________________________

# Reusing and Recycling Materials

What recycled materials are used to build structures in Saskatchewan? Research your answer to this question. Share your findings with your classmates.

| Type of Material | Reusable For ... | Can Be Recycled Into ... |
|---|---|---|
| | | |
| | | |
| | | |
| | | |
| | | |
| | | |
| | | |
| | | |
| | | |
| | | |
| | | |
| | | |

**Internet Search Word-Combination Suggestions**

- Saskatchewan+recycling+materials+locations
- Saskatchewan+recycling+new construction

**Remember:** The more words you have in your search, the better your results will be!

# Tipi Cover Template

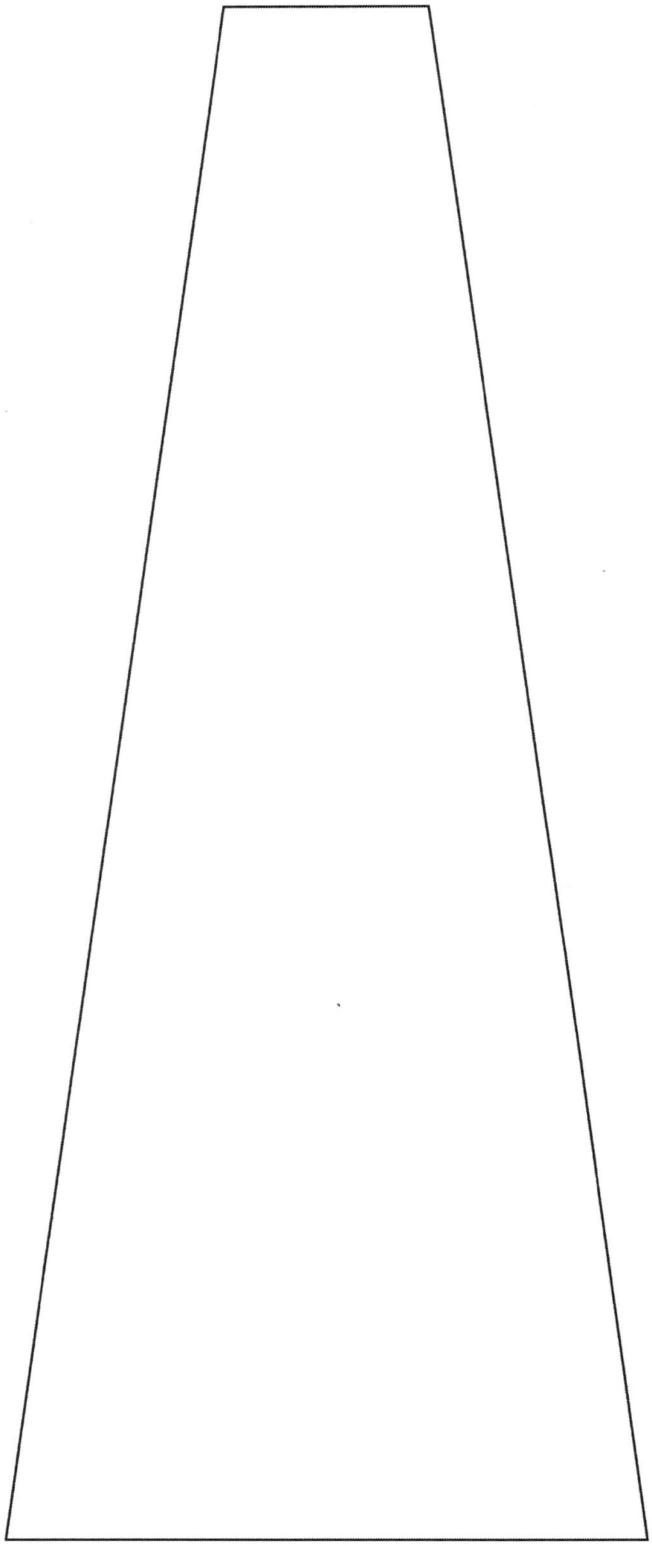

Name: ______________________________

# Building a Dog House

You have been asked to estimate the material required to build a dog house. The dog house has two roof pieces, one floor, and four walls. Cut out the pattern pieces and lay them on the rectangle below, which represents one sheet of plywood. How many sheets of plywood would you need to make one dog house? How many would you need to make two dog houses?

**Plywood**

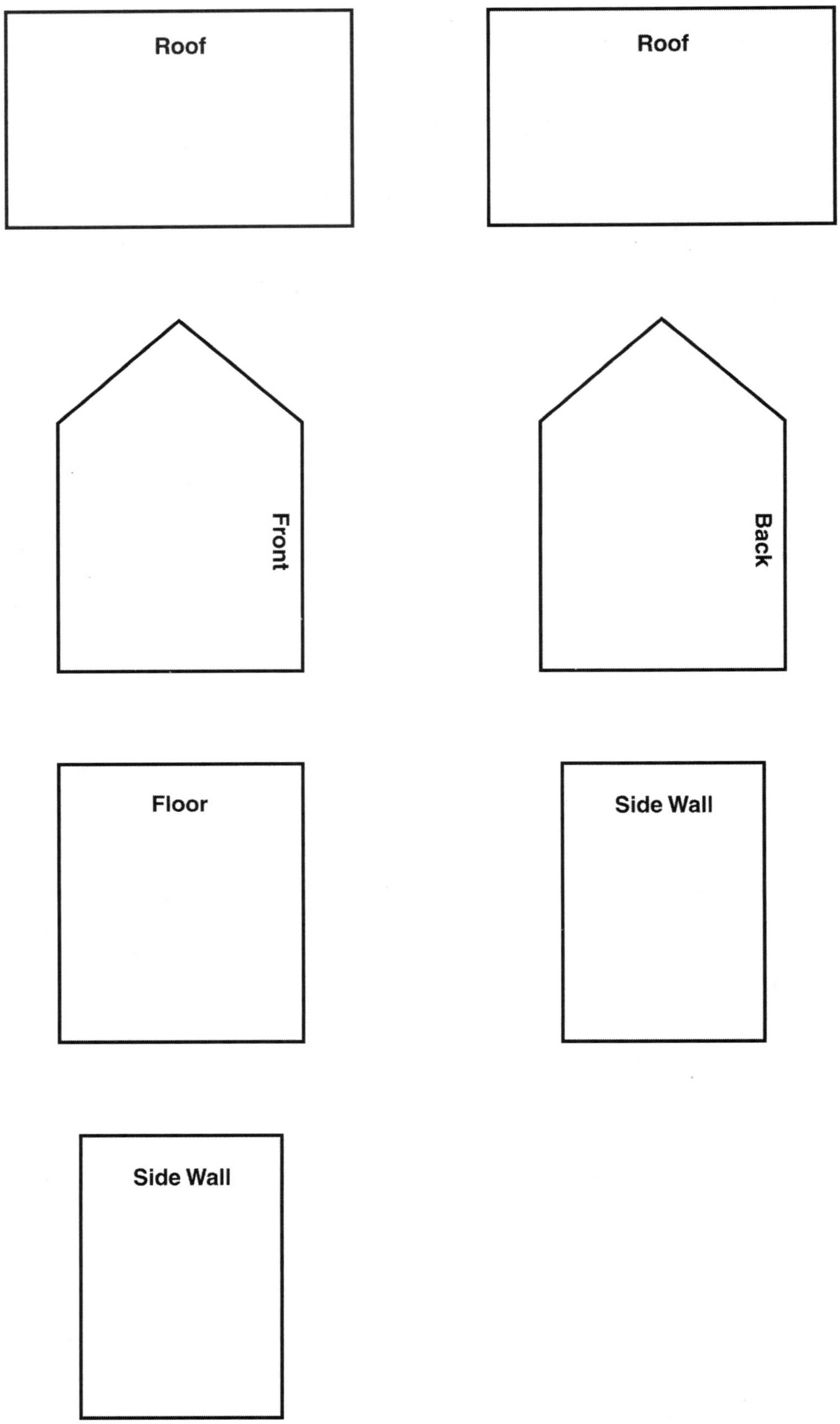
Roof
Roof
Front
Back
Floor
Side Wall
Side Wall

Name: ______________________________

Due Date: ____________________________

# Design a Bridge

## Design Project Planner

To design and build:

_______________________________________________________________

What it must be able to do:

_______________________________________________________________

_______________________________________________________________

_______________________________________________________________

Other things to think about or questions to ask:

_______________________________________________________________

_______________________________________________________________

_______________________________________________________________

_______________________________________________________________

Brainstorming ideas:

_______________________________________________________________

_______________________________________________________________

_______________________________________________________________

_______________________________________________________________

The best idea:

______________________________________________

______________________________________________

______________________________________________

______________________________________________

Why I chose this idea:

______________________________________________

______________________________________________

______________________________________________

______________________________________________

Materials and equipment list:

______________________________________________

______________________________________________

______________________________________________

______________________________________________

**The drawing that I will build from**

**View from the top**

**View from the side or front**

**Building Steps**

Step 1:

______________________________________________

______________________________________________

______________________________________________

Step 2:

______________________________________________

______________________________________________

______________________________________________

Step 3:

______________________________________________

______________________________________________

______________________________________________

Step 4:

______________________________________________

______________________________________________

______________________________________________

**Assessment Checklist**

I made sure that I

□ followed safety rules while building my bridge

□ built a bridge that spans 25 cm

□ built a bridge that holds at least 50 pennies

Name: ______________________________

# Connecting Bridges

Match the type of bridge to its image by drawing a line to connect them.

Cantilever bridge

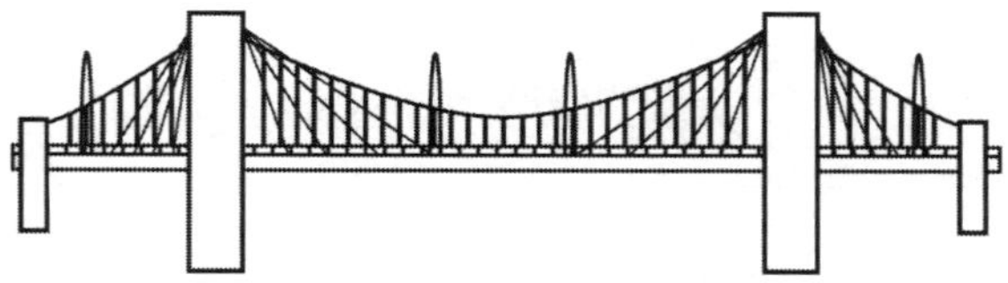

Arch bridge

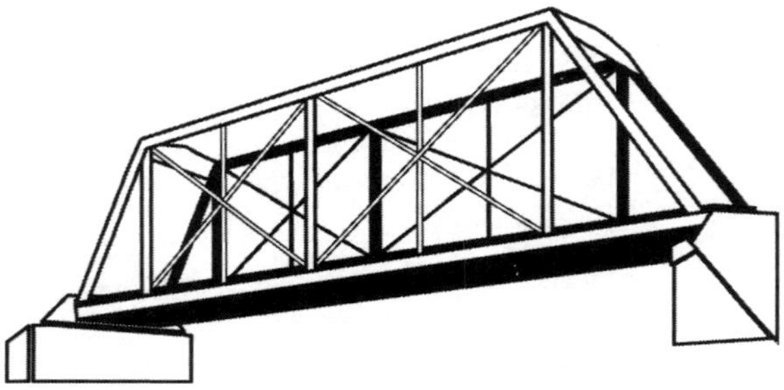

Suspension bridge

Beam bridge

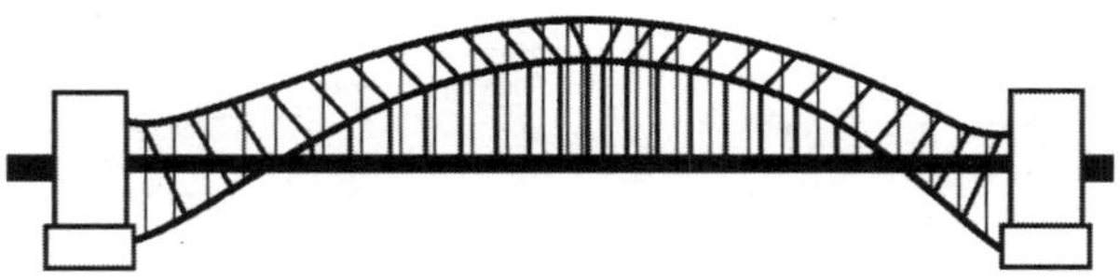

Truss bridge

**Name:** ______________________________

# Design Project Rubric: Build a Bridge

| | 1 Star ★ | 2 Stars ★★ | 3 Stars ★★★ | 4 Stars ★★★★ |
|---|---|---|---|---|
| **Followed safety rules** | You had to be reminded to follow the safety rules. | You followed some of the safety rules. | You followed most of the safety rules. | You followed all of the safety rules. |
| **Use of equipment** | You had to be reminded to use equipment and materials safely. | You used equipment and materials safely some of the time. | You used equipment and materials safely most of the time. | You used equipment and materials safely. |
| **Bridge construction** | It does none of the things it is supposed to do. | It does one thing it is supposed to do. | It does both of the things it is supposed to do. | It does both of the things it is supposed to do, and is made stable through adding bulk, layering, or triangle shapes. |
| **Planning** | You needed help forming an idea for your bridge. | You had more than one idea about your bridge and started building right away. | You had more than one idea about your bridge and drew a schematic of the bridge. | Your schematic included a top view, side view, and overall diagram. |
| **Testing** | You were not able to test your bridge. | Your bridge does only one thing it was supposed to do. | Your bridge successfully did both things it was supposed to do. | Your bridge did more than it was supposed to do. |

Name: ______________________________

# Show What You Know

1. Look at the shapes on page 80 of your student book. Order them from most to least stable. (**Hint:** Think about points of contact with the ground.)

_______________________________________________

2. Look at your answer to question 1. Explain why the shape you placed first is the most stable.

_______________________________________________

_______________________________________________

_______________________________________________

3. There are different types of structures. Look at the photos on page 80 of your student book. Name the type of structure in each.

**a)** _______________________________________________

**b)** _______________________________________________

**c)** _______________________________________________

4. Most materials can be recyclable, reusable, or renewable. Give an example of each.

_______________________________________________

_______________________________________________

_______________________________________________

_______________________________________________

_______________________________________________

5. Why do First Nations and Métis people offer tobacco or food to Mother Earth when using her resources?

6. Give one example of how to make materials stronger.

7. Give three examples of how to make structures stronger.

8. How does shape help humans and other animals stay stable? Give one example for humans and one for animals.

9. Draw a picture to show how a First Nations structure is like one of nature's structures.

10. List four ways that structures can be joined together. What materials can be joined each way?

11. What materials are suitable for building houses? Research your answer and make a list of five materials.

12. Are the materials you listed in question 11 suitable for building skyscrapers? Explain your answer.

13. A new playground is being built at your school. It must be stable and made of recycled materials. Draw a design for the playground. Label the material that each part of the playground is made from.

**Looking Back**

14. Give one example that shows that structures are important to think about.

______________________________________________

______________________________________________

______________________________________________

15. What did you learn about structures that you did not know before this unit?

______________________________________________

______________________________________________

______________________________________________

Name: ______________________________

# Unit 2 Review Word Search

| | | | | | | | | | | | | | | | | | | | | | | | | | | | |
|---|---|---|---|---|---|---|---|---|---|---|---|---|---|---|---|---|---|---|---|---|---|---|---|---|---|---|---|
| M | H | E | H | T | G | V | E | U | Z | D | S | V | I | S | N | M | O | S | Q | A | J | T | Z | I | Y | S | G |
| T | L | G | L | K | Q | E | F | K | I | A | Y | C | T | U | F | G | M | V | Q | D | Z | O | T | H | I | J | G |
| E | L | G | N | A | I | R | T | V | E | I | I | R | S | D | J | S | A | T | N | U | Y | W | W | H | P | L | Z |
| K | L | C | C | W | N | M | C | H | Q | D | E | L | C | R | I | C | T | G | I | G | X | W | Y | A | V | W | P |
| X | H | F | Z | P | M | I | E | R | R | N | I | D | L | Q | B | G | E | N | L | L | Q | U | R | M | J | V | W |
| A | W | Q | L | S | E | G | T | X | G | E | I | M | Y | Q | B | R | R | G | A | Y | V | S | E | M | I | V | R |
| X | P | B | Y | F | A | D | I | T | O | Z | W | T | A | G | D | B | I | E | W | J | E | E | C | E | E | N | F |
| L | K | W | R | Y | R | J | H | C | V | J | A | O | G | R | E | N | A | S | P | E | K | A | Y | R | D | J | N |
| A | O | A | D | E | P | Q | C | Z | T | E | O | Q | T | O | Y | W | L | G | Q | T | A | Q | C | E | A | J | P |
| M | M | M | E | D | W | K | R | N | O | C | B | Z | A | X | Z | P | S | L | J | X | N | Z | L | E | M | T | A |
| E | Q | D | S | H | I | V | A | E | T | R | Y | F | S | M | L | E | O | B | Q | G | S | X | E | N | N | G | T |
| K | C | R | I | O | R | I | W | N | W | Y | R | O | J | H | S | U | R | V | G | R | S | Q | F | I | A | A | X |
| E | E | H | G | P | L | N | Q | V | Y | T | L | C | X | O | E | D | U | V | E | P | G | N | J | G | M | J | M |
| B | J | S | N | O | I | J | Z | Y | Y | I | Q | I | P | O | A | V | U | Y | I | Z | X | L | D | N | U | F | H |
| O | M | B | Y | E | J | T | G | B | D | L | G | E | P | P | S | U | A | D | F | G | H | K | F | E | H | S | E |
| T | S | D | R | G | W | G | O | X | I | I | D | M | U | A | P | L | E | E | L | E | B | X | Y | E | M | C | J |
| P | P | F | G | D | V | K | I | Y | E | B | G | V | S | S | W | R | S | E | L | A | K | J | N | O | U | Z | P |
| B | W | G | D | I | A | V | K | U | D | A | B | X | X | E | W | Q | N | C | X | T | Z | J | I | D | R | B | D |
| X | V | C | C | R | U | C | R | R | A | R | O | X | K | E | K | V | G | X | C | T | N | T | E | A | D | R | F |
| K | V | X | Y | B | M | U | E | D | A | U | Z | Y | B | A | I | A | R | I | A | A | H | R | O | T | U | K | T |
| O | C | V | X | P | F | C | Q | C | X | D | K | P | D | R | S | E | U | B | F | C | R | W | I | U | M | L | V |
| B | H | V | U | X | T | C | E | N | I | G | V | O | O | A | L | Y | C | Q | M | F | R | U | D | E | U | L | G |
| R | R | S | T | A | B | I | L | I | T | Y | G | N | B | C | O | L | V | N | H | O | N | A | T | U | R | E | S |
| E | X | O | N | C | U | G | X | J | Z | J | M | P | E | V | O | R | J | H | A | T | Q | B | T | D | M | H | X |
| S | Y | G | K | O | T | O | R | T | K | E | C | Q | X | N | T | S | E | G | R | L | R | B | R | H | O | S | H |
| U | L | H | V | P | S | Y | Q | N | N | O | C | L | I | I | K | V | M | Z | J | W | A | A | Z | R | V | N | Q |
| E | G | Y | S | P | H | G | S | T | Y | A | X | F | M | L | N | Z | M | Y | F | K | I | B | E | G | L | P | H |
| R | R | X | Y | B | U | T | B | X | J | K | V | I | B | F | L | Y | D | S | T | R | U | C | T | U | R | E | S |

STRUCTURES
RECYCLE
REUSE
REDUCE
SOLID
FRAME
SHELL
PYRAMID
TOWER
BALANCE
STABILITY
DESIGN
ENGINEER
ARCHITECT
NATURE
HUMANMADE
MATERIALS
BRIDGE
ROAD
STRENGTH
DURABILITY
TOOLS
HAMMER
GLUE
NAIL
TRIANGLE
RECTANGLE
CIRCLE
BRACE
LAYERS
TIPI
SPIDER WEB
EARTHQUAKE
ENVIRONMENT

Name: ______________________________

# Unit 2 Review Crossword

**ACROSS**

1. Structure made of hides or canvas and tall flexible trees.
3. Made of firm parts that are fastened together.
6. Something that holds a weight.
7. Weight that a structure supports.
10. A round tent found in Saskatchewan and Mongolia.
11. Has a hard outer case that holds the structure together.
13. Materials that we take from nature.
14. Made of one material, not hollow.
15. Things that can be replaced by new growth.

**DOWN**

1. The most stable shape.
2. Used to strengthen a tower or bridge.
4. Objects that fix or hold materials together.
5. The middle of the points that touch the ground.
8. Things that can be used more than once.
9. A curved tent made of strong trees and hide
12. Things that can be made into new products.

# Answers to Unit 2 Line Masters

**LM 2-12: Connecting Materials**

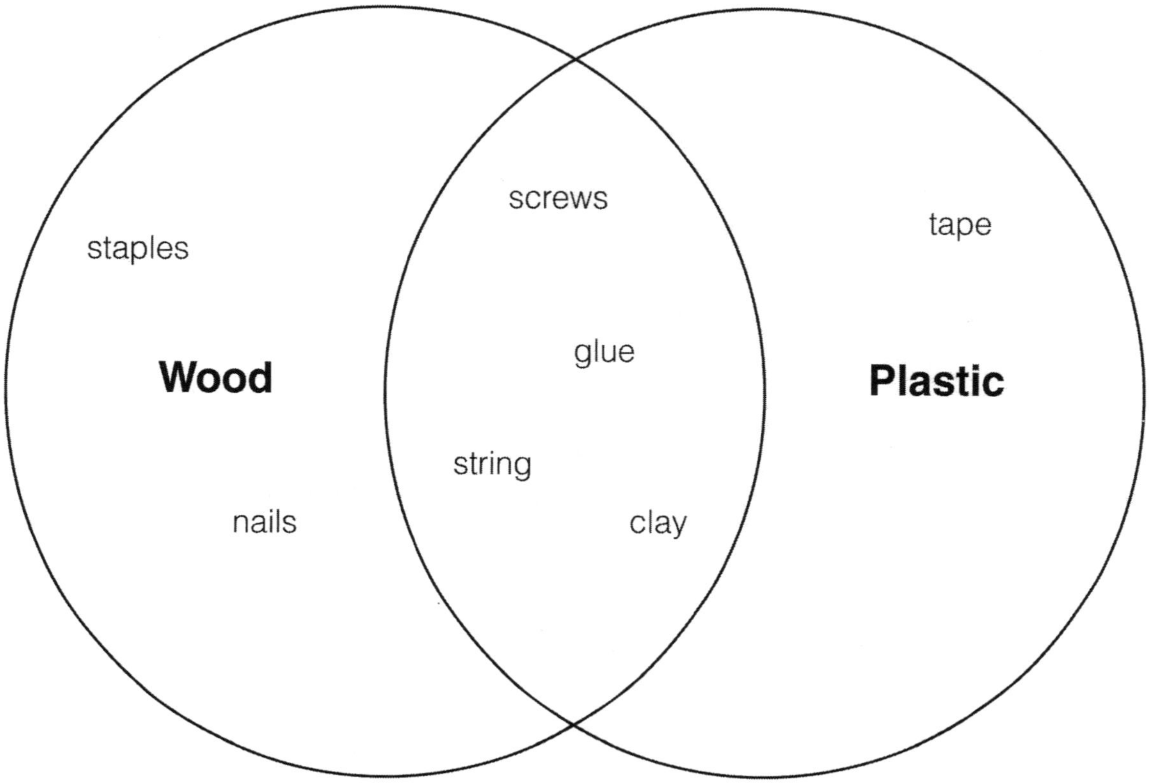


Note: Screws can be used to fasten plastic only if there is a pilot hole in the plastic. Without the hole, the plastic would crack.

**LM 2-18: Building a Dog House**

You would need two sheets of plywood to make one dog house and three sheets of plywood to make two dog houses.

## LM 2-20: Connecting Bridges

Cantilever bridge

Arch bridge

Suspension bridge

Beam bridge

Truss bridge

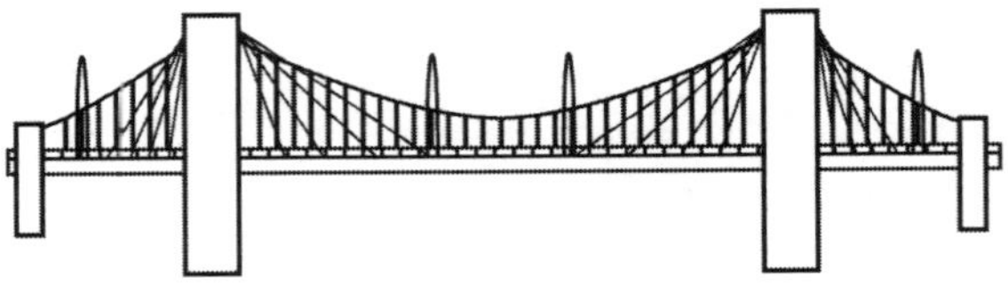

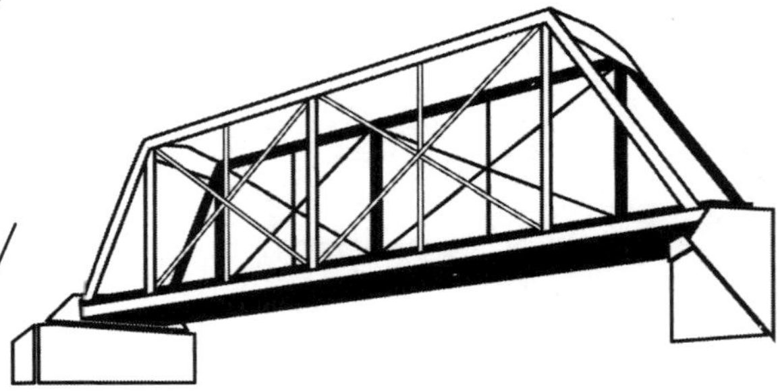

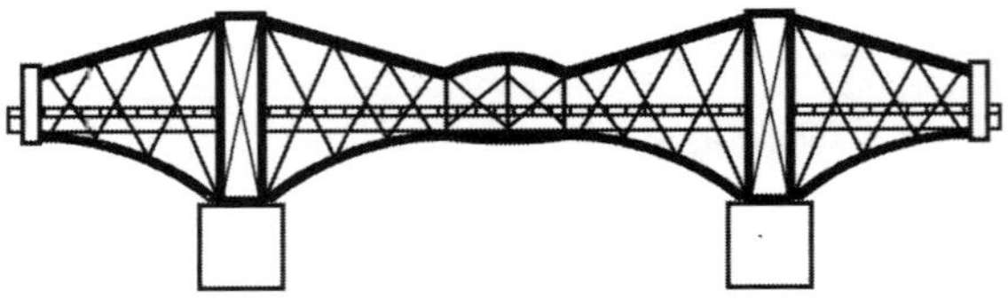

## LM 2-23: Unit 2 Review Word Search

| | | | | | | | | | | | | | | | | | | | | | | | | | | | |
|---|---|---|---|---|---|---|---|---|---|---|---|---|---|---|---|---|---|---|---|---|---|---|---|---|---|---|---|
| M | H | E | H | T | G | V | E | U | Z | D | S | V | I | S | N | M | O | S | Q | A | J | T | Z | I | Y | S | G |
| T | L | G | L | K | Q | E | F | K | I | A | Y | C | T | U | F | G | M | V | Q | D | Z | O | T | H | I | J | G |
| E | L | G | N | A | I | R | T | V | E | I | I | R | S | D | J | S | A | T | N | U | Y | W | W | H | P | L | Z |
| K | L | C | C | W | N | M | C | H | Q | D | E | L | C | R | I | C | T | G | I | G | X | W | Y | A | V | W | P |
| X | H | F | Z | P | M | I | E | R | R | N | I | D | L | Q | B | G | E | N | L | L | Q | U | R | M | J | V | W |
| A | W | Q | L | S | E | G | T | X | G | E | I | M | Y | Q | B | R | R | G | A | Y | V | S | E | M | I | V | R |
| X | P | B | Y | F | A | D | I | T | O | Z | W | T | A | G | D | B | I | E | W | J | E | E | C | E | E | N | F |
| L | K | W | R | Y | R | J | H | C | V | J | A | O | G | R | E | N | A | S | P | E | K | A | Y | R | D | J | N |
| A | O | A | D | E | P | Q | C | Z | T | E | O | Q | T | O | Y | W | L | G | Q | T | A | Q | C | E | A | J | P |
| M | M | M | E | D | W | K | R | N | O | C | B | Z | A | X | Z | P | S | L | J | X | N | Z | L | E | M | T | A |
| E | Q | D | S | H | I | V | A | E | T | R | Y | F | S | M | L | E | O | B | Q | G | S | X | E | N | N | G | T |
| K | C | R | I | O | R | I | W | N | W | Y | R | O | J | H | S | U | R | V | G | R | S | Q | F | I | A | A | X |
| E | E | H | G | P | L | N | Q | V | Y | T | L | C | X | O | E | D | U | V | E | P | G | N | J | G | M | J | M |
| B | J | S | N | O | I | J | Z | Y | Y | I | Q | I | P | O | A | V | U | Y | I | Z | X | L | D | N | U | F | H |
| O | M | B | Y | E | J | T | G | B | D | L | G | E | P | P | S | U | A | D | F | G | H | K | F | E | H | S | E |
| T | S | D | R | G | W | G | O | X | I | I | D | M | U | A | P | L | E | E | L | E | B | X | Y | E | M | C | J |
| P | P | F | G | D | V | K | I | Y | E | B | G | V | S | S | W | R | S | E | L | A | K | J | N | O | U | Z | P |
| B | W | G | D | I | A | V | K | U | D | A | B | X | X | E | W | Q | N | C | X | T | Z | J | I | D | R | B | D |
| X | V | C | C | R | U | C | R | R | A | R | O | X | K | E | K | V | G | X | C | T | N | T | E | A | D | R | F |
| K | V | X | Y | B | M | U | E | D | A | U | Z | Y | B | A | I | A | R | I | A | A | H | R | O | T | U | K | T |
| O | C | V | X | P | F | C | Q | C | X | D | K | P | D | R | S | E | U | B | F | C | R | W | I | U | M | L | V |
| B | H | V | U | X | T | C | E | N | I | G | V | O | O | A | L | Y | C | Q | M | F | R | U | D | E | U | L | G |
| R | R | S | T | A | B | I | L | I | T | Y | G | N | B | C | O | L | V | N | H | O | N | A | T | U | R | E | S |
| E | X | O | N | C | U | G | X | J | Z | J | M | P | E | V | O | R | J | H | A | T | Q | B | T | D | M | H | X |
| S | Y | G | K | O | T | O | R | T | K | E | C | Q | X | N | T | S | E | G | R | L | R | B | R | H | O | S | H |
| U | L | H | V | P | S | Y | Q | N | N | O | C | L | I | I | K | V | M | Z | J | W | A | A | Z | R | V | N | Q |
| E | G | Y | S | P | H | G | S | T | Y | A | X | F | M | L | N | Z | M | Y | F | K | I | B | E | G | L | P | H |
| R | R | X | Y | B | U | T | B | X | J | K | V | I | B | F | L | Y | D | S | T | R | U | C | T | U | R | E | S |

## LM 2-24: Unit 2 Review Crossword

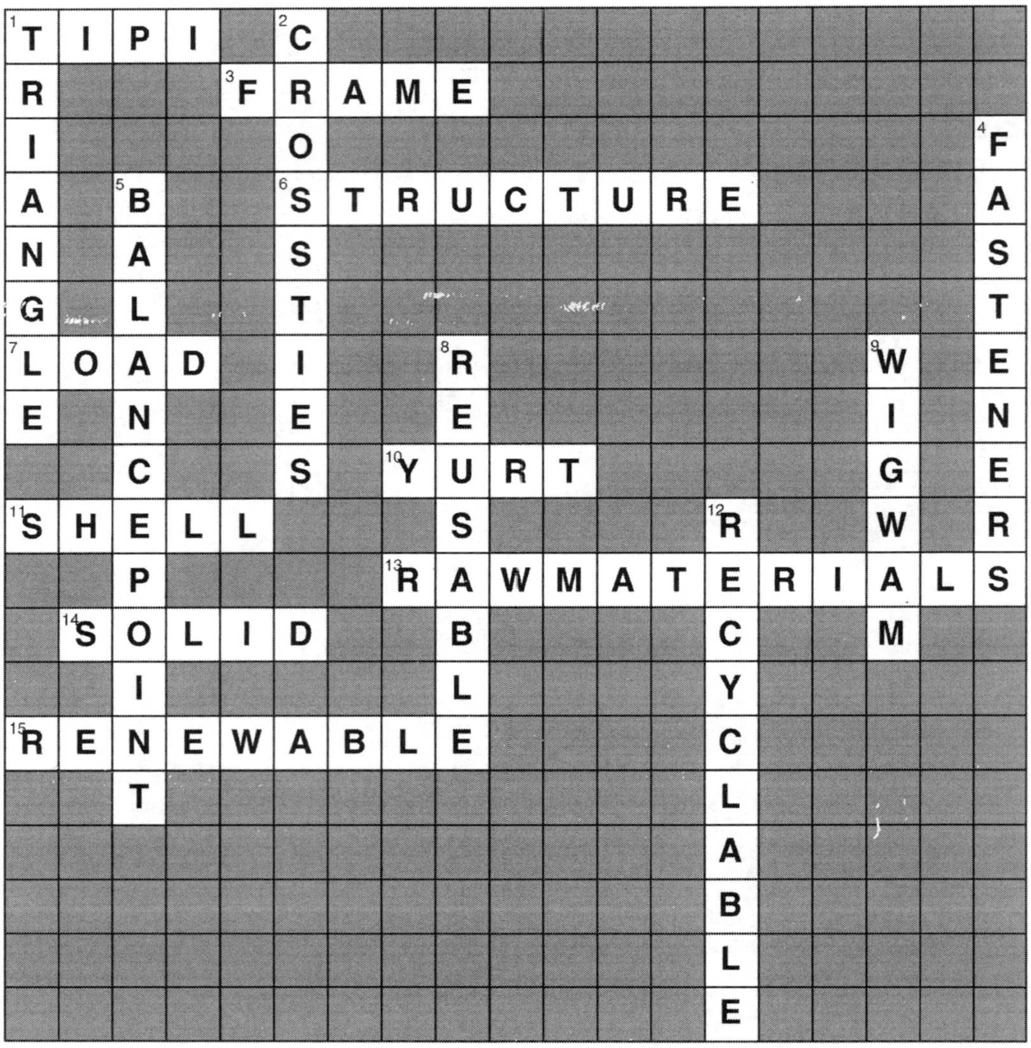

UNIT 3

# Magnetism and Static Electricity

## Table of Contents

## Table of Contents *(continued)*

## Unit Indicators Correlation Chart

| Indicator | Lesson References | Assessment Opportunities |
|---|---|---|
| By the end of grade 3, students will be able to: | | |
| **ME3.1 Investigate the characteristics of contact (e.g., push, pull, and friction) and non-contact (e.g., magnetic and static electric) forces.** | | |
| a. Pose questions related to the characteristics of magnetic and static electric forces. | Lesson 3<br>Lesson 11<br>Show What You Know | Communicate, p. 91, q. 3<br>Communicate, p. 107, q. 3<br>Show What You Know, q. 14 |
| b. Demonstrate how contact and non-contact forces are able to cause objects to start moving, speed up, slow down, and stop; cause moving objects to change direction; and cause changes to the shape of objects. | Lesson 1<br><br>Lesson 2<br><br>Lesson 3<br><br>Lesson 9<br>Lesson 11<br>Lesson 12<br><br>Show What You Know | Work On It, p. 87<br>Communicate, p. 87, q. 1, 2<br>Work On It, p. 89<br>Communicate, p. 89, q. 1, 2, 4<br>Work On It, p. 90<br>Communicate, p. 91, q. 1, 2<br>Communicate, p. 103, q. 2<br>Work On It, p. 107<br>Work On It, p. 108<br>Communicate, p. 109, q. 3<br>Show What You Know, p. 122, q. 1–5 |
| c. Compare the characteristics of contact, magnetic, and static electric forces, including the range over which they act, and propose methods of increasing or decreasing effects of these forces. | Lesson 2<br><br>Lesson 3<br>Lesson 6<br><br>Lesson 13<br><br>Show What You Know | Work On It, p. 89<br>Communicate, p. 89, q. 3<br>Work On It, p. 90<br>Work On It, p. 96<br>Communicate, p. 97 q. 3<br>Work On It, p. 111<br>Communicate, p. 111 q. 2<br>Show What You Know, p. 122, q. 9 |
| d. Group materials according to criteria such as their attraction to magnets and ability to be magnetized, based on personal observation. | Lesson 4<br><br>Lesson 7 | Work On It, p. 93<br>Communicate, p. 93, q. 1, 2, 3<br>Communicate p. 99, q. 1–4 |
| e. Compare the characteristics and effects of different types and shapes of magnets, including the location and type of magnetic poles (if any exist), and the shape of magnetic field produced by the magnet. | Lesson 5 | Work On It, p. 94<br>Communicate, p. 95, q. 3 |

| Indicator | Lesson References | Assessment Opportunities |
|---|---|---|
| f. Predict and test the number of objects a magnet can pick up under different conditions and develop simple conclusions about conditions that affect strength of magnetic forces. | Lesson 6<br><br>Lesson 9 | Work On It, p. 96<br>Communicate, p. 97, q. 1–4<br>Work On It, p. 102<br>Communicate, p. 103, q. 1, 3 |
| g. Investigate how charged materials interact with each other and with other charged and uncharged objects. | Lesson 11<br><br>Lesson 12 | Work On It, p. 107<br>Communicate, p. 107, q. 1, 2<br>Work On It, p. 108<br>Communicate, p. 107, q. 1, 2 |
| h. Demonstrate ways to use materials found in their environment to investigate conditions which affect the strength of static electric forces. | Lesson 13<br>Design Project | Work On It, p. 111<br>Work On It, p. 119 |
| i. Make and record relevant observations during investigations to identify conditions which affect the strength of static electric forces, and develop simple conclusions about these conditions. | Lesson 13<br><br>Lesson 14 | Work On It, p. 111<br>Communicate, p. 111, q. 1<br>Communicate, p. 113, q. 1 |
| **ME3.2 Assess effects of practical applications of magnetic and static electric forces on individuals and society.** | | |
| a. Investigate how magnets are used at home, school, and in business and industrial applications. | Lesson 8<br>Ask ...<br>Show What You Know | Work On It, p. 100<br>Research, p. 115<br>Show What You Know, p. 122, q. 6, 7 |
| b. Classify magnets that are used at home, school, and in business and industrial applications as natural, temporary, and permanent. | Lesson 8<br>Show What You Know | Communicate, p. 101, q. 1–4<br>Show What You Know, p. 122, q. 8 |
| c. Explore how magnetic compasses can provide evidence for and information about magnetic fields, including those created by current travelling through a conductor, and Earth's magnetic field. | Lesson 10 | Work On It, p. 104<br>Communicate, p. 105, q. 1–3 |
| d. Design, construct, and test an object such as a toy or game whose function depends on attractive or repulsive magnetic forces. | Lesson 15<br><br>Design Project | Work On It, p. 117 (if student uses magnets)<br>Work On It, p. 119 (if student uses magnets) |
| e. Describe the operation of a toy or game whose function depends on magnetic forces using terms such as *attract*, *repel*, *push*, and *pull*. | Lesson 15<br><br>Design Project<br><br>Show What You Know | Communicate, p. 117, q. 1, 2 (if student uses magnets)<br>Communicate, p. 119, q. 2 (if student uses magnets)<br>Show What You Know, p. 123, q.13 |

## Unit Indicators Correlation Chart *(continued)*

| Indicator | Lesson References | Assessment Opportunities |
|---|---|---|
| f. Explain safety procedures to be followed when interacting with magnetic and static electric forces. | Lesson 3<br>Lesson 5<br>Lesson 7<br>Lesson 10<br>Lesson 14<br><br>Show What You Know | Work On It, p. 90<br>Work On It, p. 94<br>Work On It, p. 99<br>Work On It, p. 104<br>Work On It, p. 113<br>Communicate, p. 113, q. 2<br>Show What You Know, p. 123, q. 12 |
| g. Describe the effects of static electric forces in their daily lives. | Lesson 11<br>Ask …<br>Show What You Know | Communicate, p. 107, q. 3, 4<br>Research, p. 115<br>Show What You Know, p. 123, q. 10 |
| h. Explain the purpose of technologies which are designed to minimize static electric forces. | Lesson 13<br>Show What You Know | Communicate, p. 111, q. 2<br>Show What You Know, p. 123, q. 11 |
| i. Investigate methods of using magnetic and static electric forces to create artistic expressions. | Lesson 9<br><br>Lesson 12 | Work On It, p. 102<br>Communicate, p. 103, q. 2<br>Communicate, p. 109, q. 3 |
| j. Generate new questions from what has been learned about applications of magnetic and static electric forces. | Lesson 3<br>Lesson 4<br>Lesson 9<br>Lesson 13 | Communicate p. 91, q. 3<br>Work On It, p. 93<br>Communicate, p. 103, q. 3<br>Communicate, p. 111, q. 3 |

## Lesson Planning Chart

Note that estimates of class times are based on 40 min per period.

| Lesson | Type of Activity | Time (number of classes) | Materials Required (for each group) | Line Masters |
|---|---|---|---|---|
| **Unit Opener** | | 1 | pencils<br>paper | LM 3-1<br>LM 3-2<br>LM 3-3 |
| **Launch:** Forces Are All Around You | confirmation inquiry | 1 | pencils<br>paper | LM 3-4 |
| **1.** Contact Forces | structured inquiry | 1 | pencils<br>paper | LM 3-5 |
| **2.** What Is Friction? | structured inquiry | 1 | pencils<br>paper<br>small toy car<br>smooth, open floor area, such as a hallway<br>ruler or measuring tape<br>towel<br>piece of string about 1 m long | LM 3-6 |
| **3.** Can You Move an Object Without Touching It? | structured inquiry | 1 | pencils<br>wooden ball or bead<br>paper clip<br>magnet<br>balloon<br>drinking straw | LM 3-7<br>LM 3-8<br>LM 3-9 |
| **4.** Exploring with Magnets | guided inquiry | 1 | pencils<br>2 different magnets<br>objects to test with a magnet such as paper clips, coins of different denominations, rocks, shells, nuts, bolts, nails, aluminum pop cans or pop can tabs, glass beads, marbles, wooden blocks, old keys, lids from frozen juice containers, plastic and metal toys | LM 3-10 |
| **5.** Magnets and Poles | structured inquiry | 1 | pencils<br>paper<br>pairs of a variety of magnets (each magnet in the pair is identical, different pairs have different-shaped magnets)<br>magnetic drawing board | LM 3-11 |
| **6.** Which Magnet Is Stronger? | structured inquiry | 1 | 2 different magnets<br>same-sized paper clips<br>ruler<br>pencils | LM 3-12 |

| Lesson | Type of Activity | Time (number of classes) | Materials Required (for each group) | Line Masters |
|---|---|---|---|---|
| **7.** Can You Make a Magnet? | structured inquiry | 1 | iron nail<br>magnet<br>paper clips<br>penny<br>nickel<br>quarter<br>aluminum foil<br>pencils<br>aluminum pop can tab | LM 3-13<br>LM 3-14 |
| **8.** Types of Magnets | confirmation inquiry | 1 | pencils<br>paper | LM 3-15 |
| **9.** Do Magnetic Forces Act Through Materials? | structured inquiry | 2 | materials to test: glass cake pan, piece of cardboard, sheet of plywood, cookie sheet, piece of cloth, paper<br>8 books<br>paper clip<br>wand, horseshoe, or bar magnet<br>sheet of unlined paper<br>pencils<br>variety of liquid paint colours | LM 3-16<br>LM 3-17 |
| **10.** What Can a Compass Tell You? | structured inquiry | 1 | 2 small magnetic compasses for each partner<br>large bar magnet to share<br>earbuds and portable music player, or computer and speakers<br>pencils | LM 3-18<br>LM 3-19 |
| **11.** What Is Static Electricity? | structured inquiry | 1 | 2 balloons<br>piece of wool fabric<br>objects to test, such as tissue and polystyrene foam bits, classroom walls, curtains, carpets, coats, and plastic and metal items<br>pencils | LM 3-20 |
| **12.** Charged Materials | structured inquiry | 1 | 2 polystyrene foam plates<br>2 pieces of string about 10 cm long<br>tape<br>piece of wool fabric or fur<br>sink and water tap<br>pencils | LM 3-21 |

| Lesson | Type of Activity | Time (number of classes) | Materials Required (for each group) | Line Masters |
|---|---|---|---|---|
| **13.** The Strength of Static Electricity | structured inquiry | 1 | balloon<br>piece of wool fabric<br>bare wall<br>stopwatch<br>pencils<br>spray bottle of water | LM 3-22 |
| **14.** Static Electricity and You | confirmation inquiry | 1 | pencils | LM 3-23<br>LM 3-24<br>LM 3-25 |
| **Ask …** Why is it important to understand forces? | | 1–5 | reference books and Internet access | LM 3-26<br>LM 3-27 |
| **15.** Tricks with Non-contact Forces | guided inquiry | 1–5 | pencils<br>various materials used in previous experiments such as:<br>a supply of magnets of different sizes and shapes<br>a supply of items such as balloons and wool cloths to create a charge with<br>metal items: containers, lids, toys<br>polystyrene plates, cups, bowls, tissue paper | LM 3-28 |
| **Design Project:** Build a Toy Boat or Sled | guided inquiry | 3–5 | pencils<br>magnets of different sizes and shapes<br>items to create a charge, such as balloons and wool cloths<br>metal items: containers, lids, toys<br>polystyrene plates, cups, bowls, tissue paper<br>items to help build the sled or boat, such as tape, glue, Bristol board, cardboard, plastic straws, Lego blocks, plastic lids to cut up, etc.<br>small tub for water, such as a baby bathtub, storage container, or large baking dish<br>ramp, such as a plastic tray, cookie sheet, or thin piece of plywood covered with a smooth piece of paper | LM 3-29<br>LM 3-30 |

traditional ***KNOWLEDGE***

## First Nations Cultural References

The following references provide information on First Nations topics. The information may not be specific to Saskatchewan First Nations and should not be generalized to all First Nations.

- Wanuskewin Heritage Park – Educational Tours – Fire starting and legend of the Thunderbird educational presentations
- Contact local Aboriginal Societies to inquire about Elders for guest speakers on the topics of fire starting, lightning and Thunderbird.

## Suggested Websites

Please note that website URLs constantly change and the addresses given below may become out of date. In this case, please use the website title and a search engine to find the appropriate website.

- Magnets:
  www.rapides.k12.la.us/region6tltc/intech2/IS%20BIGGER%20BETTER/Magnet%20websites.htm
  http://library.thinkquest.org/11924/emagnet.htmlnkquest.org/11924/emagnet.html
- Static Electricity:
  www.EnchantedLearning.com/physics/staticelectricity.shtml
  www.mos.org/sln/toe/
  http://science.jrank.org/kids/pages/230/All-About-Electricity.html
- Lightning:
  www.exploratorium.edu/ronh/weather/weather.html
- Earth's Magnetic Field and Northern Lights:
  http://gsc.nrcan.gc.ca/geomag/index_e.php
- Free Power Points for Kids:
  http://science.pppst.com/magnets.html
- Magnet Identification Online Game:
  www.fossweb.com/modules3-6/MagnetismandElectricity/index.html
- Everything Magnets and Electricity:
  www.physicssource.ca/pgs/3006_forces.html
- Free Applets to demonstrate Magnetism and Static Electricity:
  http://phet.colorado.edu/en/simulations/category/physics/electricity-magnets-and-circuits
- Northern lights:
  www.northernlightscentre.ca/northernlights.html
  www.webexhibits.org/causesofcolor/4C.html
  www.suite101.com/content/legends-behind-the-northern-lights-a12230

## Suggested Field Trips

- Saskatchewan Science Centre, Regina: Magnets Classroom Program
- Royal University Hospital, Saskatoon, or Regina General Hospital: MRI information
- Saskatoon Public Libraries, Regina Public Libraries, Prince Albert Public Library: Discuss how magnets help prevent book theft in libraries.
- Local stores or businesses that use a magnetic alarm system to help prevent theft (e.g., Wal-Mart, movie rental stores, Home Depot).

## Suggested Guest Speakers

- Local First Nations Elders, to discuss the legend of Thunderbird and lightning or to demonstrate fire starting with friction
- University of Regina, Educating Youth in Engineering and Science (EYES)
- Local doctor or MRI technician to discuss how an MRI works
- Photocopier service technician to discuss how static electricity helps make copies
- Mechanic to discuss how magnets are important to motors
- Scientific researcher or teacher: Innovators in the Schools—A Program through the Saskatchewan Science Centre—to discuss science careers and innovations

## Suggested Additional Student Resources

- *Magnetic and Non-magnetic* by Angela Royston (Heinemann Library, 2003)
- *What Does a Magnet Do?* by Jacqui Bailey (Smart Apple Media, 2007)
- *Shocking Science & Fascinating Electrical Experiments* by Shar Levine (Sterling Publishing, 1999)
- *The Attractive Story of Magnetism with Max Axiom, Super Scientist* by Andrea Gianopoulos, Cynthia Martin and Barbara Schulz (Capstone Press, 2008)
- *The Way Things Work* DVD (Schlessinger Media, 2003)
- *Attract and Repel* by Jennifer Boothroyd (Lerner Publications, 2011)
- *Electrically Charged* by Nancy Moore (Exclusive Educational Products, 1994)

## Materials and Equipment Needed for Unit 3

(based on 30 students)

| Launch: Forces Are All Around You (p. 84) | |
|---|---|
| **Materials**<br>• pencils<br>• paper | **Equipment**<br>• no equipment needed |
| **1. Contact Forces (p. 86)** | |
| **Materials**<br>• pencils<br>• paper | **Equipment**<br>• no equipment needed |
| **2. What Is Friction? (p. 88)** | |
| **Materials**<br>• pencils<br>• paper | **Equipment**<br>• 15 metre sticks, metric rulers, or metric measuring tapes<br>• 15 small toy cars<br>• 15 1-m pieces of string<br>• 15 small towels |
| **3. Can You Move An Object Without Touching It? (p. 90)** | |
| **Materials**<br>• pencils<br>• 15 balloons<br>• 15 drinking straws | **Equipment**<br>• 15 paper clips<br>• 15 wooden balls or beads<br>• 15 magnets |
| **4. Exploring with Magnets (p. 92)** | |
| **Materials**<br>• pencils | **Equipment**<br>• 15 sets of 2 different magnets<br>• objects to test with a magnet, such as paper clips, coins of different denominations, rocks, shells, nuts, bolts, nails, aluminum pop cans or pop can tabs, glass beads, marbles, wooden blocks, old keys, lids from frozen juice containers, plastic and metal toys |
| **5. Magnets and Poles (p. 94)** | |
| **Materials**<br>• pencils<br>• paper | **Equipment**<br>• 15 sets of 2 identical magnets<br>• 15 sets of 2 identical magnets that are different from the first set<br>• 15 sets of 2 identical magnets that are different from the second set<br>• 2 or 3 magnetic drawing boards (Groups can share one or two that are centrally located, and then return to their work area; they only need the item for one step in the activity.) |

## Materials and Equipment

*(continued)*

| 6. Which Magnet Is Stronger? (p. 96) | |
|---|---|
| **Materials**<br>• pencils | **Equipment**<br>• 15 same-sized paper clips<br>• 15 magnets<br>• 15 magnets of a different shape and size<br>• 15 metric rulers |
| **7. Can You Make a Magnet? (p. 98)** | |
| **Materials**<br>• pencils<br>• aluminum foil cut into small pieces | **Equipment**<br>• 15 magnets<br>• supply of several of each of these, for groups to share:<br>- iron nails<br>- paper clips<br>- pennies, nickels, quarters<br>- pencils with metal around the eraser end<br>- aluminum pop can tabs |
| **8. Types of Magnets (p. 100)** | |
| **Materials**<br>• pencils | **Equipment**<br>no equipment needed |
| **9. Do Magnetic Forces Act Through Materials? (p. 102)** | |
| **Materials**<br>• pencils<br>• 15 sheets of unlined paper | **Equipment**<br>• 15 wand, horseshoe, or bar magnets<br>• some books or other heavy items for each group<br>• 15 paper clips<br>• a supply of materials to test such as<br>- letter-sized pieces of cardboard, Bristol board, or plywood<br>- metal cookie sheets<br>- glass baking pans<br>- plastic serving trays<br>- large plastic lids<br>- pieces of cloth of several different materials<br>• liquid paint in a variety of colours |
| **10. What Can a Compass Tell You? (p. 104)** | |
| **Materials**<br>• pencils | **Equipment**<br>• 60 small magnetic compasses<br>• 15 large bar magnets to share<br>• earbuds and a music player or a computer and speakers |

# Materials and Equipment

*(continued)*

| 11. What Is Static Electricity? (p. 106) | |
|---|---|
| **Materials**<br>• pencils<br>• 30 small balloons<br>• 15 tissues | **Equipment**<br>• 15 small pieces of wool fabric<br>• polystyrene foam bits<br>• plastic items such as spoons, containers<br>• metal items such as spoons and paper clips, containers |
| **12. Charged Materials (p. 108)** | |
| **Materials**<br>• pencils<br>• 5 rolls of adhesive tape to be shared by the groups | **Equipment**<br>• 30 small polystyrene foam plates<br>• sink with running water<br>• 15 small pieces of wool fabric or fur<br>• 30 pieces of string pre-cut to about 10 cm |
| **13. The Strength of Static Electricity (p. 110)** | |
| **Materials**<br>• 15 small balloons<br>• pencils | **Equipment**<br>• 15 stopwatches<br>• 15 small pieces of wool fabric<br>• 5 small spray bottles of water |
| **14. Static Electricity and You (p. 112)** | |
| **Materials**<br>• pencils | **Equipment**<br>• no equipment needed |
| **15. Tricks With Non-contact Forces (p. 116)** | |
| **Materials**<br>• pencils<br>• 15 balloons<br>• a supply of items for students to use to build their tricks such as<br>- polystyrene plates, cups, and bowls<br>- tissue paper. | **Equipment**<br>• 15 small pieces of wool fabric<br>• supply of items for students to use to build their tricks such as<br>- magnets of different sizes and shapes<br>- metal items such as containers, lids, toys |
| **Design Project: Build a Toy Boat or Sled (p. 118)** | |
| **Materials**<br>• balloons<br>• a supply of items such as<br>- polystyrene foam plates, cups, bowls,<br>- tissue paper<br>- tape<br>- glue<br>- Bristol board<br>- cardboard<br>- plastic lids<br>- plastic straws | **Equipment**<br>• supply of magnets of different sizes and shapes<br>• 15 small pieces of wool fabric<br>• a supply of items such as<br>- metal containers, lids, toys<br>- Lego building blocks<br>• small tub such as a baby bathtub, storage container, or large baking dish<br>• ramp, such as a plastic tray, cookie sheet, or thin piece of plywood covered with a smooth piece of paper |

## Materials and Equipment

*(continued)*

### Overall Unit Requirements

| Materials | Equipment |
|---|---|
| • pencils<br>• paper<br>• 10 boxes of paper clips, all the same size<br>• 15 1-m pieces of string<br>• 30 plastic drinking straws<br>• 60 small balloons (water balloon sized)<br>• 60 balloons<br>• 60 small polystyrene plates<br>• 5 tissues<br>• 5 rolls of adhesive tape<br>• 60 pieces of string pre-cut to 10 cm<br>• several bottles of liquid Tempera paints in different colours<br>• 15 small pieces of aluminum foil<br>• 15 sheets of unlined paper<br>• 15 plastic container lids, to cut up<br>• 5 bottles of glue<br>• 15 containers of cut-up tissue paper<br>• 15 polystyrene cups<br>• 15 polystyrene bowls<br>• 15 pieces of cardboard<br>• 15 plastic container lids | • 15 metre sticks or metric tape measures<br>• 15 small toy cars<br>• 15 small towels<br>• 30 metric rulers (30 cm)<br>• bulletin board<br>• cut outs of magnet and lightning shapes to record class ideas<br>• 15 wooden balls or beads<br>• 2 magnetic drawing boards<br>• 30 bar magnets<br>• 30 horseshoe magnets<br>• 30 wand magnets<br>• 15 large bar magnets<br>• 30 magnets of various shapes and sizes<br>• 15 keys<br>• 15 math manipulatives<br>• 15 letter-sized pieces of cardboard, Bristol board, or plywood<br>• 15 iron nails<br>• 15 pennies<br>• 15 nickels<br>• 15 quarters<br>• 15 pencils with metal around the eraser end<br>• 15 aluminum pop can tabs<br>• pieces of cloth of several different materials<br>• 60 small magnetic compasses<br>• 2 sets of earbuds and a music player or 2 computer and speakers<br>• 30 small pieces of wool fabric or fur<br>• sink with running water<br>• 5 small spray bottles of water (fine mist atomizers are best.)<br>• 2 small tubs for water, such as a baby bath tub, storage container, or large baking dish<br>• 2 ramps, such as plastic serving trays, cookie sheets, or a thin piece of plywood covered with a smooth piece of paper<br>• 15 metal cookie sheets<br>• 15 glass baking pans<br>• 15 plastic serving trays, or large plastic containers |

UNIT 3

# Unit Opener

Page 82

| Time |
| --- |
| 40 min |
| **Line Masters** |
| • LM 3-1<br>• LM 3-2<br>• LM 3-3 |

In this unit, students will explore how forces act on objects. They will learn about the forces of magnetism and static electricity. They will also learn how we use forces to make our lives better. Throughout the unit, focus will be brought to First Nations and Métis ways of knowing and learning. One important strategy is the careful observation and connection to nature. The Big Ideas of the unit are

- Forces make objects move or change.
- Some forces touch those objects, but others make no contact at all.
- We can use what we know about forces to help us in our daily lives.
- Forces in nature are important to the ways of First Nations and Métis people.

Before the unit begins, have students come up with a list of questions they have about magnetism, static electricity, and forces in general. Some questions that students may generate could include the following:

- What is a force?
- How do forces make things move?
- How can you make things move without touching them?
- What is static electricity?
- What is magnetism?
- How do magnets make things move?
- What do magnets and static electricity have to do with each other?
- Where do you see static electricity or magnetism in nature?
- How are forces used in my daily life?
- Is static electricity useful?

## Assess Prior Knowledge

- Discussing the Big Ideas that appear on student book page 82 is an excellent opportunity to assess prior knowledge and student preconceptions about magnetism and static electricity.

## Introduce the Unit

- Read the opening text on student book page 83 with the class.
- Ask students to share their observations of the forces listed in the opening text, such as wind, waves, and magnetism and static electricity, and things that change.
- Have them look at the opening picture of the northern lights. Tell them that these lights are created when the forces of magnetism and static electricity meet. Ask them, *Can you see static electricity?*
- Once you have determined students' prior knowledge, you may want to hand out LM 3-1 Unit 3 Summary and LM 3-2 Unit 3 Vocabulary to help students record their understanding of the unit and vocabulary terms.

## Introduce the Design Project

- Tell students that their task is to build a small toy boat or sled that will move by means of a non-contact force, either magnetism or static electricity. The boat or sled will have to move and carry a small load.
- Inform students that throughout the unit, the "Build on What You Know" sections in the student book will prompt them to think about how they could use their new knowledge to help plan their Design Project.
- Tell students to start planning and collecting materials, and to continue doing so as the unit progresses. This will make the Design Project much easier for them at the end.

| Time |
| --- |
| 30 min |
| **Skills** |
| • communicating |
| **Grouping** |
| pairs or groups |
| **Line Masters** |
| • LM 3-3 |

## Looking Forward

- Have students fill in LM 3-3 Looking Forward as they answer the Looking Forward questions.
- As students think about objects that are moving and changing and the forces making the objects move or change, consider asking them whether each force they have thought of is a pushing force or a pulling force.
- Students' answers to question 1 will vary but might include those in the table below.

| Objects that Are Moving or Changing | Forces that Made These Objects Move or Change |
| --- | --- |
| The swings on the playground | My friend pushed me |
| A toboggan going down a hill | We pushed the toboggan at the top of the hill |
| My bike moving forward | My legs pushed the pedals. |

- Students' questions about magnetism and static electricity will vary, but they could include such questions as: Why do magnets stick only to metal? What makes a magnet stick? What is static electricity? Why does static electricity make my hair stand up? Why does it sometimes give me a shock?

# LAUNCH Forces Are All Around You

Page 84

| Time |
|---|
| 40 min |

| Time |
|---|
| 20 min |

**Learning Context**

inquiry

**Level of Inquiry**

confirmation

**Skills**

- observing
- classifying
- inferring
- interpreting
- communicating

**Grouping**

pairs or groups

**Materials and Equipment**

(per group)
- pencils
- paper

**Line Masters**

- LM 3-4

## Get Started ▶

- Read the Get Started text together as a class.

## Work On It

### Purpose

To give students the opportunity to identify different forces

### Activity Notes

- Have the class look at the large cartoon to find objects that are being affected by a force. Identify a few together to get them started.
- Discuss with the class that some items might be pushed or pulled by a force you can see, such as a person or animal, but that some items might be affected by unseen forces such as static pulling causing hair to fly up or the wind blowing snow.
- Then students can fill in more items they find on LM 3-4 Forces Are All Around You.
- Students may have difficulty identifying stationary items that are being acted on by a force, such as a piece of paper held on a fridge by a magnet. Point out to students that the paper is being stopped from moving by magnetism. Get them to reread the first sentence of the Get Started paragraph.

## Communicate

**1, 2.** Students' answers may vary, but may include the following.

| Objects that Are Moving, Being Stopped, or Changing Direction or Shape | What I Think Is Causing the Movement or Change |
|---|---|
| CD/DVD player – spins the discs | Motor |
| Backpack flap has popped open | Too many papers in it for the magnet to stick |
| Notes stuck on fridge | Magnet |
| Dust – gets cleaned off TV | Static cling duster |
| Socks stick to laundry | Static |
| Hair stands up when you take off your toque | Static |
| Car tires spin | Ice |
| Horse-drawn sled | Horse pulling it |

*continued→*

| Objects that Are Moving, Being Stopped, or Changing Direction or Shape | What I Think Is Causing the Movement or Change |
|---|---|
| Snow moves when shovelled | Person pushing the shovel |
| Snow falls off roof | Wind |
| Snow moves in front of grader | Grader blade pushing it |
| Snow changes shape to make a snowman | Hands pushing the snow into a ball |
| Checkers on board move | Hand moving the checkers |
| Snow gets brushed off car | Hand pushing the brush to move the snow |
| Snowballs fly | Hand and arm throwing them |
| Sledders move down the hill | Sledders sliding on the snow; gravity pulling them down |
| Snowmobile drives down the road | Motor |
| Snow flies out of snow blower | Motor |

## DI Differentiating Instruction

### *For Reteaching*

If students do not recognize that forces stop or change objects, refer them to the first sentence of the Get Started paragraph, which states that forces move, change, and stop objects. If students are still unable to identify objects that are being stopped by a force, offer other examples, such as a headband. It stops hair from falling—which is movement—into a person's face. Another example is a stair rail. It stops a person from tumbling over into the stairwell. If they are unable to find objects that are changing shape, describe how gum changes shape by the force of a person's teeth and mouth. If a person blows a bubble, his or her breath is the force that changes shape of the gum into a bubble.

## Assessment *for* Learning

| What to Look for in Student Work | What to Do |
|---|---|
| Students can identify objects that are being acted upon by a force, which makes them move, stop, or change shape or direction. | • Monitor student discussions as they do the Communicate section of the lesson.<br>• Use student lists to assess their ability to identify forces acting on objects. |

# 1 Contact Forces

Page 86

| Time |
|---|
| 40 min |

| Vocabulary |
|---|
| • force<br>• contact forces |

| Line Masters |
|---|
| • LM 3-5 |

## Indicator Assessment Chart

| Indicator | Assessment Opportunities |
|---|---|
| **ME3.1 b.** Demonstrate how contact and non-contact forces are able to cause objects to start moving, speed up, slow down, and stop; cause moving objects to change direction; and cause changes to the shape of objects. | • Work On It, p. 87<br>• Communicate, p. 87, q. 1, 2 |

## Lesson Goal

To find examples of forces that touch objects

## Background Information

A force is any influence that can produce a change in the movement of an object. This definition goes further than "push" or "pull" in that no direct contact is necessarily implied.

A force acting on an object may increase or decrease the object's speed and/or change direction. A force may also move the particles that the object is composed of, thus changing its shape.

A force is a vector quantity, meaning that it has both magnitude and direction. Forces are measured in newtons (abbreviated N), after Sir Isaac Newton. One newton is the amount of net force required to accelerate a mass of 1 kg a rate of 1 $m/s^2$ .One newton is equal to the force of gravity acting on a mass of 102 g (roughly equal to the mass of a small apple).

## Curriculum Connections

In this lesson, students have the opportunity to develop skills and concepts in these areas:

### *Social Studies*

RW3.3 a. Recognize that technology includes more than electronics (i.e., paper, forging steel, manufacturing, vehicles, making cloth, products created for construction).

IN3.1 a. Describe characteristics of daily life in communities studied, and compare the ways in which the needs are met by individuals in diverse communities (e.g., housing, tools, work, use of the land, games, education).

## Misconceptions

Students often focus on the push or pull part of the definition of a force. It needs to be stressed that a force may also stop movement, change an object's direction of movement, or change the shape of the object.

Students often visualize the term "contact forces" as a person or thing touching another object, but things such as wind and air can cause movements and changes. Even though they cannot be seen, they are still contact forces.

## Get Started ▶

- Read the Get Started text with students.
- Discuss the effects of forces that students experience in their everyday lives, using the illustrations on pages 86 and 87 of the student book. Explain to students that although they do not yet know what a force is, they have experienced what forces can do.
- Discuss any questions students may have about the information on this page.

| Time |
| --- |
| 20 min |
| **Learning Context** |
| inquiry |
| **Level of Inquiry** |
| confirmation |
| **Skills** |
| • observing<br>• interpreting<br>• communicating |
| **Grouping** |
| pairs or groups |
| **Materials and Equipment** |
| • pencils<br>• paper |
| **Line Masters** |
| • LM 3-5 |

## Work On It

### Purpose

To allow students to find examples of forces that actually make contact with the objects that are moving or changing

### Activity Notes

- Students work in pairs or small groups to identify what things in the cartoon are being moved, changed, or stopped by a force.
- Students can use LM 3-5 Pushing and Pulling Forces to record their observations.
- Students may have difficulty identifying the wind that moves the clothes drying on the line and the kite as a force because they cannot see it.
- Monitor groups as they work, and redirect to the "contact force" definition as necessary.

## Additional Activity

Have students go outside to see what items are being moved, stopped, or changed. Recess is a great time to do this. Or, have students watch a gym class or kindergarten playtime to look for objects moving or changing.

## Communicate

1.

| Examples of Pushing Forces | Examples of Pulling Forces |
|---|---|
| Leaves pushed by wind<br>Flag pushed by wind<br>Football pushed to throw it<br>Beach ball pushed to throw it<br>Man pushing wheelbarrow<br>Boy pushing lawnmower<br>Arms pushing ski poles<br>Batter hitting baseball<br>Girl pushing ringette ring<br>Hot chocolate gets blown on<br>Snowman gets pushed into shape | Man pulling rake<br>Kite pulling on a string, parasail handle<br>Water skier pulling the tow rope handle<br>Sleigh pulled by horse<br>Kayaker pulling paddle<br>Grain pulled up into combine<br>Swimmer pulls himself through water<br>Climber pulls self up ladder to go down the slide<br>Apple pulled down by gravity<br>Player pulls strings on guitar |

2. Scientists call them contact forces because they must touch something to make it move or change. Contact is something that you feel, so even the wind is a contact force because even though you can't see it, you can feel it.

## DI Differentiating Instruction

### *For Reteaching*

Some students may have difficulty understanding how a force that isn't moving or actually pushing or pulling something could change an object's shape or direction, or that stopping movement is also part of the definition. Having students play with modelling clay provides them with a concrete example of how the force of their hands changes the shape of the clay. Having them roll a ball of clay across the floor to hit a wall or having them drop it on the floor, are good ways to show stopping and shape-changing forces, even though nothing was actually moving to make those changes.

## Assessment *for* Learning

| What to Look for in Student Work | What to Do |
|---|---|
| Students can identify examples of contact forces. | • Observe students and monitor their group discussions to see if they are able to identify the various forces acting on objects. |

# 2 What Is Friction?

Page 88

| Time |
| --- |
| 40 min |

| Vocabulary |
| --- |
| • friction |

| Line Masters |
| --- |
| • LM 3-6 |

## Indicator Assessment Chart

| Indicator | Assessment Opportunities |
| --- | --- |
| **ME3.1 b.** Demonstrate how contact and non-contact forces are able to cause objects to start moving, speed up, slow down, and stop; cause moving objects to change direction; and cause changes to the shape of objects. | • Work On It, p. 89<br>• Communicate, p. 89, q. 1, 2, 4 |
| **ME3.1 c.** Compare the characteristics of contact, magnetic, and static electric forces, including the range over which they act, and propose methods of increasing or decreasing effects of these forces. | • Work On It, p. 89<br>• Communicate, p. 89, q. 3 |

## Lesson Goal

To explore the force of friction and its effects

## Background Information

Friction is the force that resists motion when a surface of one object comes into contact with a surface of another.

Friction is produced whenever two surfaces rub against each other. It is caused by the attractive forces of the surfaces in contact with each other. The force of friction acts in the opposite direction of the movement. For example, if a block slides to the left, friction pulls to the right. If you drop a ball, the ball moves downward and the friction acts upward.

All surfaces, even smooth ones, have some bumps or hollows. You can see and feel the irregularities on rough surfaces such as sandpaper. You would need a magnifying lens or microscope to see the irregularities on smooth surfaces, such as linoleum or an ice rink. The fewer the surface irregularities, the lower the friction. However, no matter how smooth a surface is, there is always friction.

Some friction is helpful. Friction allows us to walk without slipping. But friction can also make work harder. For example, various parts of an engine move against one another, which produce friction. Lubricants, such as oil, need to be added to make the surfaces smoother and thus reduce friction. Without the lubricants, the friction would hinder the work of the engine.

traditional **KNOWLEDGE**

Many First Nations cultures traditionally used friction as a tool to help them in their daily lives to make fire. One method of fire starting was with the use of a fire drill. This type of drill contains several components: a hearth board (made of hardwood), an upright stick (made of the same wood as the hearth board), a small bow, and a hand pad made out of stone or antler. The hearth board is placed on the ground and the stick is placed upright on the board. The bow's string is secured around the upright stick so that the bow can saw back and forth, causing the upright to spin on the hearth board. The top of the upright is held securely by the hand pad. The spinning of the upright stick on the hearth board causes friction, which creates heat that ignites dry tinder.

## Curriculum Connections

In this lesson, students have the opportunity to develop skills and concepts in these areas:

### *Mathematics*

SS3.3 Demonstrate understanding of linear measurement (cm and m) including measuring and recording length.

## Misconceptions

Many students believe that with friction, it is only the rubbing that is the force. In reality, it is the *resistance* to the movement of the attractive forces between the two objects that creates the heat energy. It is important to stress to students that friction is the resistance to movement or rubbing.

## Get Started ▶

- Read the Get Started text with students, view the visuals, and read the captions.
- Discuss any questions students may have about the information on this page.
- A simple demonstration of the force of friction could be added when discussing the fire starting photo. Have all students rub their hands together and feel the heat that is the result of the force of friction.

## Work On It

### Purpose

To allow students to explore the force of friction and feel how an increase or decrease in friction affects the amount of work done to make an object move

*continued→*

| Time |
| --- |
| 20 min |
| **Learning Context** |
| inquiry |
| **Level of Inquiry** |
| structured |
| **Skills** |
| • observing<br>• collecting data<br>• interpreting<br>• comparing<br>• measuring<br>• communicating<br>• controlling variables<br>• predicting |
| **Grouping** |
| pairs or groups |
| **Materials and Equipment** |
| (per group)<br>• pencils<br>• paper<br>• small toy car<br>• smooth, open floor area, such as a hallway<br>• ruler or measuring tape<br>• towel<br>• string about 1 m long |
| **Line Masters** |
| • LM 3-6 |

## Activity Notes

- Carefully read the instructions to the class. Remind students that they have to measure the distance the car travels after only *one push* of one finger or *one pull* on the string. If they push or pull more, the distance the cars may travel may be too large to measure accurately.
- Give students time to "play" (open exploration) with the cars for a few minutes before doing the experiment. This may help students stay on task, and avoid behaviour issues before they happen.
- Space out the groups around the room and/ or hallway to remove students' temptation to race the cars.
- Carefully monitor students during the measurement and data recording steps to ensure they obtain accurate data. This will help them interpret their data properly and draw the correct conclusions.
- You may wish to give students LM 3-6 Friction and Toy Cars to record their predictions and data.
- Students should be able to predict that friction will slow down the car when it is pushed or pulled.
- Data will vary widely depending on the type of toy car used. However, the car should travel much farther when pushed or pulled on the floor than when pushed or pulled on a towel.

## Communicate

Students can work individually or in pairs to answer the questions. Group discussion and sharing answers among several groups or with the whole class is an excellent opportunity for assessing students' understanding of friction.

1. It was easier to push the car across the floor than across the towel.
2. It was easier to pull the car across the floor than across the towel.
3. I think the towel created more friction because its surface is bumpy.
4. When the car was on the towel, there was more friction and it was harder to push or pull it. On the smooth floor, it was easier.

## DI Differentiating Instruction

### *For Enrichment*

Have students look at their hands under a magnifying lens to see the skin surface in more detail. Ask, *What does the surface of your skin surface look like? Is one part smoother than other parts? If rubbed, which part would create the most friction?*

## Assessment *for* Learning

| What to Look for in Student Work | What to Do |
| --- | --- |
| Students understand that friction is a force of resistance to movement.<br>Students understand that rougher surfaces create more friction. | • Have students answer questions orally or have a class discussion after the groups have completed the Communicate section. |

# 3 Can You Move an Object Without Touching It?

Page 90

**Time**

40 min

**Vocabulary**

- non-contact forces

**Line Masters**

- LM 3-7
- LM 3-8
- LM 3-9

## Indicator Assessment Chart

| Indicator | Assessment Opportunities |
|---|---|
| **ME3.1 a.** Pose questions related to the characteristics of magnetic and static electric forces (e.g., Do all magnets attract objects? Do all magnets have a North pole? Why do I get a shock when I rub my shoes on a carpet and touch a door knob?). | • Communicate, p. 91, q. 3 |
| **ME3.1 b.** Demonstrate how contact and non-contact forces are able to cause objects to start moving, speed up, slow down, and stop; cause moving objects to change direction; and cause changes to the shape of objects. | • Work On It, p. 90<br>• Communicate, p. 91, q. 1, 2 |
| **ME3.1 c.** Compare the characteristics of contact, magnetic, and static electric forces, including the range over which they act, and propose methods of increasing or decreasing effects of these forces. | • Work On It, p. 90 |
| **ME3.2 f.** Explain safety procedures to be followed when interacting with magnetic and static electric forces. | • Work On It, p. 90 |
| **ME3.2 j.** Generate new questions from what has been learned about applications of magnetic and static electric forces. | • Communicate, p. 91, q. 3 |

## Lesson Goal

To explore forces that do not touch objects

### Background Information

The two non-contact forces being introduced in this lesson are magnetism and static electricity. Magnetism is the force that causes certain metals to move toward or away from a magnet. A magnet is an object that is surrounded by a magnetic field and that has the property, either natural or induced, of attracting some metals, such as iron and steel. Magnetism is a force that can act over a distance. This means that a magnet need not actually touch an object in order to push or pull it, or to change an object's direction or shape. In fact, the force of magnetism can pass through many types of matter, including air, water, glass, cardboard, book covers, cloth, tabletops, plastic, and skin.

*continued→*

Static electricity is also a non-contact force. How many times in the winter has your hair stood on end long after you have removed your toque or scarf? The two forces are similar: they both attract and repel, and they both display polarity. In fact, they can create each other.

A collapsing magnetic field can create an electric spark, which happens in the starter of a vehicle's engine. Magnetism is more commonly related to current electricity, which is different from static electricity. Wires carrying a current of electricity have a magnetic field around them that can be detected with a compass. Electromagnets have a magnetic field caused by current electricity. The relationship of the forces of magnetism and electricity can be compared to the two sides of a coin: while they are different, they are also inseparably intertwined.

## Focus On Literacy

### *Before Reading: Previewing Unfamiliar Vocabulary and Activating Prior Knowledge*

Tell students, *Knowing the meaning of prefixes and root words can help us make sense of unfamiliar terms used in science. By breaking apart a word into its prefix and root word and using our knowledge of what these two word parts mean, we can make sense of new words we encounter in our science reading.*

Have the following list of words posted on chart paper or on the board:

| | | | |
|---|---|---|---|
| non-stop | non-stick | non-smoker | non-fiction |
| non-iron | nonsense | | |

Ask students to identify the small word part each of these words has in common ("non"). Tell students that this small word part is the prefix of the word and circle it in each word on the chart.

Now have students identify the root word in each of the words above; underline each root word as they are given. Ask students to turn to a partner and discuss what the prefix "non" does to each root word. For example, ask them, *If "stop" means "to cease doing something," what does "non-stop" mean? What has the prefix "non" done to the root word?* Invite students to share their thinking and answers. Record key information on the chart paper to serve as an anchor chart that can be revisited in future lessons. For example, Lesson 5 presents the words "magnetic" and "non-magnetic."

Invite students to scan student book page 90 and find a word(s) that starts with the prefix "non." They will offer the word "non-contact." Remind students that they learned about a contact force in Lesson 1 of this unit; review the meaning of "contact force." Ask students, *Using your new knowledge of the prefix "non," what do you think the phrase "non-contact force" might mean?* Students can further verify their definition of "non-contact force" by viewing the photos and captions in Lesson 3 to see if they are correct.

## Misconceptions

Students often misinterpret an invisible contact force as being a non-contact force, so they often think wind, or moving air, is a non-contact force. But because air is matter, it takes up space. Therefore, it can make contact and cause movement or shape change.

**Time**

30 min

**Learning Context**

inquiry

**Level of Inquiry**

structured

**Skills**

- collecting data
- inferring
- observing
- interpreting
- experimenting
- comparing
- communicating
- controlling variables
- predicting

**Grouping**

pairs

**Materials and Equipment**

(per group)
- pencils
- wooden ball or bead
- paper clip
- magnet
- balloon
- drinking straw

**Line Masters**

- LM 3-7
- LM 3-8

**SAFETY CAUTION!**

Never put a magnet in your mouth or swallow a magnet.
Severe risks of choking or intestinal perforation exist if magnets are swallowed.

## Get Started ▶

- Question students about their understanding of the prefix "non."
- Read the Get Started text with students and review the pictures and captions.
- Refer students to the non-fiction elements, such as photos, captions, and headings, to help them infer the meanings of new concepts.

## Work On It

### Purpose

To provide students with an opportunity to identify which forces are non-contact forces

### Activity Notes

- Read the instructions with the class, and stress that step 2 is the only step in which they are allowed to touch the wooden ball, hair, or paper clip directly. In steps 3 and 4, the magnet, the balloon, and the straw must not touch any of the items as students try to move them.
- Students can make their predictions and record their data on LM 3-7 Can You Move an Object Without Touching It? and record their ideas and questions on LM 3-8 Non-contact Forces KWL Chart.
- Students' predictions will vary but may include
  - The force from my fingers will move the ball, paper clip, and hair.
  - The force from the magnet will move the paper clip without contact.
  - The force from the balloon will move my hair without contact.
  - The force from the straw will move the items with contact.
- Most students will have enough prior knowledge of magnets and static charged balloons to use them move the paper clip and their own hair without any contact.
- Most students will realize quickly that they need to blow through the straw to make the items move. If a group is not getting it, ask them *Could wind move those things?* to put them on the right track.
- Students' data may be as follows.

| Object/Was It Moved by the Force of ... | Wooden Ball | Paper Clip | Your Hair | Did Anything Touch the Object? If So, What? |
|---|---|---|---|---|
| Your fingers | Yes | Yes | Yes | Yes. My hands |
| The magnet | No | Yes | No | Nothing touched the paper clip at first |
| The balloon | No | No | Yes | Nothing touched my hair. |
| The straw | Yes | Yes | Yes | Yes. My breath |

## Communicate

This section is critical to student understanding of the difference between contact and non-contact forces. They need to understand that even though they cannot see the air they can feel it. The air is touching each object to make it move, and therefore the air is a contact force. But magnetism and static electricity are truly non-contact—they cannot be felt.

At the end of the Communicate, students can begin to fill in a KWL chart to keep track of their learning about these two forces: what they know, what they want to know, and what they have learned. Students will use this chart in several lessons throughout the unit to continue adding to their knowledge and posing new questions.

1. The magnet moved the paper clip without touching it. The balloon moved my hair without touching it.
2. Blowing air is a contact force because you can feel it pushing. It actually touches things to make them move, even if you can't see it.
3. Responses may vary but may include the following. I learned that a magnet and a balloon produce non-contact forces. Wind is a contact force. What makes a balloon produce a non-contact force? What makes a magnet produce a non-contact force?

### BUILD ON WHAT YOU KNOW

Students are now asked to list some forces they could use to make a toy boat or sled move. Responses could include push it with a finger, pull it with a string, use a magnet to pull it, and use wind to push it. Students can record their ideas on LM 3-9 Build On What You Know.

## DI Differentiating Instruction

***For Reteaching***

Some students may still be convinced that air moving things is an example of a non-contact force, since they can't see the air. Help these students to feel the difference with a simple activity. Ask these students to close their eyes as first the magnet and then the balloon are passed over their heads. Then, while they still have their eyes closed, blow through the straw at the top of their heads. Ask them which one they actually felt touching them. That one is a contact force!

## Assessment *for* Learning

| What to Look for in Student Work | What to Do |
| --- | --- |
| Students can identify and distinguish between contact and non-contact forces. | • Monitor answers to and discussion of Communicate question 2 to gauge understanding and whether reteaching is needed. See For Reteaching activity above. |

# 4 Exploring with Magnets

Page 92

| Time |
| --- |
| 40 min |
| **Line Masters** |
| • LM 3-10 |

## Indicator Assessment Chart

| Indicator | Assessment Opportunities |
| --- | --- |
| **ME3.1 d.** Group materials according to criteria such as their attraction to magnets and ability to be magnetized, based on personal observation. | • Work On It, p. 93<br>• Communicate, p. 93, q. 1, 2, 3 |
| **ME3.2 j.** Generate new questions from what has been learned about applications of magnetic and static electric forces. | • Work On It, p. 93 |

## Lesson Goal

To explore what magnets do and their special properties

### Background Information

Magnetite is the most magnetic naturally occurring mineral. All forms of magnetite are attracted to magnets. Only one form, called lodestone, acts as a magnet, attracting other magnetic materials, such as iron and nickel. It is believed that natural magnets were first discovered over 2500 years ago in a region of Ancient Greece called Magnesia, now known as Thessaly. Pieces of lodestone suspended by a string were the first rudimentary magnetic compasses and were used in navigation. Magnetism remained a mystery for centuries. It wasn't until the 19th century that the relationship between magnetism and electricity was discovered.

Magnetite/lodestone is an iron oxide. In addition to magnetite, another mineral called pyrrhotite is weakly magnetic. Earth itself is also a weak magnet. It has two magnetic poles.

Magnets attract metal objects made from iron, nickel, or cobalt. Steel is manufactured from iron ore, and is therefore also magnetic. Aluminum and copper, two common metals that students will have encountered, are not attracted to magnets.

In the Get Started on student book page 92, the text says that "magnets cause your doorbell to ring and motors to turn." An electromagnet (a magnet that uses electric current) works against a spring to hit a chime on a doorbell. In a motor, an electrical current causes a magnetic field, which turns a rotor and the motor shaft, which can be used to power things such as appliances.

*continued→*

**traditional KNOWLEDGE**

First Nations and Métis peoples understand that rocks and all things found in nature have Spirit and are part of Creator. Traditionally, a deep connection is felt with both the animate and inanimate beings that inhabit the environment. First Nations and Métis people understand that everything around us is imbued with special powers, even rocks and trees. This spiritual relationship with nature permeates all aspects of daily life, not only ceremonies or special occasions.

## Curriculum Connections

In this lesson, students have the opportunity to develop skills and concepts in these areas:

### *Social Studies*

DR3.1 a. Demonstrate understanding that the surface of Earth can be represented through maps, aerial photographs, and satellite images.
RW3.3 a. Evaluate the ways in which technologies have impacted daily life, and recognize that technology includes more than electronics (i.e., paper, forging steel, manufacturing, vehicles, making cloth, products created for construction).

## Focus On Literacy

### *Before Writing: Collecting and Focusing Ideas and Information*

Tell students, *Before writers begin the process of actually writing, they gather information and think about how they can organize this information so that it makes sense to the reader. They need to consider who they are writing for—the audience—and what their purpose is. For example, do they want to persuade us to do something or tell us something?*

Then tell students, *We know the audience for our science textbook is grade 3 students, so the information is written at a level we can understand. Since this is the first of several lessons on magnets in this unit, the writer probably wanted to start by building up our background knowledge on the topic of magnets. As we read, we will record the important information in each paragraph and see if we can discover how the writer organized this information.*

Begin by reading the first paragraph aloud. Work with students to identify the most important information in this paragraph. Record points such as "special rocks can be shiny, smooth" in one grouping and come up with a subtitle for this information, such as "characteristics of special rocks." Another grouping of information from the first paragraph would include "First Nations and Métis peoples believe rocks have Spirit and are part of Creator." Record this information and identify an appropriate subtitle, such as "beliefs." As you collect information with the class, organize it into groupings so that it begins to resemble a web.

Continue as a class, or have pairs of students read the second paragraph to identify more important information. Have students share the important information from this paragraph on magnetite and where it is found. Record this information with an appropriate subtitle on another part of the web. If students do not offer information from the map in the margin, point it out to them as a good source of information. Add the word "magnetic" to the "characteristics" grouping from paragraph one. Repeat this process with the third paragraph, which provides information on the various products that use or contain magnets.

Tell students, *As we can see, the writer did organize the information into special groupings so that by the end of the page we have information on a variety of topics that relate to magnets. This type of writing is called "description." We can see that a good graphic organizer for collecting and organizing information when doing descriptive writing is a web.* Prompt students to consider using a web to organize their information when they write on a topic and their purpose is to describe or tell about something.

## Misconceptions

Some students believe that all metals are attracted to magnets, which is not true. Magnets attract iron, steel, nickel, and cobalt. This lesson will allow them to discover that magnets attract only certain metals. This concept will be reinforced later in Lesson 7 Can You Make a Magnet?

### Get Started ▶

- Read the first two sentences of the Get Started section. Pause to let students make connections to the text and share their background knowledge.
- Continue to read the rest of the section with the class. Pause to refer them to the non-fiction structures on the page: the picture, map, and captions. Invite inferences regarding the origin of the word "magnet" and the area of Greece called Magnesia.
- "Magnet" is not defined in the student book. Providing a definition would give away what students are supposed to explore in the Work On It, namely, that magnets are objects that can attract certain metal objects.
- Finish reading the section, and again invite students to make connections and share their prior knowledge about magnets in their daily lives and how magnets work. This may help you assess which lessons you need to spend more or less time on, and may help you uncover any misconceptions students have.

## Time

15–30 min

## Learning Context

inquiry

## Level of Inquiry

guided

## Skills

- observing
- classifying
- inferring
- interpreting
- experimenting
- hypothesizing
- comparing
- communicating
- predicting

## Grouping

pairs or groups

## Materials and Equipment

(per group)
- pencils
- 2 different magnets
- objects to test with a magnet, such as paper clips, coins of different denominations, rocks, shells, nuts, bolts, nails, aluminum pop cans or pop can tabs, glass beads, marbles, wooden blocks, old keys, lids from frozen juice containers, plastic and metal toys

## Line Masters

- LM 3-10

**SAFETY CAUTION!**
Remember to handle sharp objects with care. Magnets should not be dropped; it weakens them, and if they chip the shards can be very sharp and could hurt you.

# Work On It

### Purpose

To allow students to explore what magnets can do and discover on their own some of a magnet's special properties

### Activity Notes

- Students will hypothesize and make predictions about what magnets can do.
- Sample predictions include metal objects will stick to magnets and non-metal objects won't stick to magnets.
- They will then engage in open exploration with the magnets and the items provided for each group.
- Give students LM 3-10 Exploring With Magnets to record their observations.
- Sample entries may look like the following.

| Object | What Happened When It Was Close to a Magnet? |
|---|---|
| Nail | Stuck to magnet. |
| Elastic bands | Did not stick to magnet. |
| Eraser | Did not stick to magnet. |
| Scissors | Stuck to magnet. |
| Key | Did not stick to magnet. |

- They will be prompted to replicate their results with a different magnet.
- During their open exploration, consider asking students the following questions to promote further understanding: *What do you notice about the types of materials sticking to your magnets? Why do you think that the pop can won't stick to the magnet, but the soup can will?*

# Communicate

The Communicate section is another way to assess student learning. Students could complete this section individually, and their answers could be used as a portfolio item.

1. Magnets attract some types of metals. These metals stick to the magnet.
2. I noticed that all the objects that stuck to the magnets were made of metal or had metal parts.
3. Students' answers will vary, but students should add to their Non-contact Forces KWL charts (LM 3-8) in the L column that magnetism is a non-contact force that attracts certain types of metal. Their additional questions might include: What types of metal are attracted to magnets? Does the size of a magnet affect how well it attracts metal objects?

## DI Differentiating Instruction

### *For Reteaching*

The lesson is meant to be an open exploration of magnets and their properties. Students are meant to choose any items they wish to test and make their own predictions and observations. If students find the number of items provided too difficult to organize or too distracting, make the activity more structured by choosing only five items for them to test. You could eliminate any test items made of aluminum for now, to help them sort the items more easily and not confuse them when it comes to answering Communicate question 2.

## Assessment *for* Learning

| What to Look for in Student Work | What to Do |
|---|---|
| Students should demonstrate an understanding that magnets attract only certain types of metal and not other substances. | • Oral questioning and monitoring of written work in the Communicate section can provide proof of student learning. |

# 5 Magnets and Poles

| Time |
| --- |
| 40 min |

| Vocabulary |
| --- |
| • attract<br>• magnetic<br>• non-magnetic<br>• magnetic field |

| Line Masters |
| --- |
| • LM 3-11 |

## Indicator Assessment Chart

| Indicator | Assessment Opportunities |
| --- | --- |
| **ME3.1 e.** Compare the characteristics and effects of different types and shapes of magnets (e.g., horseshoe, disc, bar, cylindrical, and block), including the location and type of magnetic poles (if any exist), and the shape of magnetic field produced by the magnet. | • Work On It, p. 94<br>• Communicate, p. 95, q. 3 |
| **ME3.2 f.** Explain safety procedures to be followed when interacting with magnetic and static electric forces. | • Work On It, p. 94 |

## Lesson Goal

To find out if magnets attract other magnets

## Background Information

Scientists believe that the rotation of Earth and the fact that its core is composed of iron and nickel cause the magnetic field that surrounds it. Earth behaves as if a very large bar magnet is located at its centre.

The space around a magnet where magnetic attraction occurs is referred to as a magnetic force field or magnetic field. It is strongest near the ends, or poles, of a magnet, but it also extends into the area around the magnet.

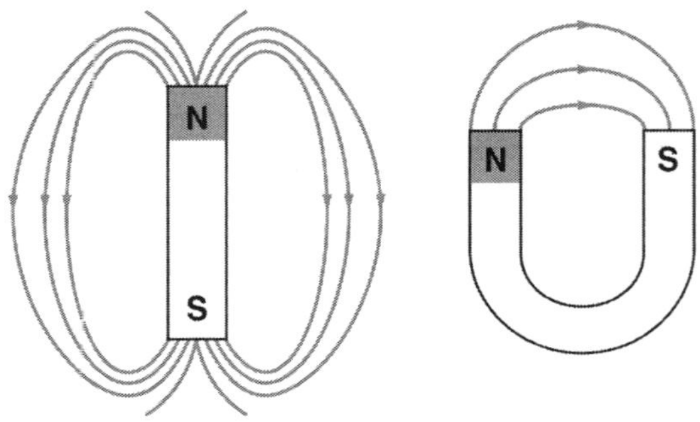


The opposite poles of two magnets attract each other. Therefore, the north pole and south pole of two magnets pull toward each other. Like poles of two magnets repel each other. Therefore, the north poles of two magnets will push away from each other, and the south poles of two magnets will push away from each other.

Attraction and repulsion can be used to determine the polarity of a magnet of unknown polarity. If a magnetized object (such as students' homemade magnet) is placed near, but not touching, one end of a hanging magnet, the hanging magnet will swing toward an unlike pole. Similarly, a hanging magnet will swing away from a like pole.

## Curriculum Connections

In this lesson, students have the opportunity to develop skills and concepts in these areas:

### *Arts Education*

CP3.8 b. Apply understanding of contour lines to form the outline of an object.
CP3.8 a. Observe visual details, and include details to enhance depictions of animals, people, and objects.

## Misconceptions

The north and south labelling of magnets' ends can cause confusion. Students wonder why a magnet's north pole would be attracted to Earth's north pole, since they have just learned that like poles repel. The confusion comes from the labelling of the magnet ends. If a bar magnet is suspended at the centre of the bar by a piece of string, the end that turns to point north is the "north-seeking" pole of the magnet. This pole is usually labelled "north." "North-seeking" is a better term to use; it explains the "opposites attract" observation. (The north-seeking pole of a magnet is really the south pole, of course, since two north poles (Earth's and the magnet's) would not attract each other.) This explanation is too complex a concept at the grade 3 level, but the terminology "north-seeking" and "south-seeking" should be reinforced to help students understand the concept when they study magnets in higher grades.

## Get Started ▶

- Preview the text as a whole class to identify new terms and activate prior knowledge to help infer what these new terms might mean.
- Read the Get Started text with students and have them interpret the non-fiction features, such as pictures and captions. Discuss the captions regarding north and south poles really being north-seeking and south-seeking.
- Discuss any questions students may have about the information on this page, and ask questions to elicit retelling and summarizing of the information.

| Time |
| --- |
| 30 min |
| **Learning Context** |
| inquiry |
| **Level of Inquiry** |
| structured |
| **Skills** |
| • making models<br>• observing<br>• interpreting<br>• comparing<br>• communicating<br>• predicting |
| **Grouping** |
| pairs and groups |
| **Materials and Equipment** |
| (per group)<br>• pencil<br>• pairs of a variety of magnets<br>• magnetic drawing board |
| **Line Masters** |
| • LM 3-11 |

**SAFETY CAUTION!**

Do not drop magnets or snap them together. They may chip and small pieces may fly off.

## Work On It

### Purpose

To find how magnets react to other magnets and what the shape of their magnetic field looks like

### Activity Notes

- Allow students time to explore how magnets react when they are placed close to each other.
- Asking students during group work about how like or opposing ends of the magnets interact can help students clarify their understanding.
- Rather than drawing their own diagrams, students can use the diagrams on LM 3-11 Magnets and Poles and add arrows to indicate the direction each magnet moved in each configuration. Students' arrows should indicate that like poles moved toward each other and unlike poles moved away from each other.
- Magnetic drawing boards are available in toy stores or even in dollar stores. Since many students have them, you could ask them to bring theirs in from home.
- Using a magnetic drawing board to show the magnetic field is much cleaner than using iron filings on paper. The iron filings in the magnetic board are visible just below the board's surface.
- When students place a strong magnet in the middle of the magnetic drawing board, they will be able to see the normally invisible force field surrounding the magnet. Drawing a picture of the usually invisible force field will reinforce their understanding. Students can draw what they see on LM 3-11 Magnets and Poles.
- If the image of the magnetic field is not clear, try placing a few magnets end to end on the board to increase their pull on the filings.
- If magnetic drawing boards are not available, or if students can't bring a few from home, they can easily be made. Fill a clear CD case with a few tablespoons of iron filings. Close the case carefully and tape up all the sides so no filings fall out. The case will now show the magnet's field just as well as the drawing board.
- Whether using the magnetic board or iron filings in a CD case, the general shape of the magnetic field is shown below.

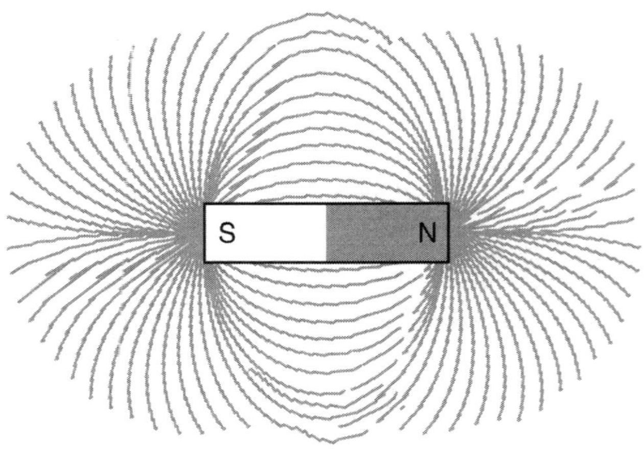

## Communicate

The Communicate section is another way to assess student learning. Students could answer these questions individually, and then add their work to their portfolios.

1. When the north pole of one magnet comes close to a south pole of another magnet, the two poles stick to each other.
2. When like poles come close, they push away from each other.
3. Bar magnets have poles at the ends. Disc magnets and ring magnets may have poles on either side. Magnets can even be in star or triangle shapes. The poles are in different places on each magnet. Magnets of different shapes have differently shaped invisible magnetic fields.

## DI Differentiating Instruction

### *For Enrichment*

Have students create art depicting the magnetic fields created by different types of magnets. They can trace the outlines of different magnets on black paper using chalk or pastels. Then they can then draw the shape of the magnetic field they observed when each magnet was placed on the magnetic board.

## Assessment *for* Learning

| What to Look for in Student Work | What to Do |
|---|---|
| Students can demonstrate an understanding that like poles repel and opposites attract. | • Student diagrams of how magnets react that include arrows to show the direction of the force will indicate understanding. They are also a good portfolio item. |
| Students can demonstrate an understanding that magnetic forces move from pole end to pole end, and that magnets are strongest at the poles. | • Questioning students regarding their diagrams of the magnetic field they viewed on the drawing board will give a good indication of their level of understanding. |

# 6 Which Magnet Is Stronger?

Page 96

**Time**

40 min

**Vocabulary**

- repel

**Line Masters**

- LM 3-12

## Indicator Assessment Chart

| Indicator | Assessment Opportunities |
|---|---|
| **ME3.1 c.** Compare the characteristics of contact, magnetic, and static electric forces, including the range over which they act, and propose methods of increasing or decreasing effects of these forces. | • Work On It, p. 96<br>• Communicate, p. 97, q. 3 |
| **ME3.1 f.** Predict and test the number of objects a magnet can pick up under different conditions (e.g., distance between magnet and object, number of identical magnets, solids between magnet and object) and develop simple conclusions about conditions that affect strength of magnetic forces. | • Work On It, p. 96<br>• Communicate, p. 97, q. 1–4 |

## Lesson Goal

To measure the strength of magnets

## Background Information

A magnet attracts paper clips in chain fashion. (Other small, magnetic metal objects will also form chains.) Each paper clip attracts the paper clip below it. This is referred to as induced magnetism. Magnetism is induced in the paper clips by the permanent magnet. If the first paper clip is removed from the permanent magnet, the whole chain of paper clips will fall apart.

## Curriculum Connections

In this lesson, students have the opportunity to develop skills and concepts in these areas:

***Mathematics***

SP3.1 Demonstrate understanding of first-hand data using tally marks, charts, lists, bar graphs, and line plots (abstract pictographs), through collecting, organizing, and representing.

## Get Started ▶

- Read the Get Started text with students, view the pictures, and read the captions.
- Discuss any questions students may have about the information on this page.
- Invite students to share connections to the text and their prior knowledge of magnet strength and of common uses for magnets.

**Time**

30 min

**Learning Context**

inquiry

**Level of Inquiry**

structured

**Skills**

- observing
- interpreting
- experimenting
- comparing
- measuring
- communicating
- controlling variables
- predicting
- collecting data

**Grouping**

pairs or groups

**Materials and Equipment**

(per group)
- 2 different magnets
- same-sized paper clips
- ruler
- pencils

**Line Masters**

- LM 3-12

## Work On It

### Purpose

To allow student to measure the strength of magnets and discover that distance rather than size limits magnetic strength

### Activity Notes

- Students work in pairs or groups to test the strength of magnetic fields with two variables: the size or shape of magnet, and the distance the magnet is placed from the paper clips.
- Use small metal paper clips, not the plastic-coated type.
- Provide a variety of magnets of different sizes and strengths for students to choose from so that they can see that size does not equal strength: the largest magnet may not be the strongest.
- Hobby stores often sell very small but strong magnets if your school does not have any.
- Students can record their predictions and their data on LM 3-12 Which Magnet Is Stronger?
- The number of paper clips picked up depends on the magnets used.

## Communicate

In this Communicate section, students analyze their results from the Work On It activity, and then compare their results with those of other groups. After the smaller groups have completed the questions, have larger groups discuss their findings or rate all the magnets used by strength. Display their findings.

1. Students' answers may vary. Responses should indicate that they analyzed their results and concluded whether their prediction about which magnet was the stronger was accurate.
2. Big magnets are not always stronger. If students ask why, explain that the strength of a magnet depends on the amount of magnetic material it has. A magnet can be made bigger by adding material that does not act as a magnet.
3. The farther away the magnet was from the paper clips, the fewer paper clips it picked up.
4. Students' answers may vary. Responses should indicate that their prediction of how many clips two magnets will pick up is roughly based on their observations of how many clips one magnet picks up.

### BUILD ON WHAT YOU KNOW

Students now know that magnetism can work from a distance to pull or push objects, as seen with like poles. Referring students to the last two experiments they completed can help them plan how they could get their boat or sled to move without touching it. Ideas can be recorded on LM 3-9 Build On What You Know.

## DI Differentiating Instruction

### *For Enrichment*

Have students engage in independent research into how magnets are used in industry and toys, as illustrated in the photos and captions on page 96 of the student book.

## Assessment *for* Learning

| What to Look for in Student Work | What to Do |
| --- | --- |
| Students can identify that magnet size does not affect magnetic strength but that distance can limit magnet strength. | • Monitor student discussion in the Communicate section of the lesson to assess the level of student understanding. |

# 7 Can You Make a Magnet?

Page 98

**Time**

40 min

**Vocabulary**

- magnetized

**Line Masters**

- LM 3-13
- LM 3-14

## Indicator Assessment Chart

| Indicator | Assessment Opportunities |
|---|---|
| **ME3.1 d.** Group materials according to criteria such as their attraction to magnets and ability to be magnetized, based on personal observation. | • Communicate, p. 99, q. 1–4 |
| **ME3.2 f.** Explain safety procedures to be followed when interacting with magnetic and static electric forces. | • Work On It, p. 99 |

## Lesson Goal

To find out if objects can be made into magnets

## Background Information

If a magnet, such as a bar magnet, is cut in half, both halves have north and south poles. If you keep dividing these magnets, each piece will have two poles. This means that magnetism is a property of the smallest particles in the magnet. The pull of a magnet is actually caused by the movement of particles called electrons, which surround the nucleus of every atom. These movements generate tiny magnetic fields. In most materials, these magnetic fields are aligned randomly, so they balance each other out and the material does not show any magnetism. When the electrons' magnetic fields are aligned, the material becomes magnetized.

Objects made from iron, nickel, or cobalt can be made into magnets. Stroking one of these objects with a magnet causes the electrons' magnetic fields within the metals to align. The object becomes a temporary magnet.

Not all metals are capable of being magnetized. Aluminum and copper, two common metals that students will have encountered, cannot be magnetized.

Canadian nickels, dimes, and quarters made before the year 2000 contain 25 percent or more nickel. The remainder of each coin is copper. Even this amount of nickel is enough to render these coins magnetic if they are touched by a magnet. (After 2000, the only nickel in nickels and quarters is in the plating (approximately 2 percent), and dimes are only 2.5 percent nickel. This is not enough to render them magnetic.)

## Curriculum Connections

In this lesson, students have the opportunity to develop skills and concepts in these areas:

***Social Studies***

RW3.3 a. Evaluate the ways in which technologies have impacted daily life: recognize that technology includes more than electronics (e.g., paper, forging steel, manufacturing, vehicles, making cloth, products created for construction).

## Misconceptions

Students often believe that all metals can be attracted to magnets, and therefore can be induced into magnetism. Only iron, nickel, and cobalt are classified as magnetic. Steel, manufactured from iron ore, is also magnetic. Magnetic metals are the only ones that can be induced into magnetism. Aluminum and copper, two common metals that students will have encountered, are not magnetic, so they will not become magnetized. This investigation should help students correct this misunderstanding.

**Time**

30 min

**Learning Context**

inquiry

**Level of Inquiry**

structured

**Skills**

- classifying
- inferring
- observing
- interpreting
- communicating
- controlling variables

**Grouping**

pairs

**Materials and Equipment**

(per group)
- iron nail
- magnet
- paper clips
- penny
- nickel
- quarter
- aluminum foil
- pencils
- aluminum pop can tab

**Line Masters**

- LM 3-13

## Get Started ▶

- Read the Get Started text with students, view the pictures, and read the captions.
- Discuss any questions students may have about the information on this page.
- Invite students to share connections to the text and prior knowledge about magnet strength and how magnets are used in society.

## Work On It

### Purpose

To allow students to predict and explore which common household items may be induced into magnetism

### Activity Notes

- Students will need to stroke each item quite a few times to magnetize it. Make sure students stroke the item in one direction only, or the item will not become magnetized.
- After students have tried to magnetize a couple of items and see how it is done, you may wish to give each pair of students a second magnet. Then both students can prepare and test the remaining items for magnetism, which reduces the time needed to complete the investigation.

**SAFETY CAUTION!**

Do not put magnets near electronic items, such as computer screens, credit cards, and CD, DVD, and MP3 players. Magnets may damage them permanently.

- Warn students that if they drop or bump the items they are trying to magnetize, any magnetism accumulated in the item will disappear. Suggest that they stand while stroking the magnet down each item. This reduces the chance of students accidentally bumping the item against desk or table or dropping the items. Remind them that if they do drop or bump the item, they have to start stroking the item all over again.
- You may wish to give them LM 3-13 Can You Make a Magnet? to record their observations.
- Circulate during group work and question students about what they have discovered. This can help clarify for them that some metals are magnetic and others are not.

## Additional Activity

As an extension activity, students can magnetize a nail using the electric current from a battery. They can follow the instructions on LM 3-14 Make Your Own Electromagnet.

## Communicate

Collecting students' answers may help assess student understanding, as would a class discussion of the Communicate questions. The last question introduces the next lesson on types of magnets.

1.

| Magnetized Objects | Non-magnetized Objects |
|---|---|
| Nail | Penny |
| Paper clip | Aluminum foil |
| Nickel | Pencil |
| Quarter | Aluminum pop can tab |

2. Students' answers may vary. Items that did not become magnetized were made of copper or aluminum.
3. Not all metals can be magnetized. Only certain metals can be induced.
4. The nail magnet was no longer magnetized after being dropped.

## DI Differentiating Instruction

### *For Reteaching*

If students are having trouble concluding that only certain metals are magnetic, refer them back to the Get Started section in Lesson 5. Rereading and even retesting some of the metal items may help them to see that only certain metals are attracted to magnets.

## Assessment *for* Learning

| What to Look for in Student Work | What to Do |
|---|---|
| Students demonstrate an understanding that certain metals can be induced into magnetism and that others cannot. | • Have students complete the Communicate questions, and/or have a class discussion to gauge student understanding. |

# 8 Types of Magnets

Page 100

| Time |
|---|
| 40 min |

| Vocabulary |
|---|
| • natural magnets<br>• temporary magnets<br>• permanent magnets |

| Line Masters |
|---|
| • LM 3-15 |

## Indicator Assessment Chart

| Indicator | Assessment Opportunities |
|---|---|
| **ME3.2 a.** Investigate how magnets are used at home, school, and in business and industrial applications (e.g., refrigerator magnet, magnetic cupboard door latches, credit card magnetic strip, radio speakers, navigation, motorized devices, scrap yard crane, magnetic levitation trains, jewellery, tools, and toys). | • Work On It, p. 100 |
| **ME3.2 b.** Classify magnets that are used at home, school, and in business and industrial applications as natural, temporary, and permanent. | • Communicate, p. 101, q. 1–4 |

## Lesson Goal

To find and sort different types of magnets

## Background Information

Natural magnets are magnets that occur in nature. A natural magnet has two unique properties: certain metals, such as iron, will cling to it, and when allowed to swing freely, it will align itself with Earth's magnetic poles. Any substance that displays these two properties without having been artificially altered is a natural magnet. Lodestone, a form of magnetite, is the most common natural magnet.

Permanent artificial magnets are the ones people are most familiar with. They have been created by people. Permanent magnets have strong magnetic fields that do not fade over time. Permanent magnets are made from "hard" magnetic metal alloys, such as alnico and ferrite. These materials are processed in a powerful magnetic field, which aligns their internal structure and makes them very hard to demagnetize.

These materials can be formed into different shapes so that their poles are in specific positions. For example, a circular ring magnet can be made to have the north pole on the inner surface of the ring and the south pole on the outer surface, or vice versa, depending on what it is used for.

Temporary magnets act in the same way as permanent magnets but only when they are within a strong magnetic field. They lose their magnetism as soon as the magnetic field disappears. Temporary magnets are dependent on some outside factor to create the field.

A simple example of this is a paper clip that can attract another paper clip because the first is touching a magnet. As soon as the first clip is removed from the magnet, it can no longer attract the second paper clip. The first paper clip was a temporary magnet because it was within the magnetic field of the magnet.

Electromagnets are always temporary because they can't function without electric current. They are made of a wire tightly wound around a metal core. A magnetic field is created when electric current is passed through the wire coil. But as soon as the current is stopped the magnetic field disintegrates. Electromagnets are the strongest type of magnet and they have many industrial applications. They are used to lift cars in scrap yards and to make school bells ring.

## Curriculum Connections

In this lesson, students have the opportunity to develop skills and concepts in these areas:

### *Social Studies*

RW3.3 a. Evaluate the ways in which technologies have impacted daily life: recognize that technology includes more than electronics (i.e. paper, forging steel, manufacturing, vehicles, making cloth, products created for construction).

## Get Started ▶

- Preview the text for the non-fiction feature, bolded new terms. Invite comments and connections about what type of magnet students created in the last lesson.
- Read the Get Started text with students. Pause after the definition of a temporary magnet to allow students to confirm their earlier thinking. Then continue reading to the end, view the pictures, and read the captions.
- Discuss any questions students may have about the information on this page.
- Invite students to share their connections to the text and prior knowledge about magnet strength and how magnets are used in society. For each example, ask students what type of magnet they think it is. Refer them to the electromagnet and the magnetic toy shown in the beginning of Lesson 6, if they are unable to think of any others.
- A good website for students to discover examples of magnets is www.fossweb.com/modules3-6/MagnetismandElectricity/index.html.

| Time |
| --- |
| 20 min |
| **Learning Context** |
| inquiry |
| **Level of Inquiry** |
| structured |
| **Skills** |
| • classifying<br>• inferring<br>• observing<br>• comparing<br>• communicating |
| **Grouping** |
| pairs or groups |
| **Materials and Equipment** |
| (per group)<br>• pencils<br>• paper |
| **Line Masters** |
| • LM 3-15 |

## Work On It

### Purpose

To allow students to identify magnets used in daily life and technology, and to then sort them by type: natural, permanent, or temporary

### Activity Notes

- Student pairs identify the magnets in the illustration, and then decide whether each example is a natural, temporary, or permanent magnet.
- Some students may have trouble identifying magnets in their environments other than fridge magnets. Refer them back to the Get Started in Lesson 4, which states that magnets are in motors. Then ask them to name appliances that have motors (blenders, lawn mowers, coffee grinders, chainsaws, etc.).
- Students may get confused about motors. Motors have both a permanent magnet and an electromagnet in them. Electromagnets are temporary magnets. So, motors have both types of magnets.
- Students can record and sort their examples of magnets by type on LM 3-15 Magnet Examples.

## Additional Activity

Students may not be aware of all the places that magnets are used in their daily lives. Display the webpage www.fossweb.com/modules3-6/MagnetismandElectricity/index.html to the whole class using a projector or interactive whiteboard. The Kitchen Magnets activity allows students to explore the illustrations to find magnets in their kitchens. Stress to students that all electromagnets are temporary because they work only when an electric current is on. Thus, the electromagnets can be turned on and off.

## Communicate

1. Student lists will vary but may include backpack closure, fridge magnets, magnetic tool bar holding tools on wall, magnet cupboard door closure, TV, DVD, magnetic utensil holder in kitchen, computer screen, key holder, paper clips, loadstone or magnetite rock, nail hanging off hammer, and screw hanging off screwdriver.
2. Students' answers may vary, but tables could include the following:

| Natural Magnets | Temporary Magnets | Permanent Magnets |
| --- | --- | --- |
| Magnetite rock<br>Magnetite paper clips | Nail<br>Screw<br>Electromagnet from Lesson 6 | Backpack closure<br>Cupboard door closure<br>Fridge magnets<br>TV /DVD/computer screen<br>Utensil holder<br>Magnetite paper clips |

3. Student suggestions of magnets used at home or in a business may vary but could include the following:

| Natural Magnets | Temporary Magnets | Permanent Magnets |
| --- | --- | --- |
| | School bell<br>Doorbell | Magnetic screwdrivers<br>Door clasp on a TV stand |

4. Students' answers may vary but could include the following:

| Natural Magnets | Temporary Magnets | Permanent Magnets |
| --- | --- | --- |
| | Fire alarm bell<br>Buzzers on appliances | Compass needle<br>Some types of can openers |

## DI Differentiating Instruction

### *For ELL*

Get students to practice English by explaining science concepts by using the think/pair/share strategy. Give students time to write a response to summarize the Work On It, Then give some additional time for them to discuss it with their neighbour before sharing their conclusion with the class. The think/pair/share technique increases student participation and involvement, and is a particularly effective way of encouraging English language learners to express science concepts in English.

## Assessment *for* Learning

| What to Look for in Student Work | What to Do |
| --- | --- |
| Students can identify and distinguish between natural, temporary, and permanent magnets in the world around them | • Monitoring student completion of the chart in the Communicate section will give a good indication of students' understanding. |

# 9 Do Magnetic Forces Act Through Materials?

Page 102

| Time |
| --- |
| 80 min |

| Line Masters |
| --- |
| • LM 3-16<br>• LM 3-17 |

## Indicator Assessment Chart

| Indicator | Assessment Opportunities |
| --- | --- |
| **ME3.1 b.** Demonstrate how contact and non-contact forces are able to cause objects to start moving, speed up, slow down, and stop; cause moving objects to change direction; and cause changes to the shape of objects. | • Communicate, p. 103, q. 2 |
| **ME3.1 f.** Predict and test the number of objects a magnet can pick up under different conditions (e.g., distance between magnet and object, number of identical magnets, solids between magnet and object) and develop simple conclusions about conditions that affect strength of magnetic forces. | • Work On It, p. 102<br>• Communicate, p. 103, q. 1, 3 |
| **ME3.2 i.** Investigate methods of using magnetic and static electric forces to create artistic expressions (e.g., mobiles, kinetic sculptures, painting, and drama). | • Work On It, p. 102<br>• Communicate, p. 103, q. 2 |
| **ME3.2 j.** Generate new questions from what has been learned about applications of magnetic and static electric forces. | • Communicate, p. 103, q. 3 |

## Lesson Goal

To investigate if magnetic forces can act through objects

## Background Information

Magnetic field lines must terminate on the opposite pole. This means that even if a non-magnetic object, such as a block of wood, is placed between the poles of a horseshoe magnet, the magnetic field will not change. Even though magnetic field lines cannot be blocked, they can be re-routed around an object. This is done by surrounding an object that needs to be protected with a specially designed magnetic material. The magnet's magnetic field will flow along this material, avoiding the object the material is shielding. The magnetic field lines are allowed to terminate on opposite poles, but the shielding redirects them and they travel to the pole by a different route.

## Time

30–40 min

## Learning Context

inquiry

## Level of Inquiry

structured

## Skills

- observing
- experimenting
- communicating
- controlling variables
- predicting

## Grouping

pairs or groups

## Materials and Equipment

(per group)
- materials to test such as cloth, plastic, and cardboard
- books, or other heavy items to act as weights
- paper clip
- wand, horseshoe, or bar magnet
- sheet of unlined paper
- pencils
- variety of liquid paint colours

## Line Masters

- LM 3-16

**SAFETY CAUTION!**

Do not go under or between the desks or tables. The books could fall if bumped.

## Curriculum Connections

In this lesson, students have the opportunity to develop skills and concepts in these areas:

***Arts Education***

CP3.8. Create art works using a variety of visual art concepts (e.g., contour lines), forms (e.g., drawing, sculpture), and media (e.g., pencils, pastels, found objects).

## Get Started ▶

- Read the Get Started text with students, view the pictures, and read the captions.
- Discuss any questions students may have about the information on this page.

## Work On It

### Purpose

To provide students with an opportunity to discover that magnetic fields act through various materials

### Activity Notes

- Possible test materials include a glass cake pan, a piece of cardboard, a sheet of plywood, or even the table or desk top, a cookie sheet, a piece of cloth, and a piece of paper. A strong magnet will move a paper clip across these materials.
- Students set up each test material across a span between two desks or tables, using books to secure it on either side. They then place a paper clip on the material's surface and try to move it across the surface using a **strong** magnet on the underside of the material.
- You may wish to test the magnets ahead of time to make sure they are strong enough to pass through all the materials. School magnets may weaken over time or if improperly stored.
- Students can use LM 3-16 Magnetic Forces to record their predictions and observations.
- In the last part of the activity, students create art without touching the paint, using the paper clip on top of the paper and the magnet below. They should be able to move and mix the paint into a creation of their making.
- Placing the paper on a stiff piece of cardboard or plastic tray will keep the paper from sagging or falling under the weight of the liquid paint.
- While they are creating their art, prompt them to describe their creation and come up with a name for it. You may be surprised with their creativity.

## Additional Activity

Students can investigate the limits of the strength of a magnet's magnetic field (LM 3-17 Magnet Challenge). Students use a strong magnet to fish a paper clip out of a glass of water. They repeat the procedure moving the magnet farther away each time until they can no longer raise the paper clip out of the glass.

## Communicate

Students should record their findings individually.

1. Students' answers may vary depending on which types of materials students tested. A strong magnet should be able to move a paper clip through all the items mentioned in the activity notes, including items such as plastic, wood, glass, cloth, and paper.
2. I could make art because the magnetic forces helped me to move the paper clip anywhere I wanted it to go on the paper. So, I was able to move it through the paint and make patterns.
3. Students' entries on their KWL charts (LM 3-8) will vary but may include: The magnetic field of a strong magnet can pass through many different materials. A new question might be: Is there anything that a magnetic field cannot act through?

## DI Differentiating Instruction

### *For Enrichment*

Challenge students to find a material that a magnet cannot move a paper clip through. Leave some items and extra magnets out for open exploration, and remind students about how magnets responded to each other in Lesson 5. Students may conclude that a magnet's magnetic field does not pass through the force field of another magnet by trying to lay a clip on top of one magnet and placing a second magnet underneath it, and seeing if the clip will move.

## Assessment *for* Learning

| What to Look for in Student Work | What to Do |
|---|---|
| Students conclude that magnetic fields can pass through most materials. | • Monitor student responses to the Communicate questions to assess learning. |
| Students can create art using magnetic forces. | • Collect student art. Ask students to name their piece, and discuss or write about what their art depicts. |

# 10 What Can a Compass Tell You? *Page 104*

| Time |
|---|
| 40 min |
| **Line Masters** |
| • LM 3-18<br>• LM 3-19 |

## Indicator Assessment Chart

| Indicator | Assessment Opportunities |
|---|---|
| **ME3.2 c.** Explore how magnetic compasses can provide evidence for and information about magnetic fields, including those created by current traveling through a conductor, and Earth's magnetic field. | • Work On It, p. 104<br>• Communicate, p. 105, q. 1–3 |
| **ME3.2 f.** Explain safety procedures to be followed when interacting with magnetic and static electric forces. | • Work On It, p. 104 |

## Lesson Goal

To explore how a compass can show non-contact forces that you cannot see

## Background Information

Scientists believe Earth's rotation and its iron and nickel core cause Earth's magnetic field. Earth behaves as if a very large bar magnet is located at its centre.

One of the first uses for lodestone (a naturally occurring magnetic form of magnetite) came from the Chinese. They discovered that when lodestone was hung by a thread, it always aligned itself north–south. They used this discovery to help navigate their ships.

A compass needle aligns with Earth's magnetic field. As mentioned in the Background Information for Lesson 5, the end that points north is the north-seeking pole of the compass needle, which is a magnet. This latter term is the preferred one to use; it explains the "opposites attract" observation: The north-seeking pole of a magnet is really the south pole, since two north poles repel each other. It is thought that the poles of a magnet were named before repulsion and attraction were really understood.

*continued→*

**traditional KNOWLEDGE**

First Nations peoples did not use compasses to tell direction. They believed in observing nature carefully, and they had intimate knowledge of directionality from the animals around them. First Nations peoples were traditionally hunting and gathering societies, migrating from place to place following the seasonal movements of wild game animals. Migratory animals act as living compasses; they move north to south and back, depending on the season.

Scientists theorize that these animals may have a sort of magnetic sense. It helps to explain the migration patterns of animals such as buffalo, whales, butterflies, and wildfowl. Special minerals have been found in the cells of these animals' brains, which may act like tiny magnets pointing these animals north.

## Curriculum Connections

In this lesson, students have the opportunity to develop skills and concepts in these areas:

### *Social Studies*

DR3.3 b. Compare the beliefs of various communities around the world regarding living on and with the land.

**Get Started ▶**

- Read the Get Started text with students, view the pictures, and read the captions.
- Refer students back to Lesson 5 to make connections to prior learning about Earth acting like a giant magnet.
- Discuss any questions students may have about the information on this page.
- Allow students to share any experiences they have had with compasses.

| Time |
|---|
| 20 min |
| **Learning Context** |
| inquiry |
| **Level of Inquiry** |
| structured |
| **Skills** |
| • observing<br>• interpreting<br>• communicating<br>• predicting |
| **Grouping** |
| pairs or groups |
| **Materials and Equipment** |
| (per group)<br>• 2 small magnetic compasses for each partner<br>• large bar magnet to share<br>• earbuds and portable music player, or computer and speakers<br>• pencils |
| **Line Masters** |
| • LM 3-18 |

**SAFETY CAUTION!**

Follow your classroom's safety rules. Never touch electrical wall outlets or wires plugged into outlets. Only use DC current for this activity, not AC current. AC current is dangerous.

## Work On It

### Purpose

To allow students to see how a compass can show the magnetic field lines around a magnet, and to realize that current-carrying wires create a magnetic field around them, which can change the direction a compass is pointing, making navigation difficult

### Activity Notes

- The purpose of the experiment is show that electricity creates a magnetic field. The best way to show it is to use the DC current that flows through the wires from an MP3 player to earbuds or from a computer to its speakers. Most other items in your classroom use AC current, which is dangerous to explore. As well, it does not show the same results because the current alternates direction, and the compass needle would swing back and forth with each alteration of current direction.
- If earbuds and a music player such as an MP3 player or iPod are not available, you can use a computer and speakers and the wire that connects them. There need not be a set for each group. They can be placed in a central spot and groups can access them as needed
- Students can use LM 3-18 What Can a Compass Tell You? to record their predictions and observations.
- As students do step 2, allow them to explore how the magnetic field affects the compass's needle. Suggest they place the compasses at different distances from the bar magnet and at different points along the sides and ends of the magnet, and so on.
- When students place all four compasses along one side of the magnet, the needles should align from one end of the magnet to the other.

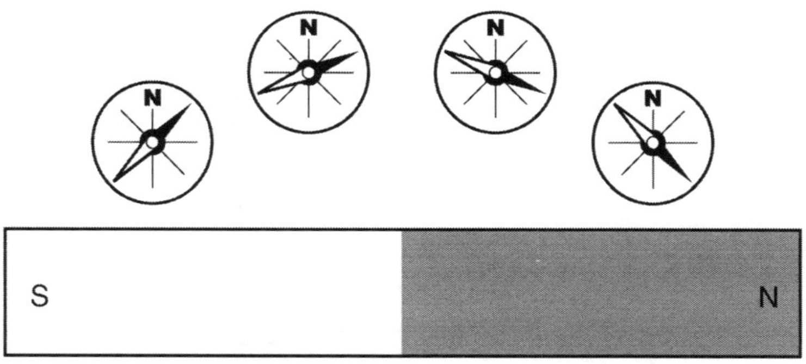


- The speaker wires or earbud wires should be laid out straight, and the computer or music player should be turned on at a very low volume.
- When students place the compass near their earbud or speaker wires, they should see that the compass's needle lines up perpendicular to the wire.
- Once they have observed the needle moving, tell them it is important to know that electricity makes a compass move. If you are using a compass to find your way when you are lost, and you are near electrical wires, the compass needle will no longer point north. The compass becomes unreliable.

## Additional Activity

Students can make their own compasses out of magnetized sewing needles. Give students LM 3-19 Make a Compass. Once they have constructed the compasses and observed them pointing north, have them place their compass needles so that they point east–west and then let go. They can then observe the needles return to the north–south position.

### Communicate

1. When I lined up the compasses, all the needles lined up to show the invisible force field from north to south poles. This is similar to magnetism moving through other materials to make the paper clip move. The compass did not touch the magnet, but the needle still moved.
2. When I put the compass near the earbud wire, the compass needle pointed toward the wire, at a right angle to the wire.
3. I knew it was a non-contact force because the compass needle moved even though it wasn't touching the magnet or the wire.

### BUILD ON WHAT YOU KNOW

Students are asked whether a compass would be a useful addition to their boats or sleds. Ask students to think carefully about what a compass does and whether that will help them move the vehicle. Students may want to include one as a navigation aid for the vehicle. Check that students don't mistakenly think it will help move their vehicle.

## DI Differentiating Instruction

### *For Reteaching*

If students need extra opportunities to see how magnets can show the magnetic field created by a bar magnet, set up a computer to display the website http://phet.colorado.edu/en/simulation/magnets-and-electromagnets. On this website, they can move a virtual compass around a bar magnet to see how the needle moves when the compass is placed in different locations.

## Assessment *for* Learning

| What to Look for in Student Work | What to Do |
| --- | --- |
| Students can describe how a compass can help detect a non-contact force field. | • Look at students' answers to the Communicate questions. These may be an item to keep for a portfolio of learning. |

# 11 What Is Static Electricity?

Page 106

| Time |
|---|
| 40 min |
| **Vocabulary** |
| • charged |
| **Line Masters** |
| • LM 3-20 |

## Indicator Assessment Chart

| Indicator | Assessment Opportunities |
|---|---|
| **ME3.1 a.** Pose questions related to the characteristics of magnetic and static electric forces (e.g., Do all magnets attract objects? Do all magnets have a North pole? Why do I get a shock when I rub my shoes on a carpet and touch a door knob?). | • Communicate, p. 107, q. 3 |
| **ME3.1 b.** Demonstrate how contact and non-contact forces are able to cause objects to start moving, speed up, slow down, and stop; cause moving objects to change direction; and cause changes to the shape of objects. | • Work On It, p. 107 |
| **ME3.1 g.** Investigate how charged materials interact with each other and with other charged and uncharged objects. | • Work On It, p. 107<br>• Communicate, p. 107, q. 1, 2 |
| **ME3.2 g.** Describe the effects of static electric forces in their daily lives (e.g., static cling, sparks when touching metal objects after walking across carpeted surfaces, and photocopiers). | • Communicate, p. 107, q. 3, 4 |

## Lesson Goal

To find out about the force of static electricity

## Background Information

The particle (atomic) theory of matter explains static electricity. This is beyond grade 3 level of understanding. The following information is included here for you. Scientists believe that all matter is composed of particles (atoms) that are held together by nuclear force. The negatively charged electrons in an atom orbit around a nucleus that is composed of positively charged protons and neutral (without an electrical charge) neutrons. Atoms are normally electrically neutral because the number of electrons (negative) is the same as the number of protons (positive) and the positive and negative charges balance each other. Some substances lose electrons easily, while others gain electrons easily.

*continued→*

When you rub a wool cloth with a balloon, the atoms in the cloth lose some of their electrons and thus they become positively charged. The balloon's atoms gain these electrons and they become negatively charged. Static electricity is the imbalance of positive and negative charges. The balloon will then attract any items that are neutral or positively charged, such as small pieces of tissue, hair, bits of polystyrene foam, a sweater or scarf, and even other items, such as a wall. These observations are similar to the behaviour of magnets, which also attract and repel.

Static electricity experiments work best when the air is dry. In winter, the air is very dry. In the spring and summer, the air is more humid. The water vapour in the air helps electrons move off objects more quickly, so they cannot build up as big a static charge.

## Curriculum Connections

In this lesson, students have the opportunity to develop skills and concepts in these areas:

***Social Studies***

IN3.2 b. Give examples of traditions and practices that have endured over time in communities studied, and discuss why these are important.

## Misconceptions

Students often think that when they get a shock from a doorknob, it is the doorknob that gave them the shock. The opposite is true: they have become electrically (negatively) charged. The shock is the movement of the charge from their body to the doorknob.

**Get Started ▶**

- Read the Get Started text with the students, view the pictures, and read the captions.
- Discuss any questions students may have about the information on this page.
- Refer students to the photos on the page and invite discussion on prior knowledge, connections to their lives, or other reading they have done.

**!**

**traditional *KNOWLEDGE***

Northern lights have a strong spiritual significance, as do most natural phenomena. Many First Nations people, including the Dené, Cree, Saulteaux, and Dakota peoples, speak about the Northern lights with reverence. They are considered to be the "spirits of the people that have come before us." In other words, the spirits of deceased relatives who now travel the spirit road or the Milky Way to the other world. Teachers must ensure that students respect that belief even if it differs from their own.

There are many stories that Elders have described from their personal experiences that may frighten children. These stories aren't intended to scare, but rather are intended for an adult audience. Elders relate these stories to describe the power of the northern lights, as they understand them. Teachers must not retell these traditional stories unless express permission has been given to them to do so.

**Time**

20 min

**Learning Context**

inquiry

**Level of Inquiry**

structured

**Skills**

- observing
- interpreting
- experimenting
- comparing
- communicating
- controlling variables
- predicting

**Grouping**

pairs or groups

**Materials and Equipment**

(per group)
- 2 balloons
- piece of wool fabric
- objects to test, such as tissue and polystyrene foam bits, classroom walls, curtains, carpets, coats, and plastic and metal items

**Line Masters**

- LM 3-20

traditional ***KNOWLEDGE***

## Work On It

### Purpose

To give students the opportunity to find out what materials a negatively charged balloon is attracted to

### Activity Notes

- Students charge balloons and try to attract objects, such as bits of tissue, foam, and other items around the room, to the balloon. Allow time for open exploration and discovery during this activity. It will help keep them focused during future investigations.
- Most students this age know that they can make a balloon stick to a wall or use it to make their hair stand up, but may not realize there are many other items that will or will not be attracted to a charged balloon.
- By using small balloons, such as the ones used for water balloon tossing games, you can have balloons blown up ahead of time. These can be stored in a large resealable bag, out of sight, if necessary.
- You may wish to give students LM 3-20 What Is Static Electricity? to record their predictions and observations for the various test items.

## Additional Activity

To visualize how the charge on your body flows to other objects, display the website http://phet.colorado.edu/en/simulation/travoltage. The animation shows how particles flow from objects, into the body, and then from the body to a doorknob.

Another activity is to have students explore how traditional peoples around the world might view Auroras. For example, How do the Māori people of New Zealand view Auroras? Possible questions related to the development of this inquiry would include:

- How do Māori people view the Auroras in the southern hemisphere?
- In what ways are their views similar to First Nations in Saskatchewan?
- In what ways are their views different?
- Why would people use legends or stories to explain the natural world?
- Create a Venn diagram to compare and contrast Māori and First Nations views about Auroras.

The following websites provide information on the Aurora borealis:

- www.northernlightscentre.ca/northernlights.html: This page provides information on the scientific and cultural explanations of the Aurora borealis.
- www.webexhibits.org/causesofcolor/4C.html: This web page provides information on Aurora folklore.
- www.suite101.com/content/legends-behind-the-northern-lights-a12230: This page provides a list of explanations of the northern lights from various cultures around the world.

## Communicate

Students can work on the Communicate in pairs or groups to facilitate discussion of their KWL chart additions and to make connections between observations about magnetism and static electricity.

1. Students' answers may vary. A charged balloon will attract bits of tissue or paper; polystyrene; cereal; string; yarn; hair; some clothing, scarves, and toques, if their cotton content is low; and some curtains, carpets, and plastics.
2. The charged balloons acted like magnets because they attracted certain types of materials and made those items move without contact. Balloons and magnets are different because magnets only attract certain metals, but static electricity attracts many objects that are not metal.
3. Students' answers may vary, but should include the observations students made during the Work On It activity, such as static electricity can attract things the way a magnet does, static electricity is a non-contact force, and static electricity has an invisible force field like magnets have.
4. Students' KWL entries will vary but may include the following. Magnetic and static electric forces are the same as contact forces because they both can change an object's direction, shape, or speed. Static electricity and friction can both be created by two objects rubbing against one another. Static electricity and magnetism are different from contact forces because they do not have to touch the object to make it change direction or speed. They are both non-contact forces.

## DI Differentiating Instruction

### *For Reteaching*

If students are having trouble visualizing how a static charge accumulates and moves, display the website http://phet.colorado.edu/en/simulation/travoltage. The animation shows how particles flow from objects, into the body, and then from the body to a doorknob.

## Assessment *for* Learning

| What to Look for in Student Work | What to Do |
|---|---|
| Students understand that charged items gain particles and then can attract items. | • Monitor student discussion about their changes and additions to their KWL charts and their explanations for those changes. |
| Students understand that charged items can act in a similar manner to magnetic forces. | |

# 12 Charged Materials

Page 108

| Time |
| --- |
| 40 min |

**Vocabulary**

- attract
- repel

**Line Masters**

- LM 3-21

## Indicator Assessment Chart

| Indicator | Assessment Opportunities |
| --- | --- |
| **ME3.1 b.** Demonstrate how contact and non-contact forces are able to cause objects to start moving, speed up, slow down, and stop; cause moving objects to change direction; and cause changes to the shape of objects. | • Work On It, p. 108<br>• Communicate, p. 109, q. 3 |
| **ME3.1 g.** Investigate how charged materials interact with each other and with other charged and uncharged objects. | • Work On It, p. 108<br>• Communicate, p. 109, q. 1, 2 |
| **ME3.2 i.** Investigate methods of using magnetic and static electric forces to create artistic expressions (e.g., mobiles, kinetic sculptures, painting, and drama). | • Communicate, p. 109, q. 3 |

## Lesson Goal

To find out how charged materials interact with each other

## Background Information

Static electricity is the accumulation of electric charge on an object. Static electricity is electricity at rest (static). Current electricity refers to electrons moving through conductors such as wires. It is important that students realize that static electricity is not the same as the electricity in wires. The electrons are not flowing through a wire, but are resting on a body or object.

A Van de Graaff generator, shown in the Get Started section, uses a continuously moving belt to create friction. As a result, a very large electrostatic charge builds up on the hollow metal dome. It was invented in 1929 by physicist Robert Van de Graaff.

When you rub an item such as a balloon or polystyrene plate with a wool cloth, the cloth loses some of its electrons and becomes positively charged. The balloon gains these electrons and becomes negatively charged. Two negatively charged plates or balloons that are brought close together repel each other.

If you rub another balloon or plate with nylon, a material that is more likely to take a charge than give it, that balloon or plate will give up some of its electrons and become positively charged. Thus the two balloons or plates would have opposite charges. When brought close together, they will attract each other. Thus, electrically charged items behave like magnets: they attract objects that have opposite charges and repel objects that have like charges.

## Curriculum Connections

In this lesson, students have the opportunity to develop skills and concepts in these areas:

***Arts Education***

CP3.1 c. Create a wide variety of movements to a given stimuli.

**Get Started ▶**

- Read the Get Started text with the students, view the picture, and read the caption.
- Discuss any questions students may have about the information on this page.
- Refer students to the photo on student book page 108 and invite discussion on prior knowledge, connections to their lives, or about when their hair may have looked like the girl's in the photo.

| Time |
| --- |
| 20 min |
| **Learning Context** |
| inquiry |
| **Level of Inquiry** |
| structured |
| **Skills** |
| • observing<br>• interpreting<br>• experimenting<br>• comparing<br>• communicating<br>• controlling variables<br>• predicting |
| **Grouping** |
| pairs or groups |
| **Materials and Equipment** |
| (per group)<br>• 2 polystyrene foam plates<br>• 2 pieces of string about 10 cm long<br>• tape<br>• piece of wool fabric or fur<br>• drier sheet (optional)<br>• sink and water tap<br>• pencils |
| **Line Masters** |
| • LM 3-21 |

## Work On It

### Purpose

To allow students to experience and feel with their hands the attraction and repulsion that can occur between charged materials

### Activity Notes

- You may wish to give students LM 3-21 Charged Materials to record their predictions and observations.
- Tell students to hold onto the strings and not to hold onto the plate. They should also hold the strings close to the plate's edge. This will help stop the plate from spinning. The charged plates act like magnets: they spin so that their opposite poles align. If this is allowed to happen, students will not see two sides of the plates that have like charges repelling.
- Each plate should lose its charge after each test. This can be done by touching a plate with a hand or with a dryer sheet.
- For the test with the running water, make sure that the stream of water is quite thin. The thinner the stream, the easier it is to see the stream bending. A single sink and tap is sufficient because groups only need to use it for a few seconds to complete the test.
- In the first test, the charged plate and the uncharged plate attract each other.
- In the second test, the two charged plates repel each other.
- In the test with the charged plate and running water, the plate attracts the stream of water, which bends toward the charged plate.

## Communicate

1. The plates attracted each other when one was charged and one was not. The plates repelled each other when both were charged. The charged plate attracted the running water. Other items tested may attract or repel.
2. Yes, the charged plates acted like magnets. Sometimes they attracted each other and sometimes they repelled each other, just like magnets do.
3. Students' answers may vary, but the improvised movements should show how charged objects attract or repel, depending on the charge of each object.

### BUILD ON WHAT YOU KNOW

Students have learned that they can move a polystyrene plate by charging one or both plates. The like charges repelled and caused one plate to move away from another plate. The unlike charges caused the uncharged plate to move toward the charged plate. Perhaps they could build their toys out of polystyrene and use a charged polystyrene plate to move the toy. Remind students that they can record their ideas in LM 3-9 Build On What You Know.

## DI Differentiating Instruction

### *For Enrichment*

Students can experiment with attraction and repulsion using a charged balloon and aluminum can. If they place the can on its side, students can make the can roll by placing the charged balloon near it.

## Assessment *for* Learning

| What to Look for in Student Work | What to Do |
|---|---|
| Students will show that they understand that charged items can attract and repel in a manner similar to magnets. | • Check students' responses to the Communicate questions and watch their improvised movement routines. |

# 13 The Strength of Static Electricity *Page 110*

| Time |
|---|
| 40 min |
| **Line Masters** |
| • LM 3-22 |

## Indicator Assessment Chart

| Indicator | Assessment Opportunities |
|---|---|
| **ME3.1 c.** Compare the characteristics of contact, magnetic, and static electric forces, including the range over which they act, and propose methods of increasing or decreasing effects of these forces. | • Work On It, p. 111<br>• Communicate, p. 111, q. 2 |
| **ME3.1 h.** Demonstrate ways to use materials found in their environment (e.g., balloon, cotton, fur, wool, confetti, acetate strip, ebonite rod, and Scotch tape) to investigate conditions which affect the strength of static electric forces. | • Work On It, p. 111 |
| **ME3.1 i.** Make and record relevant observations during investigations to identify conditions (e.g., humidity, type of materials, and distance between charged objects) which affect the strength of static electric forces, and develop simple conclusions about these conditions. | • Work On It, p. 111<br>• Communicate, p. 111, q. 1 |
| **ME3.2 h.** Explain the purpose of technologies which are designed to minimize static electric forces (e.g., fabric softeners and dryer sheets, antistatic bags, chains hanging from combines, antistatic safety boots, grounding straps on cars, and dusters). | • Communicate, p. 111, q. 2 |
| **ME3.2 j.** Generate new questions from what has been learned about applications of magnetic and static electric forces. | • Communicate, p. 111, q. 3 |

## Lesson Goal

To investigate the strength of static electricity

## Background Information

Friction can cause static electricity. (Students learned this in the last investigation.) Certain conditions must be present for a static electric charge to build up. Dry air and dry surfaces are needed. In certain situations, such as refuelling a vehicle, a build-up of static charge can be very dangerous. Knowing how to limit static electricity can make your life safer and easier. There are various static control methods.

- Use a humidifier to add moisture to the air. This moisture will make the surface of the objects in your home more conductive, which will decrease the ability of things in your home to retain a static charge.
- Wear more cotton. Some materials have a tendency to lose electrons and become positively charged (air, skin, fur, glass, nylon, wool, silk, and aluminum). Other materials have a tendency to gain electrons and become negatively charged (Teflon, silicon, polystyrene, polyester, gold, and brass). Cotton is a neutral material, thus does not become charged at all.
- Wear shoes made of materials that have good conductivity, such as rubber-like polymers. These anti-static safety boots conduct static charges that accumulate on the body from the sole of the foot to the bottom of the boot. Basically, they ground the wearer so he or she does not retain any static charge.
- Add dryer sheets to the dryer. They contain a chemical that coats the surfaces of the clothing. This chemical makes the surface of the clothes slightly conductive. Conductive items do not hold onto a charge. They pass it on. If the clothes have no charge, there is no static cling.
- Use a grounding strap on a vehicle. This strap is usually made of a metal such as copper, aluminum, nickel or silver plate, in a braided or mesh wire that has good conductivity. It is supposed to drain static electricity off the car to the ground. It is supposed to prevent painful static shocks when exiting the vehicle and eliminate an electrostatic discharge, which could cause a fire when filling the fuel tank at a gas station. However, there is much debate about whether grounding straps actually work.
- The first photo on student book page 110 shows a person filling up a fuel tank from a tanker truck. In situations such as this, they do have the truck and the nozzle grounded to reduce the risk of sparks due to static charge accumulation.

## Curriculum Connections

In this lesson, students have the opportunity to develop skills and concepts in these areas:

### *Social Studies*

RW3.1 c. Describe ways in which communities help ensure basic human needs are met (e.g., food and water, shelter, clothing, education, safety).

## Get Started ▶

- Read the first paragraph of the Get Started text with students. Invite discussion on prior knowledge and connections to their lives. Most students will have stories about times they have gotten shocked or even given someone a shock.
- Have students look at the pictures of the fuel truck and the person at the gas pump. Have them brainstorm how static electricity might make each situation dangerous, and then share their ideas with the class.
- Read the second paragraph of the Get Started text with students, and the captions with the pictures below it. Invite discussion of their prior knowledge of ways to limit static electricity.
- Discuss students' questions about the information on this page.

**Time**

20 min

**Learning Context**

inquiry

**Level of Inquiry**

structured

**Skills**

- observing
- experimenting
- comparing
- measuring
- communicating
- controlling variables
- predicting

**Grouping**

pairs or groups

**Materials and Equipment**

(per group)
- balloon
- piece of wool fabric
- bare wall
- stopwatch
- pencils
- spray bottle of water

**Line Masters**

- LM 3-22

**SAFETY CAUTION!**
Students need to be reminded that spraying anything at another student is never safe, even if it is only water.

## Work On It

### Purpose

To give students an opportunity to investigate the strength of static electricity and factors that can affect the strength of static electricity

### Activity Notes

- Students charge a balloon and measure how long it stays put on a wall in three different situations: contact with the wall, no contact with the wall, and humidity around the site.
- The last test asks students to begin timing after you mist water in the area of the balloon. A water bottle that sprays a very fine mist works best. If you are comfortable with your students using the spray bottle responsibly, feel free to allow them to spray on their own. This makes it easier for groups to complete the activity, since they do not have to wait for an adult to mist the water above the balloon. Each group need not have a spray bottle. A couple at the front of the room that you can monitor and students can use to do one small spray would be sufficient.
- Students can record their data on LM 3-22 The Strength of Static Electricity.

## Communicate

1. Distance from the wall and humidity in the air both shortened the amount of time the balloon stayed still on the wall.
2. Students' answers may vary. Students should include at least two of the following: use a humidifier, use dryer sheets, and wear clothing that does not allow static electricity to build up.
3. Students should add new learning to their KWL charts about the effects of distance and humidity on the strength of a static charge, and how devices are used to eliminate static electric charges. They should also record any new questions they may have.

## DI Differentiating Instruction

### *For Enrichment*

Students could hypothesize whether the type of material the balloon is rubbed with affects the strength of the static charge. They can test the materials using steps 1 to 4 in the What You Will Do in the Work On It activity. Some materials they could test include cotton, dryer sheets, nylon, aluminum foil, or even their scarves or toques.

## Assessment *for* Learning

| What to Look for in Student Work | What to Do |
| --- | --- |
| Students can identify some ways to limit static electricity. | • Monitor student answers to Communicate question 2, as well as additions they make to their KWL charts in Communicate question 3. |

# 14 Static Electricity and You

Page 112

**Time**

40 min

**Vocabulary**

- Thunderbird

**Line Masters**

- LM 3-23
- LM 3-24
- LM 3-25

## Indicator Assessment Chart

| Indicator | Assessment Opportunities |
|---|---|
| **ME3.1 i.** Make and record relevant observations during investigations to identify conditions (e.g., humidity, type of materials, and distance between charged objects) which affect the strength of static electric forces, and develop simple conclusions about these conditions. | • Communicate, p. 113, q. 1 |
| **ME3.2 f.** Explain safety procedures to be followed when interacting with magnetic and static electric forces | • Work On It, p. 113<br>• Communicate, p. 113, q. 2 |

## Lesson Goal

To find out about static electricity in nature and how to stay safe when it occurs

## Background Information

Friction between water molecules in raindrops and hail inside clouds occurs as air currents cause them to move and rub together. This causes a build-up of static electric charge. Negative charges build up at the bottom of the cloud, while positive charges build up in the top of the cloud.

Negative charges from the cloud can jump suddenly to a nearby cloud, to a building, or to the ground. This rapid discharge of electricity causes the air to be heated to a very high temperature and light to be given off. This heat causes rapid expansion of the air, resulting in the crackling noise that we call thunder.

Benjamin Franklin invented the lightning rod in the mid-1700s. His famous kite experiment proved that lightning is an electric spark. He then used a metal strip to carry electricity to the ground if the building was struck by lightning. Today, lightning rods are pointed metal rods mounted on the roofs of buildings. A metal wire, such as copper, runs from the rod to the ground. A grounding rod attaches to the wire to the ground.

Without a lightning rod, if lightning hits a building, it will still find its way to the ground. However, it will likely cause a lot of damage to the structure and its contents on the way down. Some of the house and its contents, such as electrically powered machines (computers, etc.) can be destroyed or a fire could start.

A lightning rod offers lightning a path to the ground that does not pass through the structure and so prevents destruction. Conductors allow electricity to travel through them. A lightning rod is a conductor. Metals are the best conductors. Water is also a conductor. Non-conductors are materials that allow little or no electricity to travel through them. Non-conductors are called insulators. Wood, paper, glass, plastic, and rubber are examples of insulators.

traditional ***KNOWLEDGE***

First Nations people describe natural phenomena in spiritual terms. Their understanding of lightning is no different. These cultural teachings describe how they have understood for millennia lightning, its properties, and its power. These cultural explanations have very strong value and validity to enable them to survive.

The figure of a powerful being called Thunderbird is the heart for traditional explanations of lightning. Thunderbird is a very mighty spirit that brings the rain and lightning. It is common to all First Nations cultures in Canada, and perhaps in some American groups. Thunderbird is typically described as a giant winged manifestation, like an eagle.

Descriptions of Thunderbird's ability to produce lightning and its role in First Nations stories vary from nation to nation. Plains Cree, the Saulteaux, and the Dené in Saskatchewan believe that lightning comes from Thunderbird's eyes. Eastern Anishinabe teach that lightning is produced by the flapping of its wings. Among the Saulteaux, Thunderbird is supposed to be the mortal enemy of a great serpent that lives in underwater channels under the earth. Their enmity explains why light sometimes strikes bodies of water. Thunderbird's attraction to water explains why storms appear more powerful over large bodies of water. Many First Nations peoples believe that Thunderbird heralds the first rains of spring, and that spring doesn't truly arrive until that time. West coast First Nations describe the flight of Killer whale who dives deep into the oceans to avoid the coming Thunderbirds.

## Curriculum Connections

In this lesson, students have the opportunity to develop skills and concepts in these areas:

### *Social Studies*

RW 3.1 c. Describe ways in which communities help ensure basic human needs are met (e.g., food and water, shelter, clothing, education, safety).

## Focus On Literacy

### *During Reading: Constructing Mental Images*

Tell students, *Sometimes writers try to give readers a different way to understand the information presented by including visual images such as pictures, photographs, and diagrams. When good readers encounter a lot of written text with few or no visual images, they often create pictures in their own mind as they are reading to help them understand the information.*

Provide students with LM 3-24 Static Electricity and You, which has the written text from student book page 112 on the left and lots of white space on the right, where students will draw pictures. Model what you would like students to do. As you do it, describe what you would like them to do: *Use the think-aloud strategy to model the mental images you create in your own mind as you read the first paragraph of this text. As you are reading, underline key words or phrases that inspire a mental image. Draw a simplified version of your image on the right-hand side of the page, next to the written text in paragraph one. Label your visual image as necessary.*

Now prompt students to try this visualizing strategy on their own with the information in paragraphs two and three. Once students have completed their reading and drawn their images, ask them to fold their page vertically and turn it over so they can only see the right-hand column. Students can now turn to their partners and explain their visual images, which are essentially summaries of key information.

### *After Writing: Sharing, Reflecting, and Considering Feedback*

Using the reverse side of LM 3-24 Static Electricity and You, students can now turn their oral retell into a one-paragraph summary. Have students turn to their partner once again and share their written summaries. Prompt students to consider whether all the key information has been captured in their summaries, and whether there is information that should be added or deleted.

## Misconceptions

There are several common misconceptions about lightning, and some can be dangerous for students. Students may have heard the saying that lightning never strikes twice in the same place. This is not true. Tall buildings, such as the CN Tower are hit many times a year. Students may think it is safe to seek shelter under a tree in a storm, but that is one of the most dangerous places to choose because lightning is more likely to strike the tallest objects in the area.

## Get Started ▶

- Read the Get Started with the class and allow time for discussing prior knowledge and experiences with lightning and storms.
- Question or prompt students for connections to the ways charged materials react with one another (Lesson 12), how static electricity reacts to water (Lesson 13), and the teachings of the Elder Betty McKenna about storms following sources of water (Ask… An Elder).

!

Help students understand the validity of cultural explanations of lightning, such as Thunderbird. While they may differ from the scientific perspective, they remain a strong spiritual belief for First Nations people, and as such need to be honoured. You may wish to use the traditional explanation for lightning as a springboard to invite students to explore their own cultural explanations of lightning and how these explanations may be valid to them or their culture. Extension activities may include exploring cultural stories about lightning and student-created stories about lightning.

traditional ***KNOWLEDGE***

**Time**

20 min

**Learning Context**

inquiry

**Level of Inquiry**

confirmation

**Skills**

- classifying
- interpreting
- communicating

**Grouping**

pairs

**Materials and Equipment**

(per group)
- pencils

**Line Masters**

- LM 3-23

## Work On It

### Purpose

To provide students with an opportunity to identify unsafe practices around static electricity and to reinforce static electricity safety rules

### Activity Notes

- Students work in pairs to read and discuss the safety rules. Pairs then decide whether or not each person in the illustration is acting safely or not, according to the rules they have read, their own background knowledge, and knowledge gained in past lessons.
- Students can record their observations on LM 3-23 Safety Around Static Electricity.
- Students' explanations may be as follows.

| Person | Safety rule the person is following or breaking |
|---|---|
| Canoeists | Are not going ashore |
| Boaters | Are coming ashore |
| Swimmers | Are not coming ashore |
| People near tree | Should not be taking shelter in a tree |
| Peron in open | Is crouching down |
| Man with video recorder | Should not be using an appliance |
| People looking out of windows | Should be away from the windows |
| Person on phone | Should not use an appliance and should not be near the window. |
| Person in bath | Should not be in the bath |
| Girl reading | Is staying away from windows and appliances |
| Boy skateboarding | Is not taking shelter |
| Man at gas station | Should not be refuelling his truck |
| People in car | Are staying in the car |

## Additional Activity

By the end of this lesson, students will have been introduced to all the new vocabulary associated with the unit. You may wish to give them LM 3-25 Magnetism and Electricity Word Search.

## Communicate

1. Electricity travels through metals and water very easily.
2. Students' answers may vary, but should include any three of the following safety procedures.
   - Stay inside your house or vehicle during a lightning storm.
   - If you are indoors, stay away from water sources, electrical appliances, telephones, windows, and doors.
   - If you are outdoors, do not take shelter under a tree. Go to a low spot and crouch down.
   - If you are in the water, go to shore.

## DI Differentiating Instruction

### *For EAL/ELL*

For students who may not yet have the vocabulary to do the Work On It, photocopy student book page 111 and have students circle actions in the picture that are safe in green and actions that are unsafe in red, rather than writing their answers.

## Assessment *for* Learning

| What to Look for in Student Work | What to Do |
|---|---|
| Students know how to stay safe when near non-contact forces. | • Monitor student discussions as they work through the Work On It, to see if students are identifying safe and unsafe practices. |

# Ask ... Why is it important to understand forces?

Page 114

| Time |
| --- |
| 40–200 min |
| **Line Masters** |
| • LM 3-26 |

## Indicator Assessment Chart

| Indicator | Assessment Opportunities |
| --- | --- |
| **ME3.2 a.** Investigate how magnets are used at home, school, and in business and industrial applications (e.g., refrigerator magnet, magnetic cupboard door latches, credit card magnetic strip, radio speakers, navigation, motorized devices, scrap yard crane, magnetic levitation trains, jewellery, tools, and toys). | • Research, p. 115 |
| **ME3.2 g.** Describe the effects of static electric forces in their daily lives (e.g., static cling, sparks when touching metal objects after walking across carpeted surfaces, and photocopiers). | • Research, p. 115 |

## A Mechanic

- Read the profile with the class.
- Allow time for students to make connections to prior knowledge and past lesson content related to uses for magnets. Prompt them if necessary.
- As a whole class or in small groups, have students brainstorm a list of parts in a car that move up and down or back and forth because of a small motor, or things in their homes that spin, turn, move back and forth, or up or down because of a motor.
- You may have to refer some students to the part of the text that explains that small motors run these items in a vehicle, and that those motors contain an electromagnet.
- Ask a mechanic to visit your classroom to share more knowledge on why magnets are important to this profession, and possibly show an electromagnet in a small motor.
- You may want to have students make electromagnets (LM 3-14 Make Your Own Electromagnet). Or use the instructions on the line master to make one to demonstrate to the class.
- Explain that as the electric current flows through the wire wrapped around the nail, it creates a magnetic field around the nail. The nail becomes magnetized and can pick up a paper clip.
- Add this information to the class display on magnetism and static electricity, or use it as a jump off point for research about electromagnets inside motors.

## A Doctor

- Read the profile with the class.
- Allow time for students to make connections to prior knowledge about medical technologies, past experiences, and past lesson content related to useful machines and technologies that use magnetic forces. Prompt if necessary.
- Invite a doctor or an MRI technician to share with the class in more detail how magnetism is important to their professions.
- Add this information to the class display on magnetism and static electricity, or have students do research about magnetism in medicine.

traditional ***KNOWLEDGE***

## An Elder

- Read the profile with the whole group.
- Have students research content from the textbook, such as why storms follow water, how lightning affects nitrogen in the soil, or growing things in that soil.
- Elder Betty's people come from the eastern Canada. The Anishinabe people are an eastern Ojibwe group. The Saulteaux people are Saskatchewan's plains Ojibwe people.
- This profile gives a slightly different view of electricity than other views that have originated from Saskatchewan. Elder Betty explains her people have traditionally explained that the flapping of Thunderbird's wings produced lightning. The Plains Cree and Saulteaux explain that the flashing of Thunderbird's eyes produced lightning. This difference is a variation of cultural teachings and one doesn't contradict the other.
- Cultural explanations have their place and are valid in their way. To understand lightning as either charged particles or as a "thunder being" has practical implications. In our profile, the validity of the cultural stories lies in their ability to help people understand lightning's danger. We understand that lightning beings are attracted to water, and thus people should avoid large bodies of water during a storm. This cultural teaching has survival value and is therefore valid knowledge.
- Help students understand that while that science and culture may differ in their methods of approaching an observation, they may draw similar insights. Elder Betty's people have observed that lightning "energized" the soil and promoted plant growth. Scientists know that lightning's energy is powerful enough to synthesize nitrates, which are critical to plant growth. Whether the amount of nitrates produced by lightning is sufficient to promote that growth remains to be seen, but we can draw parallels between cultural understandings and scientific ones.
- Help students understand that we need to honour different perspectives, even if contradict our own views. Science consists of shifting paradigms. While some scientific theories and models may be true today, new evidence and new observations might render them invalid in the future.

## Focus On Literacy

### *Before Writing: Summarizing and Synthesizing*

Divide the class into groups of three and have students letter themselves off as A, B, or C. Give each group a copy of LM 3-26 Placemat Graphic Organizer. They will record information from the student book in this graphic organizer as they read pages 114 and 115 of the student book. Point out that the outer area of the placemat is divided into three sections, one for each career featured in the student book: A: mechanic, B: doctor, and C: Elder. Have each student in the group read about the career that corresponds to their letter choice.

Students use their corresponding lettered section of the placemat to record how the person they have just read about uses non-contact forces in their job. Once all three students have completed their summary, they share the specific information on their career with the rest of their group.

Next, prompt the groups to discuss the focus question found at the top of page 114 of the *Ask ... Why is it important to understand forces?* After reflecting on what they have learned about the three careers, students record ideas/answers to this question in the centre part of the placemat.

As a group, students can now write a paragraph that answers the question *Why is it important to understand forces?* Prompt students to use specific examples from each of the three careers to support their answer.

## Research

- Office administrators, printers, and copier technicians use and repair photocopiers and laser printers. These devices use static electricity to make clean and precise images of the items they are copying.
- Laundry workers need to know how to limit static electricity to be safe in their workplace.
- A vehicle painter uses static electricity in his or her work. Static electricity helps attract the paint to the car's surface and helps the paint go on evenly.
- An airport security worker uses magnetism. The scanners that sense metal on people as they pass through the security area use magnets.

## Assessment *for* Learning

| What to Look for in Student Work | What to Do |
|---|---|
| Students recognize that understanding magnetism and static electricity is important and helpful to many people in their lives or careers. | • Have students research, write and share on a topic of their choice related to magnetism and static electricity. Assess the information found and presented. |

# 15 Tricks with Non-Contact Forces

Page 116

| Time |
| --- |
| 40 min |

| Line Masters |
| --- |
| • LM 3-27 |

## Indicator Assessment Chart

| Indicator | Assessment Opportunities |
| --- | --- |
| **ME3.2 d.** Design, construct, and test an object such as a toy or game whose function depends on attractive or repulsive magnetic forces. | • Work On It, p. 117 (if student uses magnets) |
| **ME3.2 e.** Describe the operation of a toy or game whose function depends on magnetic forces using terms such as *attract, repel, push,* and *pull.* | • Communicate, p. 117, q. 1, 2 (if student uses magnets) |

## Background Information

Static electricity and magnetism are forces that can work at a distance. In the fictional narrative, Ann uses her knowledge of how these two forces work to do tricks for her younger sister. Ann has two "magic wands," one of glass and the other a long bar magnet. Rubbing a glass rod with a bit of silk causes the rod to become charged and attract some small tissue-paper dolls. The bar magnet also works from a distance to lift a small metal toy soldier without actually touching it.

traditional ***KNOWLEDGE***

First Nations and Métis peoples have a long history of sharing knowledge through oral storytelling, with the story left open for the learners to discover meaning on their own. The story in this section of the text is meant to honour that tradition, and allow students to create their own understanding of these two non-contact forces.

## Misconceptions

At this age, magic is still a very real possibility for children, but at the same time, students in grade 3 are beginning to question everything, and are always looking for the truth behind Santa Claus, the Tooth Fairy, or the Easter Bunny. Also, students of this age are often the best tricksters, and April Fool's Day can be a highlight for them. So, handling the topic of magic and whether students believe it is real may be a bit of a challenge. While you don't want to trample on any long-held beliefs students may have around magic, the idea that siblings often want to play tricks on each other should be safe common ground for the believers and non-believers in the class.

## Get Started ▶

- Read the narrative with students, and allow time for discussion of connections to prior knowledge, experiences with magic tricks or magicians, and sibling rivalry.
- List any questions students have about the content on chart paper. As students do the Work On It, they might discover some of the answers. When students explain their tricks, you can highlight how their work has helped them answer their questions.

**Time**

120–200 min

**Learning Context**

problem solving

**Level of Inquiry**

guided

**Skills**

- inferring
- experimenting
- making models
- communicating
- predicting

**Grouping**

pairs or groups

**Materials and Equipment**

(per group)

- pencils
  various materials used in previous experiments that students are familiar with, such as magnets of different sizes and shapes
- items to create a static charge, such as balloons and wool cloths
- metal items: containers, lids, toys
- polystyrene plates, cups, bowls, tissue paper

**Line Masters**

- LM 3-28

## Work On It

### Purpose

To provide an opportunity for students to describe how a game uses magnetic and static electric forces using the words *attract*, *repel*, *push,* or *pull,* and to give students a chance to design their own trick that uses either static electricity or magnetism

### Activity Notes

- Student pairs can reread and retell the story to each other to check for understanding.
- To complete step 2 of the Work On It, ask students to think-pair-share (think about the answer for one whole minute, pair up with their partner, and share answers).
- Remind students to use the words *attract*, *repel*, *push,* or *pull* when describing how the tricks work, and to use these words when describing how their own tricks work.
- You may wish to give them LM 3-27 Tricks with Non-contact Forces to record their ideas and list their materials.
- Make a note of those students whose trick used static electricity. Tell them that they will have to use magnetism in their Design Project, so that you can assess the indicators "Design, construct, and test an object such as a toy or game whose function depends on attractive or repulsive magnetic forces," and "Describe the operation of a toy or game whose function depends on magnetic forces using terms such as *attract, repel, push,* and *pull.*"
- Student pairs may have very different ideas about what type of magic trick to do. This can lead to tension. To help pairs reach a consensus, have each student write down all the ideas they have about types of tricks, and then have them trade lists and look for similar ideas in their lists. This may help them choose a single trick to test. Or allow the pairs to prepare two tricks for presentation, so that each can follow their own inquiry path.

## Communicate

As students show their tricks and describe how the tricks work, refer to questions students had at the beginning of the lesson and reflect on their learning and answers that students may have found.

1. The toy soldier was moved by a magnet attracting the metal of the soldier. Rubbing the glass rod with a silk cloth created a static electric charge that attracted the tissue-paper dolls.
2. Students' answers may vary, but student explanations of how the trick worked should include the words *push, pull, attract*, or *repel*.

DI

## Differentiating Instruction

### *For EAL/ELL*

Change the expectations for the Communicate. Asking ELL students to explain how their trick works could be difficult for them, especially with all the new terminology and vocabulary. Allow them to use graphic organizers or charts to help them explain the trick. Charts and diagrams can communicate concepts with minimal use of spoken or written language.

## Assessment *for* Learning

| What to Look for in Student Work | What to Do |
| --- | --- |
| Students can use their knowledge of static electricity and magnetism to solve a real-life problem and create a trick that shows that learning. | • Watch student presentations of their magic tricks and read their explanations of how the trick works to assess their understanding of the forces used and their ability to apply that knowledge in a real-life situation. |

DESIGN PROJECT

# Build a Toy Boat or Sled

Page 118

### Time

120–200 min

### Learning Context

problem solving

### Level of Inquiry

guided

### Skills

- making models
- inferring
- observing
- interpreting
- experimenting
- hypothesizing
- communicating

### Grouping

pairs

### Materials and Equipment

(per group)
- pencils
- magnets of different sizes and shapes
- items to create a charge, such as balloons and wool cloths
- metal items: containers, lids, toys
- polystyrene plates, cups, bowls, tissue paper
- items to help build the sled or boat, such as tape, glue, Bristol board, cardboard, plastic straws, Lego blocks, plastic lids to cut up, etc.
- small tub for water, such as a baby bathtub, storage container, or large baking dish
- ramp, such as a plastic tray, cookie sheet, or thin piece of plywood covered with a piece of paper

### Line Masters

- LM 3-28
- LM 3-29

## Curriculum Indicators

| Indicators Met in Design Project |
|---|
| **ME3.2 d.** Design, construct, and test an object such as a toy or game whose function depends on attractive or repulsive magnetic forces. |
| **ME3.2 e.** Describe the operation of a toy or game whose function depends on magnetic forces using terms such as *attract, repel, push,* and *pull.* |

## Background Information

The Design Project is introduced with pictures of a magnetic levitation (maglev) train. This is a real-world application of using magnetism to move a vehicle. Magnetic levitation in trains is still largely in the research and development stages. Japan and Germany are two major countries involved in this research. The train in the photograph is from Japan. Test runs on this train started in January of 1993. It has attained speeds of over 400 km/h in unmanned and manned test runs.

Maglev technology uses electromagnetism and forces of repulsion or attraction to magnetically levitate vehicles. It is being researched extensively as a means of providing high-speed travel that is safe, reliable, and has a low environmental impact.

## Curriculum Connections

In this lesson, students have the opportunity to develop skills and concepts in these areas:

***Social Studies***

IN3.1 a. Describe characteristics of daily life in communities studied, and compare the ways in which the needs are met by individuals in diverse communities (e.g., housing, tools, work, use of the land, games, education).

## Get Started ▶

- Have students look at the photo of the train in the Get Started. Discuss how it is an example of a vehicle being moved by a non-contact force—magnetism. Invite students' comments on how they might use a non-contact force to make their toy vehicle move.
- Read the Get Started with the class, and allow time for discussion of connections to prior knowledge and experiences.

- Discuss any questions students have about the content.
- If students are having difficulty understanding how a train can levitate, give a simple demonstration using two ring magnets on a pencil. Place the two magnets on a pencil so that their like poles are adjacent to each other. Hold the pencil upright. The top magnet levitates over the bottom one. (You can buy commercial ring magnet kits such as this, but a pencil works just as well.)

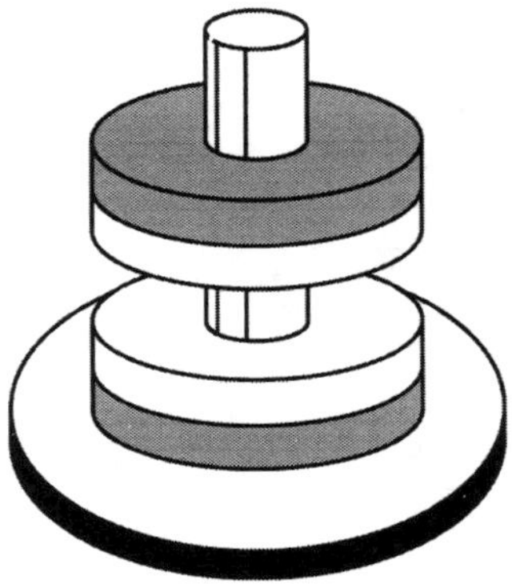

- Remind students that all they have learned about magnetism (and static electricity) in their readings and investigations will help them plan and execute their Design Projects. For example, they know that magnetism passes through water (boat) and paper (sled).
- Hand out LM 3-28 Design Project Rubric: Build a Toy Boat or Sled. There is too much material in it to go over with a large group. Assign small groups a section of the rubric to learn. Then have them report on their section to the rest of the class.

## Work On It

- Read the Work On It instructions to the class.
- With the whole class, discuss the design choices available to them: whether to build a boat or sled, and whether to use magnetism or static electricity as the force to make the vehicle move.
- You may need to give some guidance to some groups so they don't try to use static electricity to move the sled up the ramp.
- Remind students to refer to the notes they made on LM 3-9 Build On What You Know.
- Hand out LM 3-29 Design Project Planner: Build a Toy Boat or Sled to help students design their sled or boat.
- Students should plan their designs following the criteria listed in the student book, and record their ideas. Students should decide and record what materials they need to build their vehicles and bring from home any objects not available in the classroom (e.g., a variety of magnetic things to glue on their vehicles).

- As students build their vehicles, they should identify any problems they had with their design and come up with solutions. They should record these data.
- Students will test the success of their designs by answering the question *Does your boat move around a tub of water holding 10 marbles?* or *Does your sled move up and down a ramp while holding a small toy person?* Students will record their findings and any design changes they need to make.

## Communicate

1. Students will demonstrate how their vehicles move using magnetism or static electricity. They should be able to use the new terms and concepts they have encountered throughout this unit. Some possible designs are the following.

**Sleds:**

- Students may place a strong magnet or piece of steel on the underside of the sled and use a strong magnet underneath the ramp to guide the sled.
- Students may place a strong magnet or piece of steel on the top surface of the sled and hold a strong magnet over the top of the sled to pull it up the ramp
- Students may place a strong magnet on the back of the sled and hold a strong magnet to the sled's magnet in such a way that the like poles are facing each other and push the sled up the ramp.

**Boats:**

- Students may place their boat that has magnetic metal on its bottom in a shallow pan suspended between two tables or desks and use a strong magnet on the underside of the pan to make the boat move.
- Students may place their boat that has magnetic metal on its bottom in a shallow pan directly on a tabletop and use a strong magnet to move the boat along the side of the pan. The boat could also have magnetic material along its sides.
- Students could have a boat that has a magnet on its top. They place their boat in a shallow pan on a table, and use a strong magnet held above the boat to make it move. The like poles of the magnets are placed close together, the poles repel, and the boat is pushed forward.
- Students may place their boat that has a polystyrene sail or top in a shallow pan. A charged balloon is held near the sail to make it move.

2. Students' answers will vary depending on vehicle designs. However, student explanations should be clear and should include the words *push*, *pull*, *attract*, or *repel*, as well as other new terms and concepts they have encountered throughout the unit.

## DI Differentiating Instruction

### *For Reteaching*

Students who are having difficulty with the task may need to spend some time working with just magnets or static electricity alone. The task of building the toy can be a bit distracting, and a review of how the two forces work may be needed to focus students. Time spent exploring how two magnets repel each other when like poles are near may help students see how to make a boat move. The same thing may be done with two charged balloons: they can place one on a wall, and the other nearby. They should observe the two balloons repelling each other.

## Assessment *for* Learning

| What to Look for in Student Work | What to Do |
| --- | --- |
| Students are able to build a toy that moves by means of magnetism or static electricity with no contact. | • Use the Design Project Rubric to assess student ability to plan, design, test, and complete their model. |
| Students are able to describe how the non-contact force they chose makes their toy move. | • Use the Design Project Rubric to assess student ability to explain how the non-contact force moved the vehicle in their project. |

## Unit 3 Summary

Page 120

Students may wish to use the unit summary as a study guide. The Unit 3 Summary is available as a line master (LM 3-1 Unit 3 Summary).

## Show What You Know

Page 122

You may want to use the review questions as a formal exam for this unit, as an open-book test, or as preparation for another sort of assessment tool. The questions, with spaces for answers, are on LM 3-30 Show What You Know.

1. A force is a push or a pull that causes an object to begin moving, stop moving, change direction, or change shape.
2. The types of forces shown are contact forces and non-contact forces.
3. Students' answers may vary. Examples: snow plough pushing snow, boy pulling a sled, wind pushing snow off the roof.
4. Students' answers may vary. Examples: static electricity making the person's hair stand on end, gravity pulling the toboggan down the hill.
5. First Nations peoples used the force of friction to help them start fires.
6. Magnets could be used to hold things on your fridge, to hold your cupboard and fridge doors closed, to make doorbells ring, and to hold tools on the wall.
7. Students' answers may vary. Examples: toys, motors, appliances, closures on backpacks and purses, speakers, electromagnets, doorbells.
8. Three types of magnets are natural magnets, temporary magnets, and permanent magnets. Natural magnets are magnetic rocks made by Earth, such as magnetite. Temporary magnets are made by contact with another magnet. They lose their magnetism quickly when the magnet is removed. Permanent magnets are manufactured and stay magnetized for a long time.
9. Both contact and non-contact forces change an object's movement, direction, or shape. Contact forces must actually touch the object. Non-contact forces do not have to touch the object to make the change happen.
10. Students' answers may vary. Examples: getting zapped when opening a door, hair standing up when taking off a toque, laundry items sticking to one another after being in the dryer.
11. Students' answers may vary. Examples: dampening her hands to wipe off the sock, or using a dryer sheet and rubbing off the sock.

12. Students' sketches may vary, but could include people doing any of the following things: not putting any electronics near a magnet, staying away from metal objects during a lightning storm, staying low to the ground during a lightning storm, avoiding using trees or other tall items for shelter, and using static limiting techniques in hazardous locations, such as gas stations. Another example might be a picture of a face or animal drawn on paper, and placed on top of a plastic tray. Iron filings are placed on top of the picture and the object of the game is to move the iron filings to put hair or features on the face or animal while holding the magnet under the tray.
13. Students' sketches may vary but might be of two toy cars made of metal on top of a plastic tray and two magnets underneath. The object of the game is to use the magnet to move your vehicle across the tray fastest without touching the car.

## Looking Back

Self-evaluation allows students to communicate their learning and their feelings about it. Seeing how students view their learning can give you insight and information on which to base your programming decisions.

Ask students to answer these questions individually, and then to share their answers with the class. Some students will likely find some areas of this unit easier than other areas. This exercise may help students identify who can give them assistance to understand difficult concepts.

# Unit 3 Line Masters

## Table of Contents

## Table of Contents *(continued)*

Name: ______________________________

# Unit 3 Summary

| Forces make objects move or change. | |
|---|---|
| **SUMMARY**<br>□ A force is a push or a pull that makes an object move, stop moving, or change direction or shape. | **MY STUDY NOTES** |

| Some forces touch objects, and other forces make no contact at all. | |
|---|---|
| **SUMMARY**<br>□ Forces that act directly on an object and cause a change are contact forces.<br>□ Forces that act from a distance to move or change an object are non-contact forces.<br>□ Magnetism and static electricity are non-contact forces. | **MY STUDY NOTES** |

| We can use what we know about forces to help us in our daily lives. | |
|---|---|
| **SUMMARY**<br>□ Knowing how to magnetize objects such as tools can be very helpful.<br><br>□ Knowing how to avoid static electricity can be useful and help us stay safe. | **MY STUDY NOTES** |

| Natural forces are important to the ways of First Nations and Métis peoples. | |
|---|---|
| **SUMMARY**<br>□ Some First Nations and Métis peoples understand thunder and lightning as Thunderbird, a powerful spirit that brings rain and healing.<br><br>□ Some First Nations and Métis peoples understand the northern lights as spirits of their people dancing in the sky. | **MY STUDY NOTES** |

Name: ____________________________

# Unit 3 Vocabulary

Check off each vocabulary term below as you learn it in this unit.

After you check off all the terms, make a concept map using as many terms as you can. Start your concept map with these words in the centre: "magnetism" and "static electricity". Use the back of this page or a separate page for your concept map.

- □ attract, p. 94
- □ charged, p. 106
- □ contact forces, p. 86
- □ force, p. 86
- □ friction, p. 88
- □ magnetic, p. 94
- □ magnetic field, p. 94
- □ magnetized, p. 98
- □ natural magnets, p. 100
- □ non-contact forces, p. 90
- □ non-magnetic, p. 94
- □ north pole, p. 94
- □ permanent magnets, p. 100
- □ poles, p. 94
- □ repel, p. 96
- □ south pole, p. 94
- □ static electricity, p. 106
- □ temporary magnets, p. 100
- □ Thunderbird, p. 112

Name: ________________________________

# Looking Forward

1. Write your ideas about moving and changing objects in the table below.

| Objects That Are Moving and Changing | The Forces That Made These Objects Move and Change |
|---|---|
| | |
| | |
| | |
| | |
| | |
| | |

2. Write the questions you have about the forces of magnetism and static electricity in the space below.

______________________________________________

______________________________________________

______________________________________________

______________________________________________

______________________________________________

______________________________________________

Name: ______________________________

# Forces Are All Around You

| Objects That Are Moving, Being Stopped, or Changing Direction or Shape | What I Think Is Causing the Movement or Change |
|---|---|
| | |
| | |
| | |
| | |
| | |
| | |
| | |
| | |

Name: ______________________________

# Pushing and Pulling Forces

| Examples of Pushing Forces | Examples of Pulling Forces |
|---|---|
| | |

Name: ______________________________

# Friction and Toy Cars

How will friction affect pushing or pulling a toy car?

______________________________________________________________

______________________________________________________________

______________________________________________________________

______________________________________________________________

**Pushing the Car**

| | Distance the Car Moved |
|---|---|
| When I PUSHED the car on the floor | |
| When I PUSHED the car on the towel | |

**Pulling the Car**

| | Distance the Car Moved |
|---|---|
| When I PULLED the car on the floor | |
| When I PULLED the car on the towel | |

**Name:** ___________________________________

# Can You Move an Object Without Touching It?

Will your fingers, the magnet, the balloon, and the straw move any objects without any contact? Write down your predictions.

_______________________________________________________________________________

_______________________________________________________________________________

_______________________________________________________________________________

_______________________________________________________________________________

_______________________________________________________________________________

_______________________________________________________________________________

_______________________________________________________________________________

| Object/ Was It Moved by the Force of… | Wooden ball | Paper Clip | Your Hair | Did Anything Touch the Object? If So, What? |
|---|---|---|---|---|
| Your hands | | | | |
| The magnet | | | | |
| The balloon | | | | |
| The straw | | | | |

Name: ______________________________

# Non-contact Forces KWL Chart

| K<br>What I KNOW About Non-Contact Forces | W<br>What I WANT to Know About Non-Contact Forces | L<br>What I LEARNED About Non-Contact Forces |
|---|---|---|
| | | |

Name: ________________________________

# Build On What You Know

**Lesson 3:** What forces might you use to move the toy boat or sled you will build? Write a list of your ideas.

______________________________________________________________________

______________________________________________________________________

______________________________________________________________________

______________________________________________________________________

**Lesson 6:** How might you use a magnet to move the sled or boat that you will build? Draw pictures of your ideas below. If you need more room, use the back of this page.

**Lesson 10:** Do you think a compass would be useful to add to the boat or sled you will build? Explain your answer.

**Lesson 12:** How could you use static electricity to move your boat or sled? Record your ideas.

Name: ______________________________

# Exploring With Magnets

| Object | What Happened When It Was Close to a Magnet? |
|---|---|
| | |

Name: ____________________________

# Magnets and Poles

Record what you found out under each diagram. Draw arrows to show which direction the magnets moved.

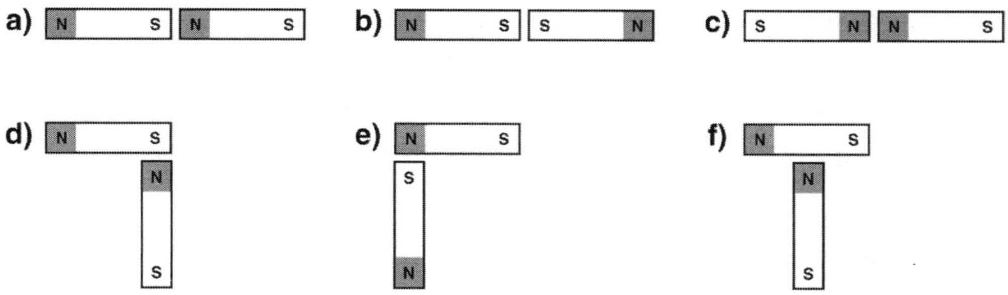


Draw what you saw when the magnet was placed on the magnetic drawing board.

**Name:** ______________________________

# Which Magnet Is Stronger?

Which magnet do you think is stronger? Write down your prediction.

_______________________________________________________________

_______________________________________________________________

Record how many paper clips each magnet picks up.

| Distance Above Paper Clips | Number of Paper Clips Picked Up by Magnet 1 | Number of Paper Clips Picked Up by Magnet 2 |
|---|---|---|
| 0 cm | | |
| 1 cm | | |
| 2 cm | | |

Name: ______________________________

# Can You Make a Magnet?

| Magnetized Object | Number of Paper Clips the Object Picked Up |
|---|---|
| | |

Name: ______________________________

# Make Your Own Electromagnet

In Lesson 7, you made a magnet by stroking the nail with a magnet. You can also turn a nail into a magnet using a battery. This type of magnet is called an electromagnet.

## What You Need

- iron nail
- 60-cm length of insulated copper wire
- 1 "D" battery
- electrical tape
- 1 box small paper clips

**SAFETY CAUTION!**
Do not touch the wires at the ends of the batteries. They get hot.

## What You Will Do

1. Carefully wrap the copper wire around the iron nail tightly 20 times. Make sure to leave a few inches of wire free at each end.
2. Ask your teacher to use the electrical tape to fasten the stripped ends of the wire to each end of the battery.

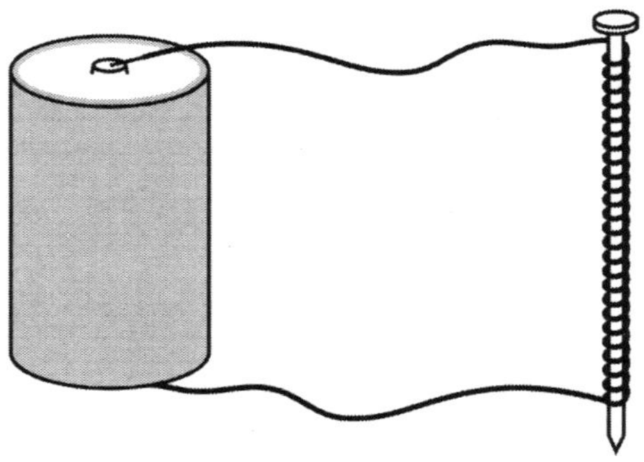

3. Hold the battery by the middle, where there is a plastic coating.
4. Predict how many paper clips your electromagnet will pick up. Record the number in the table below.
5. Hold the nail close to the paper clips. Record the number of paper clips you can pick up with your electromagnet.
6. Remove one end of the wire from the battery. Hold the nail close to the paper clips. Observe what happens.

| Number of Paper Clips I Predict the Electromagnet Will Pick Up | Number of Paper Clips the Electromagnet Picked Up |
|---|---|
| | |

**What Did You Find Out?**

1. Why do you think your electromagnet did or did not work?

_______________

_______________

2. How do you think you could make the electromagnet pick up more clips?

_______________

_______________

3. Do you think it would work if you wound the wire around your pencil instead of a nail? Why?

_______________

_______________

**Name:** ____________________________________

# Magnet Examples

List the magnets you can find in the picture on page 101 of the student book. Then, add any other examples of magnets that you can think of.

_______________________________________________________________________________

_______________________________________________________________________________

_______________________________________________________________________________

_______________________________________________________________________________

_______________________________________________________________________________

_______________________________________________________________________________

Use the table below to sort your list of magnets.

| Natural Magnets | Temporary Magnets | Permanent Magnets |
|---|---|---|
| | | |

Name: ______________________________

# Magnetic Forces

| Material | I Predict That Magnetism Will Act Through the Material (Yes or No) | Did Magnetism Act Through the Material? (Yes or No) |
|---|---|---|
| | | |
| | | |
| | | |
| | | |
| | | |
| | | |
| | | |
| | | |
| | | |

Name: ______________________________

# Magnet Challenge

Try to move a paper clip out of a glass of water without touching it!

## What You Need

- drinking glass
- water
- strong magnet
- paper clip
- ruler
- pencil

## What You Will Do

1. Fill the glass half full of cool water.
2. Drop the paper clip into the glass.
3. Use the magnet to get the paper clip out of the water without getting yourself or the magnet wet. Place the magnet on the outer surface of the glass beside the paper clip.
4. Slide the magnet upward toward the top of the glass. Take the paper clip from the inner surface of the glass once it is above the water.
5. Repeat steps 2 to 4 several times, but each time move the magnet farther away from the glass. Measure the distance with a ruler. Try to keep the magnet the same distance away from the glass as you move it upward. Each time, record how far away the magnet was from the glass.

| Distance Between Magnet and Glass | Could the Paper Clip be Removed from the Water? (yes or no) |
|---|---|
| 0 cm | |
| | |
| | |
| | |

## What Did You Find Out?

1. How far away was the magnet from the glass when it could no longer move the paper clip?

______________________________

Name: ______________________________

## What Can a Compass Tell You?

What do you think will happen when you put your compasses near the magnet? Write down your prediction.

_______________________________________________

_______________________________________________

Draw a picture to show you placed the four compasses along the magnet. Draw an arrow on each compass to show the magnet's field.

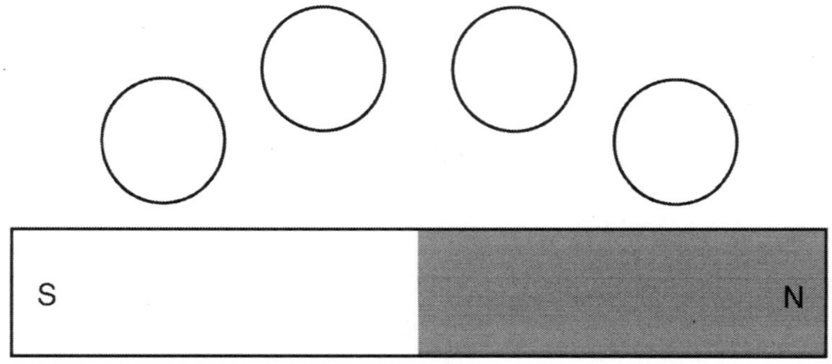


Put your compass near the earbud wires of a music player. Record what you see.

_______________________________________________

_______________________________________________

Name: ____________________

# Make a Compass

You can make your own homemade compass out of a magnetized sewing needle.

**What You Need**

- sewing needle
- small piece of foam
- glass or plastic bowl
- water

**SAFETY CAUTION!**
Be careful when using the sewing needle. The end is sharp.

**What You Will Do**

1. Magnetize the sewing needle. Do you remember how to do this? If not, look back at Lesson 7 Work on It.
2. Slowly put the needle through the foam.
3. Float the foam and needle in the bowl of water. Observe what happens to the needle.

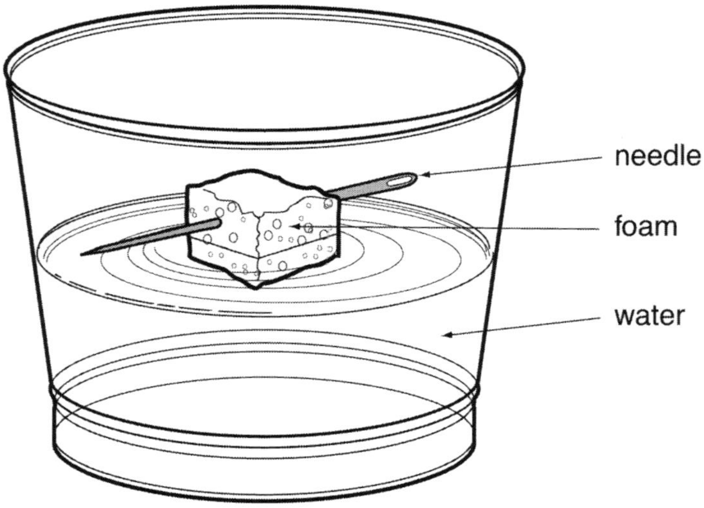

**What Did You Find Out?**

1. Which way does the needle swing?

2. Does your homemade compass point in the same direction as a compass from a store?

**Name:** ______________________________

# What Is Static Electricity?

| Object | What I Think Will Happen If I Place the Charged Balloon Near the Object | What Happened When I Placed the Charged Balloon Near the Object |
|---|---|---|
| | | |
| | | |
| | | |
| | | |
| | | |
| | | |
| | | |

Name: ______________________________

# Charged Materials

What do you think will happen when you bring the plate close to the plate you did not rub? Write down your prediction.

_______________________________________________

_______________________________________________

| What I Did | What Happened |
|---|---|
| Rubbed one plate and held it near the other plate | |
| Rubbed both plates and held them close together | |
| Rubbed one plate and held it near running water | |
| Rubbed one plate and held it close to an object I chose | |

Name: ______________________________

# The Strength of Static Electricity

Test your charged balloon under the different conditions and record the times in the table below.

| What I Did | Time the Balloon Stayed on the Wall |
|---|---|
| I rubbed the balloon with wool and pushed it onto the wall. | ____________ seconds |
| I rubbed the balloon with the wool fabric, held the balloon 1 cm from the wall, and then let it go. | ____________ seconds |
| I rubbed the balloon with the wool fabric, then water was misted, and then I pushed it onto the wall. | ____________ seconds |

Name: ______________________________

# Safety Around Static Electricity

Look at the picture on page 113 of your textbook. Find all the people. Explain the safety rule each person is following or breaking.

| Person | Safety Rule the Person Is Following or Breaking |
|---|---|
| | |

Name: ______________________________

# Static Electricity and You

Have you ever seen a thunder and lightning storm? The loud booms and bright light are awesome and we respect their power. Some First Nations and Métis peoples understand thunder and lightning as **Thunderbird** (***Piyisew*** in Cree), a powerful spirit that brings rain and healing. They let us know the rain is coming.

Today, we can understand lightning as Thunderbird or as static electricity. Charged particles build up in the clouds. When there are too many charged particles, they can move very quickly to a nearby cloud. You see this movement as lightning. They can also move to a tree or building. They move to the tallest object nearby.

Static electricity can travel through some materials and not others. It can travel through metal and water but not rubber. Knowing which materials it can travel through and which materials it cannot travel through can help you stay safe.

Name: ______________________________

# Magnetism and Electricity Word Search

Find each word in the table and circle it below.

| | | | | | | | | | | | | | | | | | |
|---|---|---|---|---|---|---|---|---|---|---|---|---|---|---|---|---|---|
| S | I | L | T | C | A | T | N | O | C | N | O | N | V | Z | E | I | F |
| L | T | N | E | N | A | M | R | E | P | T | N | B | L | M | T | Y | R |
| F | H | A | X | S | O | J | W | O | B | E | A | T | T | R | A | C | T |
| F | L | I | T | J | E | R | Y | E | S | M | T | F | M | J | P | N | R |
| E | V | E | Z | I | E | L | T | L | P | P | U | F | K | P | K | H | T |
| L | M | E | P | K | C | I | O | H | H | O | R | B | J | N | Q | H | S |
| E | Y | A | D | E | T | E | P | P | Y | R | A | K | P | F | U | M | C |
| C | V | E | G | E | R | X | L | E | Y | A | L | V | Q | N | A | H | C |
| T | S | S | N | N | Z | O | K | E | G | R | P | C | D | R | A | Y | O |
| R | L | G | D | Z | E | Z | P | J | C | Y | W | E | K | R | Z | Y | N |
| O | A | Z | G | T | D | T | D | A | P | T | R | V | G | S | C | S | T |
| M | M | V | U | J | L | U | I | F | X | B | R | E | U | M | L | E | A |
| A | I | A | S | O | U | T | H | S | I | C | D | I | R | U | O | C | C |
| G | X | N | G | B | R | N | V | R | M | A | F | W | C | E | T | R | T |
| N | C | C | N | N | E | C | D | O | D | X | Q | W | K | I | Y | O | M |
| E | X | O | O | T | E | F | R | I | C | T | I | O | N | I | T | F | X |
| T | F | I | R | P | G | T | Z | Z | E | T | Z | N | N | X | K | Y | A |
| R | W | Q | O | Z | E | Z | C | J | Z | K | W | G | B | C | M | Z | L |

ATTRACT
CHARGED
CONTACT
ELECTROMAGNET
FORCES
FRICTION
MAGNET
MAGNETISM
MAGNETITE
NATURAL
NORTH
PERMANENT
POLES
REPEL
SOUTH
STATIC ELECTRICITY
TEMPORARY
THUNDERBIRD

Name: ______________________________

# Placemat Graphic Organizer

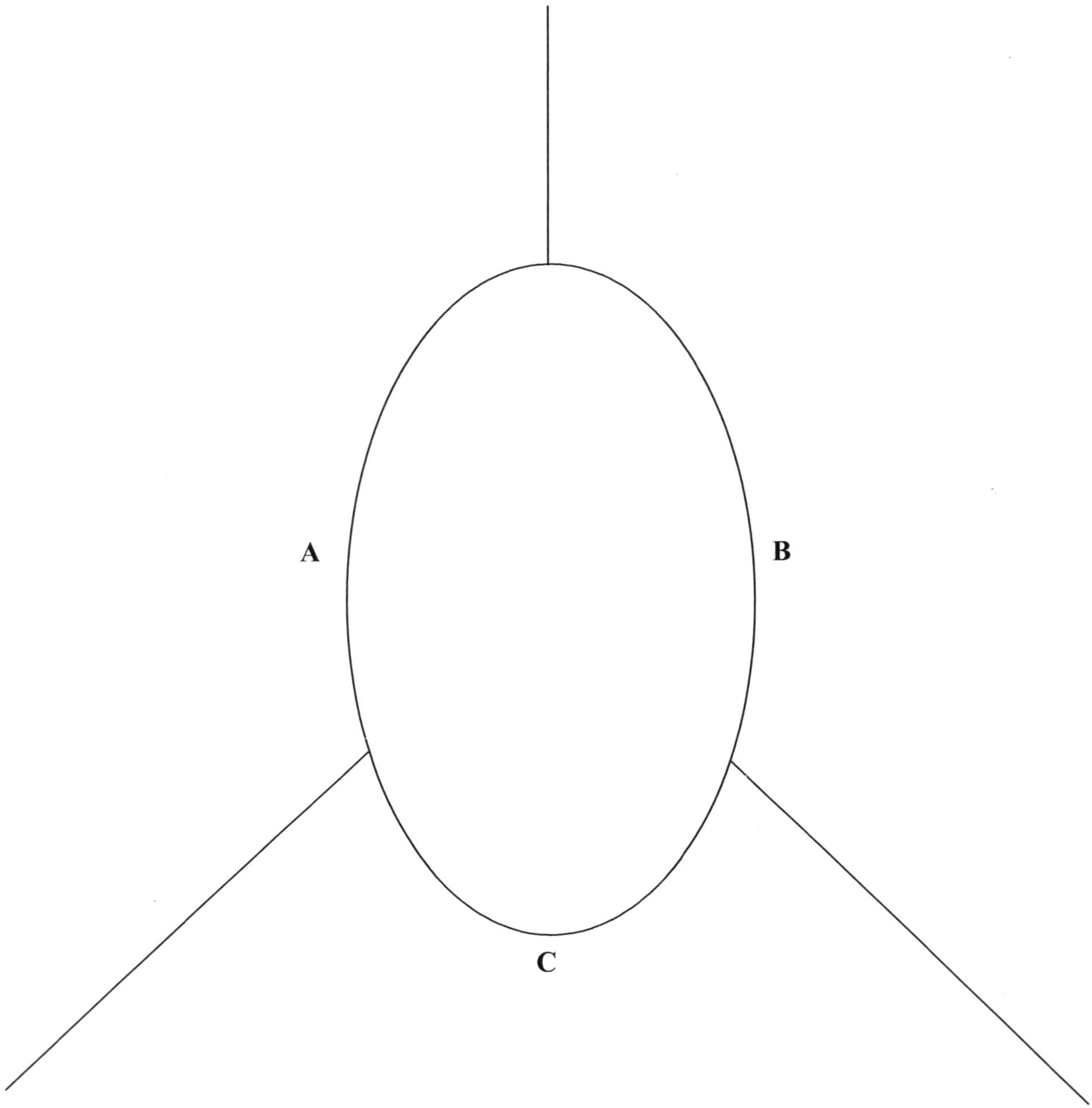

Name: ______________________________

# Tricks with Non-contact Forces

2. How do you think Ann did each trick? Think about what you have learned about non-contact forces. Write down your ideas.

________________________________________________

________________________________________________

________________________________________________

________________________________________________

________________________________________________

________________________________________________

________________________________________________

3. Make a list of the materials you need to test your ideas.

________________________________________________

________________________________________________

________________________________________________

________________________________________________

________________________________________________

**Name:** ______________________________

# Design Project Rubric: Build a Toy Boat or Sled

| | 1 Star ★ | 2 Stars ★★ | 3 Stars ★★★ | 4 Stars ★★★★ |
|---|---|---|---|---|
| **Safety:** How well did you follow safety rules when building your vehicle? | You had to be reminded to follow the safety rules. | You followed some of the safety rules. | You followed most of the safety rules. | You followed all the safety rules. |
| **Safety:** How safely did you use materials and equipment? | You had to be reminded to use equipment and materials safely. | You used equipment and materials safely some of the time. | You used equipment and materials safely most of the time. | You used equipment and materials safely. |
| **Finished Vehicle:** How well does your vehicle do what it is supposed to do? | It does none of the things it is supposed to do. | It does one thing it is supposed to do. | It does both things it is supposed to do, some of the time. | It does both things it is supposed to do, all the time. |
| **Recording Your Design:** Planning | You recorded one idea about your vehicle when you first planned it. | You recorded two ideas about your vehicle when you first planned it. | You recorded three ideas about your vehicle when you first planned it. | You recorded four ideas about your vehicle when you first planned it. |
| **Recording Your Design:** Building | You did not record any challenges you had in building or how you solved them. | You recorded a challenge you had in building but not what you did to solved it. | You recorded one challenge you had during building and what you did to solve it. | You recorded one or more challenges you had during building and more than one solution. |
| **Recording Your Design:** Testing | You did not record how your tested your vehicle or you did not test it at all. | You did not record very well how you tested your vehicle. You needed more details about the test and its success. | You recorded how you tested your vehicle in detail and if it was successful. | You recorded how you tested your vehicle in detail and if it was successful. You also described plans for changes or improvements. |
| **Presenting Your Design:** Explain Your Work. | You did not explain how your vehicle worked at all. | You explained only a few details about how your vehicle worked. | You explained how your vehicle worked and any challenges you had. | You explained how your vehicle worked in detail, any challenges you had, and how you made changes to make it work better. |

Name: ______________________________

# Design Project Planner: Build a Toy Boat or Sled

1. Circle the force you want to work with:
   - magnetism
   - static electricity

2. Circle one of the vehicle choices that you want to build:
   - A toy boat that can move around a tub of water while holding 10 marbles
   - A toy sled that can move up and down a ramp while holding a small toy person

3. Brainstorm many designs for your vehicle. Look at your LM 3-9 Build on What You Know page for ideas. Draw any design ideas you have on the back of this sheet.

4. Decide which is the best design and record your idea. Include a drawing.

______________________________________________________________

______________________________________________________________

______________________________________________________________

______________________________________________________________

______________________________________________________________

5. What will you use to build your toy? List the materials.

______________________________________________________________

______________________________________________________________

______________________________________________________________

______________________________________________________________

______________________________________________________________

6. Ask your teacher to approve your design and list of materials.

7. Build your toy. Check to see that your boat or sled does what it is supposed to do. (Circle Yes or No)

   Does your toy move using magnetism or static electricity? Yes or No

   Does your boat float while holding 10 marbles? Yes or No

   Does your sled move up and down the ramp while holding a toy person? Yes or No

8. Do you need to make changes to your design after you have tested it? If so, record what changes you might make.

_______________________________________________

_______________________________________________

_______________________________________________

_______________________________________________

_______________________________________________

9. Record whether your design was successful and any more changes you might make.

_______________________________________________

_______________________________________________

_______________________________________________

_______________________________________________

_______________________________________________

Name: ______________________________

# Show What You Know

1. How does a scientist describe a force?

______________________________________________

______________________________________________

______________________________________________

______________________________________________

2. Look at the picture on page 122 of your textbook. What types of forces can you find in it?

______________________________________________

______________________________________________

______________________________________________

______________________________________________

3. List three examples of contact forces shown in the picture on page 122 of your textbook.

______________________________________________

______________________________________________

______________________________________________

______________________________________________

4. List one example of a non-contact force shown in the picture on page 122 of your textbook.

______________________________________________

______________________________________________

______________________________________________

______________________________________________

5. Explain how First Nations people have used the force of friction to help them in their daily lives.

6. Give examples of two ways that magnets are used in your home.

7. Give examples of two ways that magnets are used in the world.

8. What are three types of magnets? Explain the differences between the types.

**9.** How are contact and non-contact forces the same? How are they different?

**10.** Describe three effects of static electricity in your daily life.

**11.** Look at the picture on page 123 of your textbook. What are two ways that the girl could get rid of her problem with static electricity?

**12.** Make a sketch to show three things you can do to be safe around static electricity.

**13.** Say you were asked to design a game that uses magnetic forces. Sketch a diagram of the game and explain how it uses magnetic forces.

______________________________________________

______________________________________________

______________________________________________

**14.** List any questions you still have about magnetism and static electricity or any new questions you would like to explore. Where might you go to research and find answers?

______________________________________________

______________________________________________

______________________________________________

______________________________________________

______________________________________________

______________________________________________

**15.** What was your favourite part of the unit or which piece of work are you most proud of from the unit? Explain your answer.

______________________________________________

______________________________________________

______________________________________________

______________________________________________

______________________________________________

______________________________________________

# Answers to Unit 3 Line Masters

## LM 3-14: Make Your Own Electromagnet

### What Did You Find Out?

1. Answers will vary depending on students' experimental results. Student answers might include: my electromagnet worked because there was electricity flowing through the wire, which turned the nail into a magnet. If students' electromagnets did not work, answers might say that it did not work because there was not enough electricity going through the wire.
2. Answers will vary but will likely include: I could make the magnet stronger by using a bigger battery.
3. It would not work if you wound the wire around a pencil because there is no metal in a pencil. It might work a bit if there was a metal ring holding an eraser on the end of the pencil.

## LM 3-17: Magnet Challenge

### What Did You Find Out?

1. Student answers will vary depending on the strength of the magnet they used. A possible distance might be 3 cm.

## LM 3-19: Make a Compass

### What Did You Find Out?

1. The needle swings to point north.
2. Yes, the homemade compass points in the same direction as a compass bought from a store.

## LM 3-24: Static Electricity and You

Students' summary paragraphs will vary but should include key points from the paragraphs. For example, First Nations and Métis people think thunder and lightning are Thunderbird, a powerful spirit. Lightning is caused by the movement of static electricity, which is charged particles, in clouds. Lightning can move from cloud to cloud or from clouds to tall objects on the ground. Static electricity can pass through metal and water, but not rubber.

## LM 3-25: Magnetism and Electricity Word Search

| | | | | | | | | | | | | | | | | | |
|---|---|---|---|---|---|---|---|---|---|---|---|---|---|---|---|---|---|
| S | I | L | T | C | A | T | N | O | C | N | O | N | V | Z | E | I | F |
| L | T | N | E | N | A | M | R | E | P | T | N | B | L | M | T | Y | R |
| F | H | A | X | S | O | J | W | O | B | E | A | T | T | R | A | C | T |
| F | L | I | T | J | E | R | Y | E | S | M | T | F | M | J | P | N | R |
| E | V | E | Z | I | E | L | T | L | P | P | U | F | K | P | K | H | T |
| L | M | E | P | K | C | I | O | H | H | O | R | B | J | N | Q | H | S |
| E | Y | A | D | E | T | E | P | P | Y | R | A | K | P | F | U | M | C |
| C | V | E | G | E | R | X | L | E | Y | A | L | V | Q | N | A | H | C |
| T | S | S | N | N | Z | O | K | E | G | R | P | C | D | R | A | Y | O |
| R | L | G | D | Z | E | Z | P | J | C | Y | W | E | K | R | Z | Y | N |
| O | A | Z | G | T | D | T | D | A | P | T | R | V | G | S | C | S | T |
| M | M | V | U | J | L | U | I | F | X | B | R | E | U | M | L | E | A |
| A | I | A | S | O | U | T | H | S | I | C | D | I | R | U | O | C | C |
| G | X | N | G | B | R | N | V | R | M | A | F | W | C | E | T | R | T |
| N | C | C | N | N | E | C | D | O | D | X | Q | W | K | I | Y | O | M |
| E | X | O | O | T | E | F | R | I | C | T | I | O | N | I | T | F | X |
| T | F | I | R | P | G | T | Z | Z | E | T | Z | N | N | X | K | Y | A |
| R | W | Q | O | Z | E | Z | C | J | Z | K | W | G | B | C | M | Z | L |

## LM 3-26: Placemat Graphic Organizer

Student answers will vary but the following might appear in each of the placemat sections.

A. Mechanic
- needs to know about magnets in order to fix the parts that use magnets
- windows, doors, and wipers all run with the help of magnetic forces
- magnets help make the spark that starts the fuel burning to make the car run

B. Doctor
- uses a machine called an MRI to look inside peoples' bodies
- the MRI uses a strong magnetic field to create the pictures
- the doctor can see if there is something wrong inside a person by looking at the MRI pictures.

C. Elder
- explains lightning as the need to connect Mother Earth and Father Sky
- explains static electricity as being created when Thunderbirds flap their wings
- storms follow river valleys
- storms are most violent over water
- lightning helps things grow

UNIT 4

# Exploring Soils

## Table of Contents

## Table of Contents

*(continued)*

## Unit Indicators Correlation Chart

| Indicator | Lesson References | Assessment Opportunities |
|---|---|---|
| By the end of grade 3, students will be able to: | | |
| **ES3.1 Investigate the characteristics, including soil composition and ability to absorb water, of different types of soils in their environment.** | | |
| a. Pose questions and make predictions about the characteristics and composition of soils that lead to exploration and investigation. | Lesson 2 | Work On It, p. 131<br>Communicate, p. 131, q. 1, 2, 3 |
| b. Examine physical characteristics of soils from different locations in their environment. | Lesson 4<br><br>Lesson 5<br><br>Design Project<br>Show What You Know | Work On It, p. 134<br>Communicate, p. 135, q. 1,2<br>Work On It, p. 136<br>Communicate, p. 137, q. 1, 2<br>Work On It, p. 161<br>Show What You Know, p. 164, q. 2, 8 |
| c. Classify soils in their environment according to location and type. | Lesson 5<br><br>Lesson 6<br><br>Design Project<br>Show What You Know | Work On It, p. 136<br>Communicate, p. 137, q. 1, 2<br>Work On It, p. 138<br>Communicate, p. 139, q. 1, 2<br>Work On It, p. 161<br>Show What You Know, p. 164, q. 4 |
| d. Analyze soil samples using tools such as spoons, hand lenses, jars, and filters appropriately and safely. | Lesson 1<br>Lesson 4<br>Lesson 6<br><br>Design Project | Work On It, p. 128<br>Work On It, p. 134<br>Work On It, p. 138<br>Communicate, p. 139, q. 1, 2<br>Work On It, p. 161<br>Communicate, p. 161, q. 1, 2 |
| e. Make and record observations and measurements in investigations related to soil composition using techniques such as notes in point form, diagrams, tables, bar graphs, photographs, and video. | Lesson 1<br><br>Lesson 4<br>Lesson 5<br>Lesson 6<br><br>Design Project<br><br>Show What You Know | Work On It, p. 128<br>Communicate, p. 129, q. 1, 2, 3<br>Work On It, p. 134<br>Work On It, p. 136<br>Work On It, p. 138<br>Communicate, p. 139, q. 2<br>Work On It, p. 161<br>Communicate, p. 161, q. 1, 2<br>Show What You Know, p. 164, q. 7 |
| f. Make predictions about the capability of different types of soil to absorb water and test these predictions through exploration and investigation. | Lesson 7 | Work On It, p. 140 |
| g. Collect and display data, using tables and bar graphs, to show the amount of water absorbed by different types of soil. | Lesson 7 | Work On It, p. 140 |

| Indicator | Lesson References | Assessment Opportunities |
|---|---|---|
| h. Sort soil samples according to one or more physical characteristics such as texture, ability to absorb water, particle size, and colour. | Lesson 4<br>Lesson 7 | Work On It, p. 134<br>Communicate, p. 141, q. 2 |
| i. Communicate procedures and results of investigations related to the testing of water absorption of soils using drawings, demonstrations, and oral and written descriptions. | Lesson 7 | Communicate, p. 141, q. 1, 2, 3 |
| j. Propose answers to initial questions related to soil composition based on the results of personal investigations. | Lesson 4<br>Show What You Know | Communicate, p. 135, q. 4<br>Show What You Know, p. 164, q. 1, 10, 13, 14 |
| **ES3.2 Analyze the interdependence between soil and living things, including the importance of soil for individuals, society, and all components of the environment.** | | |
| a. Suggest ways in which individuals and communities value and use soil, including the importance of Mother Earth for First Nations and Métis peoples. | Lesson 3<br><br>Lesson 13<br><br>Design Project<br><br>Show What You Know | Work On It, p. 133<br>Communicate, p. 133, q. 1, 2<br>Work On It, p. 153<br>Communicate, p. 153, q. 1, 2, 3<br>Work On It, p. 161<br>Communicate, p. 161, q. 1, 2<br>Show What You Know, p. 161, q. 3 |
| b. Examine the interdependence between animals and soils | Lesson 8<br><br>Lesson 9<br><br>Design Project<br>Show What You Know | Work On It, p. 142<br>Communicate, p. 143, q. 1<br>Work On It, p. 144<br>Communicate, p. 145, q. 1, 2<br>Work On It, p. 161<br>Show What You Know, p. 164, q. 6 |
| c. Examine the interdependence between plants and soils. | Lesson 8<br><br>Design Project<br>Show What You Know | Work On It, p. 142<br>Communicate, p. 143, q. 1<br>Work On It, p. 161<br>Show What You Know, p. 164, q. 5 |
| d. Relate the characteristics of soils to their uses. | Lesson 13<br><br>Show What You Know | Work On It, p. 153<br>Communicate, p. 153, q. 1, 2, 3<br>Show What You Know, p. 164, q. 11 |
| e. Observe the effects of moving water on soils in different environments. | Lesson 11 | Work On It, p. 148<br>Communicate, p. 149, q. 1, 2 |
| f. Collaboratively design and safely carry out procedures to determine the effects of moving water on different types of soils. | Lesson 10 | Work On It, p. 146<br>Communicate, p. 147, q. 1, 2, 3 |

## Unit Indicators Correlation Chart *(continued)*

| Indicator | Lesson References | Assessment Opportunities |
|---|---|---|
| g. Propose practices that individuals and communities can take to reduce the effects of erosion on a small-scale and large-scale. | Lesson 12<br><br>Design Project<br><br>Show What You Know | Work On It, p. 151<br>Communicate, p. 151, q. 1, 2, 3<br>Work On It, p. 161<br>Communicate, p. 161, q. 1, 2<br>Show What You Know, p. 164, q. 9 |
| h. Suggest sustainable practices that can affect soils positively and reduce or prevent harmful effects such as compaction and contamination of soils. | Lesson 14<br><br>Lesson 15<br><br>Design Project<br><br>Show What You Know | Work On It, p. 155<br>Communicate, p. 155, q. 1, 2, 3<br>Work On It, p. 159<br>Communicate, p. 159, q. 1, 2<br>Work On It, p. 161<br>Communicate, p. 161, q. 1, 2<br>Show What You Know, p. 164, q. 12, 15 |
| i. Research careers that involve an understanding of soils. | Ask … | Research, p. 157 |

## Lesson Planning Chart

Note that estimates of class times are based on 40 min per period.

| Lesson | Type of Activity | Time (number of classes) | Materials Required (for each group) | Line Masters |
|---|---|---|---|---|
| **Unit Opener** | | 1 | pencils | LM 4-1<br>LM 4-2<br>LM 4-3 |
| **Launch:** How Do We Depend on Soil? | confirmation inquiry | 1 | 1 piece of chart paper<br>1 coloured marker<br>pencils | none |
| **1.** A Cup of Soil | structured inquiry | 1–2 | digging trowel<br>resealable plastic bag or plastic container with a lid<br>2–3 pill bottles or baby food jars<br>2 pairs of rubber gloves (optional)<br>old newspaper<br>cupful of soil<br>sieve<br>spoon<br>magnifying lens<br>camera (optional)<br>pencils | LM 4-4 |
| **2.** How Do Scientists Understand Soil? | confirmation inquiry | 1 | pencils | LM 4-5 |
| **3.** How Do Indigenous Peoples Understand Soil? | guided inquiry | 2-3 | clipboards or pieces of stiff cardboard with metal clips (one per student)<br>216 by 279 mm paper<br>pencils for sketching<br>camera (optional) | LM 4-6 |
| **4.** What Makes Soils Different? | structured inquiry | 2 | newspaper<br>marker<br>3 spoons<br>3 different soil samples<br>magnifying lens<br>pencils | LM 4-7 |
| **5.** What Is in Soil? | structured inquiry | 2 | soil samples from three different places (keep these soil samples for use in Lesson 7)<br>3 paper towels<br>marker<br>spray bottle of water<br>3 spoons<br>pencils | LM 4-8<br>LM 4-9 |

## Lesson Planning Chart *(continued)*

| Lesson | Type of Activity | Time (number of classes) | Materials Required (for each group) | Line Masters |
|---|---|---|---|---|
| **6.** Separating Soil | structured inquiry | 2–3 | glass jar with a lid<br>soil sample<br>container of water<br>marker<br>spoon<br>paper towel<br>magnifying lens<br>pencils | LM 4-10 |
| **7.** How Much Water? | structured inquiry | 2 | equal amounts of dry sand, silt, clay, and loam<br>7 paper cups<br>7 pieces of fabric<br>nail or skewer<br>2 measuring cups<br>water<br>soil samples from Lesson 5<br>pencils | LM 4-11<br>LM 4-12 |
| **8.** What Lives in Soil? | confirmation inquiry | 3–4 | pencils | LM 4-13 |
| **9.** Meet the Earthworms! | confirmation inquiry | 2 | large, clear jar<br>small rocks or pebbles<br>sand<br>soil<br>spoon<br>water<br>earthworms<br>worm food, such as leaves<br>aluminum foil<br>tape<br>pencils | LM 4-14<br>LM 4-15 |
| **10.** How Does Moving Water Affect Soil? | guided inquiry | 3 | equal amounts of sandy soil, silty soil, soil high in clay, and loamy soil high in humus<br>4 cookie sheets or baking pans<br>8 blocks or books<br>measuring cup<br>water<br>camera (optional)<br>pencils | LM 4-16 |
| **11.** Erosion Changes Soil | confirmation inquiry | 1 | pencils | LM 4-17 |

| Lesson | Type of Activity | Time (number of classes) | Materials Required (for each group) | Line Masters |
|---|---|---|---|---|
| **12.** How Can We Prevent Soil Erosion? | guided inquiry | 3 | loam (enough for 2 cookie sheets or baking pans ¾ full)<br>2 cookie sheets or baking pans<br>water<br>camera (optional)<br>pencils | LM 4-18 |
| **13.** Using Earth's Soils | guided inquiry | 3 | clay<br>water<br>plastic or wood board<br>tools for cutting and shaping clay (e.g., plastic knives, pizza cutters, rolling pins)<br>pencils | LM 4-19 |
| **14.** Preventing Harm to Our Soil | guided inquiry | 2–3 | loam<br>2 cookie sheets or baking pans<br>6 books<br>water<br>watering can<br>camera (optional)<br>pencils | LM 4-20 |
| **Ask …** Why is it important to understand soil? | | 2–3 | pencils | LM 4-21 |
| **15.** Taking Care of Our Soil | structured inquiry | 3 | pencils | LM 4-22<br>LM 4-23 |
| **Design Project:** Create Soil for a Garden | guided inquiry | 4–6 | soil sample from your schoolyard<br>humus or compost<br>earthworms<br>silt<br>sand<br>clay<br>hand lenses<br>water<br>glass jar with a lid<br>watering can<br>spray bottle<br>container or pan for healthy soil<br>vegetable seeds<br>pencils | LM 4-24<br>LM 4-25 |

traditional **KNOWLEDGE**

## First Nations Cultural References

The following references provide information on First Nations topics. The information may not be specific to Saskatchewan First Nations and should not be generalized to all First Nations.

- As suggested in Lesson 3, take your students on a field trip to the natural environment and observe the gifts of Mother Earth.
- First Nations or Métis Elders and Traditional Knowledge Keepers may be invited to the classroom to share their wisdom about Mother Earth. Follow the "Protocol for Contacting Elders and Traditional Knowledge Keepers" in the Program Overview of this Teacher's Resource.

## Suggested Websites

Please note that website URLs constantly change and the addresses given below may become out of date. In this case, please use the website title and a search engine to find the appropriate website.

- Just for Kids—Soil Biological Communities, National Science & Technology Center: www.blm.gov/nstc/soil/Kids/index.html
- Dr. Dirt—K-12 Teaching Resources and Activities: www.wtamu.edu/~crobinson/DrDirt.htm
- Discovery Education—The Dirt on Soil: http://school.discoveryeducation.com/schooladventures/soil/
- University of Illinois Extension—The Great Plant Escape, Case 2, Soiled Again!: http://urbanext.illinois.edu/gpe/case2/index.html
- TLC Family—Science Projects for Kids: Soil Experiments: http://tlc.howstuffworks.com/family/science-projects-for-kids-soil-experiments.htm
- United States Department of Agriculture, National Resources Conservation Service—S.K. Worm Answers Your Questions About Soil and Stuff: www.nrcs.usda.gov/feature/education/squirm/skworm.html
- The Kids Garden—Teaching Kids About Soil: www.thekidsgarden.co.uk/TeachingKidsAboutSoil.html
- Saskatchewan Waste Reduction Council—Composting: www.saskwastereduction.ca/resources/Composting/composting-index.html
- National Occupational Classification Profiles: www5.hrsdc.gc.ca/NOC/English/NOC/2006/SearchAlphabetical.aspx
- Saskatchewan JobFutures: Careers in Saskatchewan: www.saskjobfutures.ca/index.cfm?event=page.careers

## Suggested Field Trips

- In Lesson 1, it is recommended that all students explore soil from the same place. Consider taking students to collect soil samples from the schoolyard for this activity. In Lesson 4, students compare three soil samples from different locations. They can use the samples from Lesson 1 as one soil type. Then, plan to take students to a nearby park, meadow, garden, and/or wooded area to collect other soil samples. (The samples will be used throughout the unit.)

- In Lesson 5, students need soil samples from three different locations. For this lesson, it is important that students accompany you to get the soil samples because they need to observe the location and the plants growing in each location in order to answer the Communicate questions. In indicator ES3.1b, the curriculum suggests that students examine the characteristics of soils from different locations, such as a garden, flower pot, river bed, slough, hill top, grassy field, lawn, ditch, and forest. Choose three of these locations to which you and your students have easy access.
- You will also need samples of sand, silt, clay, and loam for activities in this unit. Consider taking your students to a beach to collect sand; to an eroded river bank or site where a basement is being dug to collect clay; to the bottom of a field washout or the mud at the edge of a stream or pond to collect silt; and to a garden or field to collect loam. You may also wish to purchase loam from a garden supply store or nursery.
- Other interesting locations you may wish to take students include:
  - a garden supply store or nursery to buy soils
  - a greenhouse to see how different soils are used for different plants
  - a ceramic studio to see how people work with clay
  - a brick-making company for a tour of the facility
  - local places where students can see signs of erosion

## Suggested Guest Speakers

- Invite guests who can share their knowledge of soils with students. You might invite farmers or gardeners, especially those who have knowledge of growing organic produce.
- Artisans who work with clay would also be interesting guests for students. Suggest that visiting guests bring along some of their materials to show students.

## Suggested Additional Student Resources

- *A Handful of Dirt* by Raymond Bial (Walker Books for Young Readers, Walker & Company, 2000)
- *Soil* by Cristin Ditchfield (True Books—Natural Resources, Children's Press, a division of Scholastic Inc., 2002)
- *Composting: Nature's Recyclers* by Robin Michel Koontz (Picture Window Books, 2002)
- *Life in a Bucket of Soil* by Alvin and Virginia Silverstein (Dover Publications, 2000)
- *Dirt —Jump Into Science* by Steve Tomecek (National Geographic Children's Books, 2002)
- *The Scoop on Soils* by Becca Hatheway, Kerry Zarlengo, Lisa Gardiner, Sandra Henderson, and Lynne Hehr (Elementary GLOBE, 2006, download the storybook and learning activities using Adobe Acrobat Reader at http://globe.gov/k-4/soil)
- *Composting for Kids* by Robert E. "Skip" Richter, (Texas AgriLife Extension Service, an online slide show at http://aggie-horticulture.tamu.edu/kindergarden/kidscompost/cover.html)

## Materials and Equipment Needed for Unit 4

(based on 30 students)

|  |  |
|---|---|
| **Launch: How Do We Depend on Soil? (p. 126)** | |
| **Materials**<br>• 15 pieces of chart paper<br>• 15 coloured markers<br>• pencils | **Equipment**<br>• no equipment needed |
| **1. A Cup of Soil (p. 128)** | |
| **Materials**<br>• 30 pairs of rubber gloves (optional)<br>• 15 old newspapers<br>• 15 cups of soil<br>• pencils | **Equipment**<br>• 15 digging trowels<br>• 15 resealable plastic bags or plastic containers with lids<br>• 10–15 pill bottles or baby food jars<br>• 15 sieves<br>• 15 spoons<br>• 15 magnifying lenses<br>• 15 sieves<br>• camera (optional) |
| **2. How Do Scientists Understand Soil? (p. 130)** | |
| **Materials**<br>• pencils | **Equipment**<br>• no equipment needed |
| **3. How Do Indigenous Peoples Understand Soil? (p. 132)** | |
| **Materials**<br>• 30–60 sheets of 216 by 279 mm paper<br>• pencils | **Equipment**<br>• 30 clipboards (or 30 pieces of stiff cardboard and 30 metal clips) |
| **4. What Makes Soils Different? (p. 134)** | |
| **Materials**<br>• 15 old newspapers<br>• 15 markers<br>• 3 different soil samples (enough soil in each sample for 15 pairs)<br>• pencils | **Equipment**<br>• 15 magnifying lenses<br>• 45 spoons |
| **5. What Is in Soil? (p. 136)** | |
| **Materials**<br>• soil samples from three different places (enough soil in each sample for 15 pairs)<br>(keep these soil samples for Lesson 7)<br>• water<br>• 3 paper towels<br>• 15 markers<br>• pencils | **Equipment**<br>• 15 spray bottles<br>• 45 spoons |

## Materials and Equipment

*(continued)*

| 6. Separating Soil (p. 138) | |
|---|---|
| **Materials**<br>• soil sample (enough soil for 15 pairs)<br>• water<br>• 15 paper towels<br>• 15 markers<br>• pencils | **Equipment**<br>• 15 glass jars with lids<br>• 15 spoons<br>• 15 containers for water<br>• 15 magnifying lenses |
| **7. How Much Water? (p. 140)** | |
| **Materials**<br>• dry sand (enough for 15 pairs)<br>• dry silt (enough for 15 pairs)<br>• dry clay (enough for 15 pairs)<br>• dry loam (enough for 15 pairs)<br>• soil samples from Lesson 5<br>• 105 paper cups<br>• 105 pieces of fabric<br>• water<br>• pencils | **Equipment**<br>• 15 nails or skewers<br>• 30 250-mL measuring cups |
| **8. What Lives in Soil? (p. 142)** | |
| **Materials**<br>• pencils | **Equipment**<br>• no equipment needed |
| **9. Meet the Earthworms! (p. 144)** | |
| **Materials**<br>• small rocks or pebbles (enough for layers in 15 large, clear jars)<br>• sand (enough for layers in 15 large, clear jars)<br>• soil (enough for layers in 15 large, clear jars)<br>• water<br>• 45–60 earthworms<br>• worm food, such as leaves<br>• aluminum foil (enough to cover 15 large, clear jars)<br>• 3–5 rolls of tape<br>• pencils | **Equipment**<br>• 15 large, clear jars<br>• 15 spoons |
| **10. How Does Moving Water Affect Soil? (p. 146)** | |
| **Materials**<br>• sandy soil*<br>• silty soil*<br>• soil high in clay*<br>• loamy soil high in humus*<br>• water<br>• pencils<br>* (enough to fill 15 cookie sheets or baking pans ¾ full) | **Equipment**<br>• 60 cookie sheets or baking pans<br>• 180–240 blocks or books (3–4 blocks or books per cookie sheet or baking pan)<br>• 15 250-mL measuring cups<br>• camera (optional) |

## Materials and Equipment

*(continued)*

| 11. Erosion Changes Soil (p. 148) | |
|---|---|
| **Materials**<br>• pencils | **Equipment**<br>• no equipment needed |

| 12. How Can We Prevent Soil Erosion? (p. 150) | |
|---|---|
| **Materials**<br>• loam (enough to fill 30 cookie sheets or baking pans ¾ full)<br>• water<br>• pencils | **Equipment**<br>• 30 cookie sheets or baking pans<br>• camera (optional) |

| 13. Using Earth's Soils (p. 152) | |
|---|---|
| **Materials**<br>• clay (enough for 30 students)<br>• water<br>• pencils | **Equipment**<br>• 30 plastic or wood boards<br>• 30 tools for cutting and shaping clay (e.g., plastic knives, pizza cutters, rolling pins) |

| 14. Preventing Harm to Our Soil (p. 154) | |
|---|---|
| **Materials**<br>• loam (enough to fill 20 cookie sheets or baking pans ¾ full)<br>• water<br>• pencils | **Equipment**<br>• 20 cookie sheets of baking pans<br>• 60 books<br>• 10 watering cans<br>• camera (optional) |

| 15. Taking Care of Our Soil (p. 158) | |
|---|---|
| **Materials**<br>• pencils | **Equipment**<br>• no equipment needed |

| Design Project: Create Soil for a Garden (p. 160) | |
|---|---|
| **Materials**<br>• soil from the schoolyard (enough for 8–10 groups)<br>• humus or compost (enough for 8–10 groups)<br>• earthworms (enough for 8–10 groups)<br>• silt (enough for 8–10 groups)<br>• sand (enough for 8–10 groups)<br>• clay (enough for 8–10 groups)<br>• water<br>• 2–3 packages of vegetable seeds<br>• pencils | **Equipment**<br>• 30 hand lenses<br>• 8–10 glass jars with lids (one per group)<br>• 8–10 watering cans (one per group)<br>• 8–10 spray bottles (one per group)<br>• 8–10 containers or pans for healthy soil (one per group) |

## Materials and Equipment

*(continued)*

### Overall Unit Requirements

| Materials | Equipment |
|---|---|
| • 15 pieces of chart paper<br>• 15 coloured markers<br>• 30 pencils<br>• 30 pairs of rubber gloves (optional)<br>• 30 old newspapers<br>• 15 markers<br>• 30–60 sheets of 216 by 279 mm paper<br>• water<br>• 45 paper towels<br>• 30 pencils<br>• 105 paper cups<br>• 105 pieces of fabric<br>• 45–60 earthworms<br>• worm food such as leaves (enough for 15 large jars)<br>• aluminum foil (enough to cover 15 large, clear jars)<br>• 3–5 rolls of tape (invisible)<br>• water<br>• 2–3 packs of vegetable seeds<br>• 30 pencils<br>• 15 cups of soil<br>• 3 different soil samples (enough soil in each sample for 15 pairs)<br>• soil samples from 3 different places (enough soil in each sample for 15 pairs)<br>• soil sample (enough soil for 15 pairs)<br>• soil samples from Lesson 5<br>• dry sand, silt, clay, and loam (enough of each for 15 pairs)<br>• small rocks or pebbles, sand, and soil (enough of each for layers in 15 large, clear jars)<br>• sandy soil, silty soil, soil high in clay, and loamy soil high in humus (enough of each to fill a 15 cookie sheets or baking pans ¾ full) | • 15 digging trowels<br>• 15 resealable plastic bags or plastic containers with lids<br>• 10–15 pill bottles or baby food jars<br>• 15 sieves<br>• 45 spoons<br>• 30 magnifying lenses<br>• camera (optional)<br>• 30 clipboards (or 30 pieces of stiff cardboard and 30 metal clips)<br>• 15 spray bottles<br>• 15 glass jars with lids (for separating soil samples in water)<br>• 15 containers for water<br>• 15 nails or skewers<br>• 30 250-mL measuring cups<br>• 15 large, clear jars (for investigating earthworms)<br>• 60 cookie sheets or baking pans<br>• 180–240 blocks or books (3–4 blocks or books per cookie sheet or baking pan)<br>• 30 plastic or wood boards<br>• 30 tools for cutting and shaping clay (e.g., plastic knives, pizza cutters, rolling pins)<br>• 10 watering cans<br>• 8–10 containers or pans for holding healthy soil (1 per group) for the design project |

## Materials and Equipment

*(continued)*

| Overall Unit Requirements | |
|---|---|
| **Materials**<br>• loam (enough to fill 30 cookie sheets or baking pans ¾ full)<br>• clay (enough for 30 students)<br>• loam (enough to fill 20 cookie sheets or baking pans ¾ full)<br>• soil from the schoolyard, humus or compost, silt, sand, and clay (enough of each for 8–10 groups) | |

# UNIT 4 Unit Opener

Page 124

| Time |
| --- |
| 40 min |
| **Line Masters** |
| • LM 4-1<br>• LM 4-2<br>• LM 4-3 |

In this unit, students will investigate the characteristics and composition of soils. As they analyze different soil samples, they will learn that soils vary by texture, particle size, colour, ability to absorb moisture, and ability to hold together, and that different types of soil are found in different locations. Students will come to understand the importance of soil to all living things. Students will identify ways in which people use soil as well as positive and negative ways in which people affect soil. Students will also learn that First Nations and Métis ways of knowing about Mother Earth add meaning to how scientists understand soil.

## Assessing Prior Knowledge

- Read the text and examine the photograph on pages 124–125 of the student book with students. Use the questions embedded in the text to initiate a discussion with students about what they know about soil.
- Use the Looking Forward activity to determine what students know about soil.

## Introduce the Unit

- Provide LM 4-2 Unit 4 Vocabulary. Guide students to check off the terms as they learn them and then use the terms to make a concept map. Ask, *What clues do these words give you about what we will be studying in this unit?*
- Explain to students that in this unit they will investigate:
  - what is in soil
  - how soil forms
  - how soils are different
  - what happens when water moves through or over different soils
  - ways in which plants, animals, and soil depend on each other
  - how people use soil in different ways
  - how people can affect soil in harmful and helpful ways
- Provide LM 4-1 Unit 4 Summary. Read each statement with students and have them put a checkmark beside the ideas they already know and understand. Students will refer to this summary throughout the unit.
- Encourage each student to bring a sealed bag with some soil from a yard or park. Students should label the bags with their names. Invite students who compost at home to bring in some humus that has been created from their compost heap. Set up a tabletop display of the soil samples and tell students to feel free to add to it throughout the unit.

## Introduce the Design Project

Explain that in this unit students will learn everything they need to know to make healthy soil. In the Design Project, they will work in groups to plan how to create healthy soil for a class vegetable garden. Then they will use a soil sample from the schoolyard to put their plan into action.

| Time |
| --- |
| 20 min |
| **Skills** |
| • communicating |
| **Grouping** |
| individuals/pairs/class |
| **Materials and Equipment** |
| • chart paper and marker<br>• pencils |
| **Line Masters** |
| • LM 4-3 |

## Looking Forward

- Use a KWL chart to stimulate interest, connect new learning to existing knowledge, generate inquiry questions, and assess your students' prior knowledge. Post a large sheet of paper. Title it "Soil," and divide it into three columns. Label the columns "What I **K**now About Soil," "What I **W**ant to Know About Soil," and "What I **L**earned About Soil." You may wish to approach this activity in one of the following ways.
- **As a whole-class activity:** Brainstorm with students for facts—things they know to be true—about soil. Record what they know in the first column of the master KWL display chart. Example statements for What I Know About Soil include the following:
  - Soil is black or brown.
  - Mud is made of soil.
  - We eat food that grows in soil.
  - Plants grow in soil.
- Then ask students what they want to know about soil and record their questions in the second column of the KWL display chart. Guide students to suggest questions such as:
  - *What is soil made of?*
  - *How does soil form?*
  - *How are soils different?*
  - *How are soils the same?*
  - *How do we learn about soil?*
  - *What lives in soil?*
  - *How is soil important to people, plants, and animals?*
  - *How do people use soil?*
  - *What changes soil?*
  - *How do people hurt soil?*
  - *How can people care for soil?*
- Inform students that they will return to this master KWL chart to record what they learn about soil as they progress through the unit. Post it where it can be easily viewed and accessed.
- **As an individual, pairs, or whole-class activity:** Hand out copies of LM 4-3 Soil KWL Chart. Ask students to work individually (or with a partner) to record facts they know to be true about soil in the first column. Then provide an opportunity for individual students (or pairs) to share what they know about soil with the class.
- Record their statements on the master KWL chart. Before you add each entry, ask the class if everyone agrees that the statement is true. If any students question whether a particular response is true, reword it as a question and enter it under the What I Want to Know About column.
- Have students work on their own (or with their partners) to think about what they want to know about soil and record their questions on LM 4-3 Soil KWL Chart. Provide an opportunity for individual students (or pairs) to share their questions about soil with the class. Record their questions on the master KWL chart. (Refer to the list of possible questions above.)
- Inform students that they will return to their KWL charts to record answers to their questions as they progress through the unit. Keep their charts in a binder or folder where they can be easily accessed and worked on. Post the master KWL chart where entries under the What I Learned About Soil can be easily added.

# How Do We Depend on Soil?

Page 126

**Time**

40 min

**Line Masters**

- none

**traditional KNOWLEDGE**

## Get Started ▶

- Many First Nations and Métis people understand soil as the "skin" of Mother Earth and revere it. Their reliance on plants harvested from the soil for food and medicine help us understand how this belief may have evolved. Tobacco is offered for all the gifts that Mother Earth gives us. Traditional tobacco is not the tobacco that people think of today. For more explanation on cultural teachings about tobacco, see Mia's Story on page 31 and Unit 2 of this Teacher's Resource.
- *Soil* may be a new word for some students, who may be more accustomed to the word *earth* or even *dirt*. Discuss these terms with students. Say, *Soil is different from dirt. Soil is an important resource that all living things need. Dirt is soil that is out of place. When soil sticks to your shoes and ends up on the floor, it is called dirt and we say it makes the floor dirty. When you step in a mud puddle made from soil and water, your feet become dirty.*
- Before students look at the picture in the student book, ask, *How do living things—plants, animals, and people— depend on soil?* Have students work in pairs to think of ways that living things depend on soil. Provide each pair with chart paper and coloured markers for recording their ideas. Then, meet as a class to share ideas. List students' ideas on a chart entitled "How Living Things Depend on Soil." Explain to students that they will add to their list of ideas as they look at pages 126–127 of the student book.

**Time**

20 min

**Learning Context**

inquiry

**Level of Inquiry**

confirmation

**Skills**

- observing
- interpreting
- communicating
- predicting

**Grouping**

pairs

**Materials and Equipment**

(per group)
- one piece of chart paper
- coloured marker
- pencils

**Line Masters**

- none

## Work On It

### Purpose

To consider how living things, including people, depend on soil and to begin to recognize and identify what makes soils different

### Activity Notes

- Review questions 1 to 4 as a guide for students' observations of the picture on pages 126–127 of the student book. Provide time for student pairs to use these questions to view and think about the elements shown in the picture.
  - Instruct pairs to record their observations in response to each question.

- Circulate among students as they work. If they need more help to focus their attention on key elements of the picture, pose questions such as:
  - *What different plants do you see growing in soil?*
  - *Which animal homes do you see? What other animals do you know that live in the soil?*
  - *What different types of food do you see growing here? What other foods grow in soil?*
  - *Why are plants important to animals? Why are plants important to people?*
  - *Why are trees important to us?*
  - *How do people use soil to make things?*
  - *How do people use things that grow in soil to make things?*

## Communicate

Provide an opportunity for each pair of students to share their lists of responses to the Work On It questions 1 to 4 with another pair.

**1.** Students' answers may vary but could include:

Living things depend on soil in the following ways:

- Plants grow in soil, including trees, vegetables, flowers, and crops.
- People eat corn, tomatoes, and beans that grow in soil. People eat other plants that grow in soil, such as vegetables, herbs, berries, and other fruits.
- Worms and ants live in soil.
- Ground squirrels dig tunnels and rabbits dig holes to live in soil.
- Animals such as deer and rabbits eat plants that need soil to grow. Other animals eat animals that eat plants that need soil to grow.

Soil is important to people in the following ways:

- People use soil to make building materials like bricks and cement.
- People use wood from trees that grow in soil to build houses and furniture.
- People use soil (clay) to make pots and mugs.
- The food people eat comes from plants that grow in soil or animals that feed on plants.
- Farmers grow crops in soil.
- Sand is a soil that is fun to play in.

Soil might be different in the following places:

- on the beach
- near the water
- in the garden
- in the field
- in the pasture
- around the house

The soil might be different in these places because:

- it might have different materials in it
- it might hold different amounts of water

**2.** Students' answers may vary but could include the points above. Model for students how to add new ideas to their lists as they share their responses with another pair of students.

**3.** Students' answers may vary but could include: Is all soil brown? Where does soil come from?

## DI Differentiating Instruction

### *For EAL/ELL*

Ensure that EAL/ELL students can name each item in the picture on the student book pages. Students can use sticky notes to label the living things in this picture. Then, they can create drawings to illustrate how living things depend on soil. For example, they could sketch plants growing in soil, animals eating plants that grow in soil, and people eating vegetables that grow in soil.

### *For Enrichment*

Provide students with magazines, such as *National Geographic, Canadian Geographic, Chickadee,* or *OWL*, and ask students to look for pictures that illustrate ways in which living things depend on soil. Challenge students to observe ways in which living things depend on soil in their community.

### *For Reteaching*

If students have difficulty understanding how some living things indirectly depend on soil (e.g., how a deer depends on soil), draw pictures to illustrate the connections (e.g., sketch the deer eating the plant that grows in the soil—without the soil, the plant would not grow, and the deer would not have food).

## Assessment *for* Learning

| What to Look for in Student Work | What to Do |
|---|---|
| Students can identify ways in which living things, including people, plants, and animals, depend on soil. | • Observe students as they complete the Work On It activity.<br>• Observe students as they share their responses to the questions of the Work On It activity. |
| Students can identify where soil might be different and why it might be different. | • Observe students as they complete the Work On It activity.<br>• Observe students as they share their responses to the questions of the Work On It activity. |

# 1 A Cup of Soil

Page 128

| Time |
| --- |
| 40–80 min |
| **Line Masters** |
| • LM 4-4 |

## Indicator Assessment Chart

| Indicator | Assessment Opportunities |
| --- | --- |
| **ES3.1 d.** Analyze soil samples using tools such as spoons, hand lenses, jars, and filters appropriately and safely. | • Work On It, p. 128 |
| **ES3.1 e.** Make and record observations and measurements in investigations related to soil composition using techniques such as notes in point form, diagrams, tables, bar graphs, photographs, and video. | • Work On It, p. 128<br>• Communicate, p. 129, q. 1–3 |

## Lesson Goal

To discover what you can find in a cup of soil

## Background Information

Soil is a mixture of tiny fragments of rock, mineral grains, and organic material, which may be waste from living things or decayed material from once-living things. There are tiny spaces between these materials called pores. The pores in soil are filled with water or air.

Soil can also be described as having three components: solid, liquid, and gas. The mineral matter (sand, silt, and clay particles) and organic matter are the solid part of soil and give soil its mass. About half of a typical soil sample is made up of mineral (about 45 percent) and organic matter (1–5 percent). The spaces between the solid particles are filled with water (liquid) and air (gas). Water and air make up the other half of a typical soil sample. Students should be able to see small, bead-like particles (mineral matter) with their magnifying lenses. They may see little rocklike pieces (mineral pieces) and organic matter (leaves, sticks, straw, worms, beetles, and so on).

## Curriculum Connections

In this lesson, students have the opportunity to develop skills and concepts in these areas:

### *English Language Arts*

CC3.1 a. Use words, symbols, and other forms, including appropriate technology, to express understanding of topics, themes, and issues and make connections to learning in other areas of study.

CC3.1 b. Communicate thoughts, feelings, and ideas clearly and, when appropriate, artistically.

## Focus on Literacy

### *During Writing: The OWL Strategy*

Making good observations and taking notes is an essential skill in science. The OWL strategy is a variation of the KWL strategy for science, where "O" stands for "What I Observed," "W" for "What I Wonder," and "L" for "What I Learned."

Provide a copy of LM 4-4 OWL Chart for each student as pairs begin the Work On It activity of the lesson. Students can record their observations about the different soils in the "O" or "What I Observed" column of the chart.

Use the following guidelines for making good observations and taking good notes to support students as they work through the activity:

- Use as many of your senses as possible to observe (e.g., sight, hearing, touch, smell).
- Caution students that using the sense of taste is not appropriate in this science activity.
- Write down only what you see and not what you imagine.
- Focus on the physical properties of matter (e.g., size, shape, texture, odour).
- Use scientific language when you can.
- Include labelled diagrams of what you are observing when possible.
- Record the date, time, and any measurements you have taken.

Once students have completed the Work On It activity, lead a whole-group sharing of observations. Focus on ensuring that students' observations are observations and not inferences and have them revise their charts as necessary.

Provide time for students to record their wonderings in the second column of the chart and what they have learned in the third column. If students made individual KWL charts in the Looking Forward activity of the Unit Opener, you may wish to have them combine the two charts.

## Misconceptions

Students may think that soil is just dirt. The focus of the activity in this lesson is to have students discover that soil is made up of different bits and things—some larger and some smaller—and that these bits are not all the same. If soil were just dirt, students would not find different bits and things as they will in the soil samples they examine in this lesson.

## Get Started ▶

- Read the text in the Get Started with students.
- Invite students to share their experiences and observations about soil. Ask, *Have you ever made a sandcastle or a mud pie? Have you ever helped plant a garden? What other ways have you worked with or played in soil?*

| Time |
| --- |
| 30 min |
| **Learning Context** |
| inquiry |
| **Level of Inquiry** |
| structured |
| **Skills** |
| • observing<br>• classifying |
| **Grouping** |
| pairs |
| **Materials and Equipment** |
| (per group)<br>• digging trowel<br>• resealable plastic bag or plastic container with a lid<br>• pill bottles or baby food jars<br>• rubber gloves (optional)<br>• newspaper<br>• cupful of soil<br>• sieve<br>• spoon<br>• magnifying lens<br>• camera (optional)<br>• pencils |
| **Line Masters** |
| • none |

**SAFETY CAUTION!**

If you collect a soil sample from your neighbourhood, your teacher will tell you which places are safe so that you do not harm plants or animals. Always wash your hands after handling soil.

You may also wish to provide rubber gloves for students to use to handle soil.

- Inquire if students have ever looked closely at soil. Ask, *What did you see or find?* Explain to students that they will be taking a close look at soil to see what they can discover.
- Ask students to bring in some soil from their yards or from indoor house plants. Explain that the sample does not need to be large (a few tablespoons is fine) and that they must ask their parents' permission before taking any such samples. Have students show these samples to the class and tell where each sample comes from and how it was collected.

## Work On It

### Purpose

To investigate and identify different materials and sizes of materials in a cup of soil

### Activity Notes

- While the type of soil sample for this lesson is not specified in the student book, it is recommended that all students work with samples from the same area, such as samples collected in the schoolyard.
- As a class, go outside to collect more soil samples. Students will investigate these samples throughout the unit. Provide small digging trowels and resealable bags or clear plastic containers with lids. Gather students at an appropriate spot outdoors to review the digging procedure. Tell students to take the sample from the top layer of the ground. The soil found just under leaves is good, as is soil found around the edges of gardens. Once back in class, have students label the bags or containers telling where each soil sample was collected.
- There is a strong possibility that students will discover tiny live specimens in the soil. These can be transferred to small pill bottles or baby food jars and returned outside after students have examined them closely with a magnifying lens.
- Review the steps in What You Will Do with students before they begin their investigations. Observe them as they work to ensure that they are following the steps in the procedure correctly.
- Direct students to provide as much detail as possible in their pictures of the groups of big and small bits in the soil. Challenge them to find the best colour match to shade the different bits they discover in their soil sample. The ability to observe something and then record those observations accurately is essential to most science activities.
- It is likely that students will find things in the soil that they are unable to identify. Encourage them to think about what the material might be and be ready to share their thoughts when they present their drawings.

## Additional Activity

With the class, develop a list of words to describe what soil looks, feels, and smells like.

## Communicate

Have pairs present their pictures of the groups they made and share what they observed in each group. As each pair presents, record the key observations on chart paper under the headings Big Bits and Small Bits. Conclude the session by asking, *Is there anything you can think of that we should add to our class KWL chart?* Record students' suggestions.

1. Students should identify the place where the soil sample came from (e.g., schoolyard, garden, forest, field).
2. Students' answers may vary depending on the type of soil examined but could include bits of leaves, pieces of twigs, dead grasses, small bits of rocks, tiny snail shells, and so on.
3. Though students' answers may vary depending on the type of soil examined, pieces of weathered rock are typically the material that students find the most of in soil samples.
4. Students' answers may vary but could include decaying bits of the plants and insects that lived in the garden where the sample is from or decaying bits from the trees and plants (e.g., leaves and twigs) and the animals (e.g., bits of bone, insect shells, droppings) that lived in the forest where the sample is from.

## DI Differentiating Instruction

### *For EAL/ELL*

Pair EAL/ELL students with students who are proficient speakers and writers of English so they receive effective modelling of the English language. EAL/ELL students could draw their responses to the Communicate questions and then meet with you to share what they drew.

### *For Enrichment*

Encourage students to think of interesting places nearby where they can find different soil samples. The class could work together to create a list or map of sites. Next, work out a way to visit some of these sites to collect samples that you can use throughout the unit.

## Assessment *for* Learning

| What to Look for in Student Work | What to Do |
|---|---|
| Students can use a sieve, spoon, and magnifying lens to examine soil samples appropriately and safely. | • Observe students as they complete the Work On It activity. |
| Students can make and record observations using diagrams. | • Observe students' pictures of the groups they made. Look for their attention to detail and accuracy (e.g., the individual bits in each group, and the colours of the bits). |
| Students can identify and/or describe what they found in their soil sample. | • Check students' responses to Communicate questions 2 and 3. |
| Students can begin to identify that the composition of soil is different depending on the location in which it is found. | • Check students' responses to Communicate question 4. |

# 2 How Do Scientists Understand Soil?

Page 130

| Time |
|---|
| 40 min |

| Vocabulary |
|---|
| • particles<br>• humus |

| Line Masters |
|---|
| • LM 4-5 |

## Indicator Assessment Chart

| Indicator | Assessment Opportunities |
|---|---|
| **ES3.1 a.** Pose questions and make predictions about the characteristics and composition of soils that lead to exploration and investigation (e.g., What colours are soil? What does soil feel like? Where does soil come from? Is there water in soil?). | • Work On It, p. 131<br>• Communicate, p. 131, q. 1–3 |

## Lesson Goal

To find out how scientists think about soil

traditional ***KNOWLEDGE***

## Background Information

Soil is formed slowly over a long period of time. Rocks and rotted plant and animal materials start to weather and break down into small parts. Plants like moss and lichen grow in the small cracks and spaces in rock, causing it to break down even further. As rainwater seeps into cracks and crevices in rock, it dissolves some of the nutrients there and creates good conditions for some plants to grow. Plant roots hold the accumulating soil in place, and as these plants die and decay, humus begins to form. All this time the rock continues to break into smaller pieces.

Over time, soil forms into layers. The top layer is called *topsoil.* The topsoil is the layer with the most humus. It is home to many small living things and plant roots. *Subsoil* is found below topsoil and has less water, air, and organic matter. Broken and solid rock is found under the subsoil.

Humus, the decayed plant and animal matter in soil, is what makes a soil fertile. Soils that are high in humus do not compress as tightly and have more air spaces. Organic particles also absorb water and help the soil hold moisture. Water is also held in the air spaces between soil particles.

Scientists and First Nations and Métis peoples have similar and different views of soil. Rocks, as scientists describe, erode and become constituent parts of soil. First Nations and Métis peoples have a differing view. They see rocks as distinctly separate from soil. Rocks are a separate entity with Spirit (see ! feature below). Along with water, air, and fire, rock is considered an element.

*continued→*

Many First Nations and Métis peoples believe that soil is a part of Mother Earth like her skin and that trees and plants grow from her body through the soil. The soil nourishes the trees, which shelter and supply people with materials for tools and other implements, and the plants, which provide food that sustains us.

In another respect, scientists and First Nations and Métis peoples understand soil similarly. Scientists see soil as a living layer, thriving in organic material, and First Nations and Métis peoples see soil as alive, as the "skin" of Mother Earth. It is appropriate to explore and discuss ways that the two groups view soil similarly and differently. The following Venn diagram illustrates how these differing views of soil can be compared and contrasted in a respectful way.

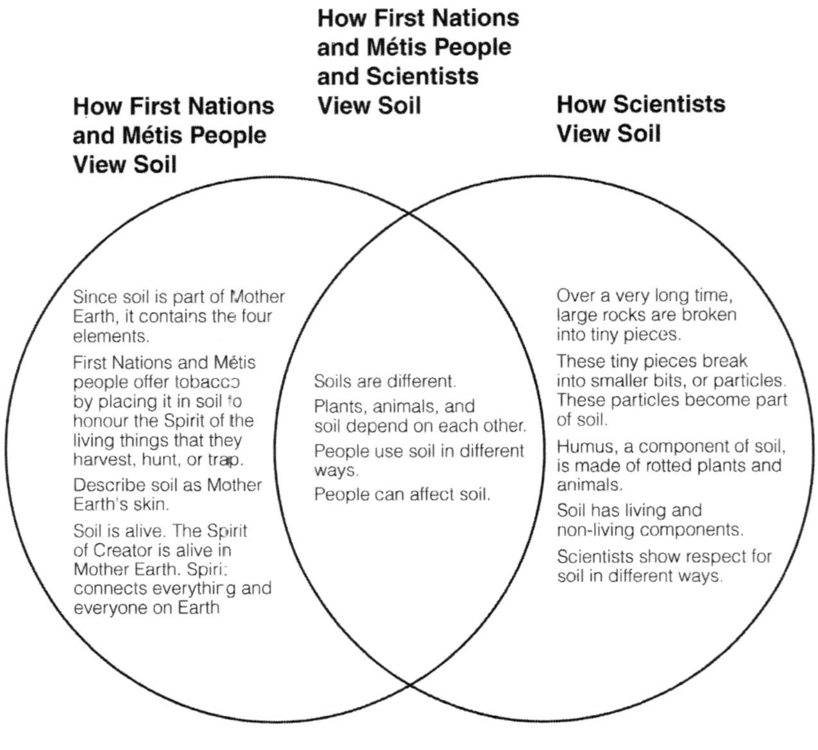

## Curriculum Connections

In this lesson, students have the opportunity to develop skills and concepts in these areas:

### *English Language Arts*

CR3.2 d. Record facts and ideas from grade-appropriate visual and multimedia texts including DVD, television program, magazine, and reference resources.
CR3.4 d. Ask questions and support answers by connecting prior knowledge with literal information found in, and inferred from, texts including First Nations and Métis resources.
CC3.1 a. Use words, symbols, and other forms, including appropriate technology, to express understanding of topics, themes, and issues and make connections to learning in other areas of study.

**Get Started ▶**

- Explain to students that they will learn how scientists say soil forms and what is in soil as they read the information in the Get Started.
- Read the text and photo captions with students and then invite students to explain in their own words what each photo reveals about soil.
- Two new words are introduced in this lesson: *particles* and *humus*. Ask students to find the little word they know in *particles*. When they identify *part*, ask them its meaning. Connect the meaning of *part* to the meaning of *particles*. A part is a piece of something. Particles are little pieces of something. To help students with the correct pronunciation of *humus* (pronounced HEW mus), relate it to *human*.
- On the board or on chart paper, develop a flow chart with students to represent the process of soil formation. Or, create a web such as the following:

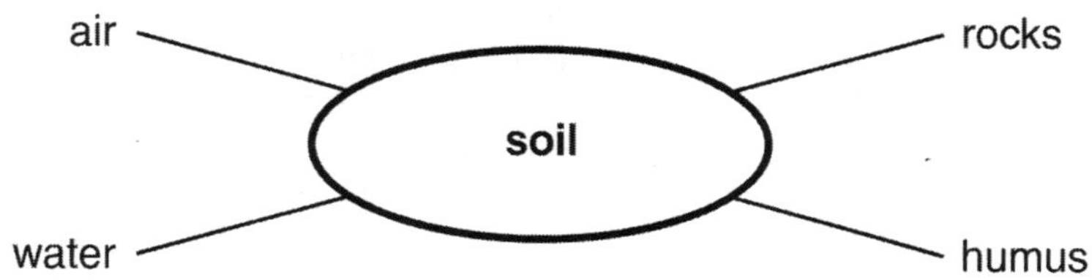


- Have students suggest details to add to each of the four sub-categories (e.g., rocks, air, water, and humus) in the web to show how each element contributes to the formation of soil.

traditional ***KNOWLEDGE***

Many First Nations peoples call rock "Grandfather Rock" [*kise-nāpē-asiniy* in Cree]. They say that rocks are the oldest beings on Mother Earth and that rocks have been on Mother Earth since the beginning of time. Many First Nations and Métis Elders believe that all things on Mother Earth are living beings and have Spirit, including rock, which may appear inanimate. In many First Nations cultures, rock is used in special ceremonies, such as the sweat lodge. Rock is also used to make the pipestone of the sacred pipe.

| Time |
| --- |
| 15–20 min |
| **Learning Context** |
| inquiry |
| **Level of Inquiry** |
| confirmation |
| **Skills** |
| • observing<br>• interpreting |
| **Grouping** |
| pairs |
| **Line Masters** |
| • none |

## Work On It

### Purpose

To examine photos of locations and identify what helps makes soil as a scientist would

### Activity Notes

- Have students work in pairs to examine the photos on page 131 of the student book and to record their ideas about what would help make the soil shown in each photo. As students examine the photos, circulate to listen to their comments and observations. Arrange for pairs with different ideas to meet and discuss their observations. Encourage students to listen to each other's ideas and to ask questions for clarification.
- Meet as a large group to review students' observations. You can make a comprehensive list of observations by listing responses from all pairs on a chart with three columns labelled "Photo 1," "Photo 2," and "Photo 3."

## Additional Activity

You may wish to use LM 4-5 Is There Air in Soil? as an additional activity to demonstrate how air fills spaces between soil particles.

## Communicate

**1.**
- Photo of beach: air, broken rock, water, broken shells. The soil would have more rock, air, and water.
- Photo of wetlands: water, air, humus from dead plants and animals, mud. The soil would have more water and humus from dead plants and animals.
- Photo of forest: air, water, grass, humus from dead plants and animals, bits of dead leaves and twigs, broken rock. The soil would have more humus in it.

**2.** Students' answers may vary depending on their familiarity with garden soil but could include rotted plants and animals, as well as living things, such as worms and insects.

**3.** Students' answers may vary depending on their familiarity with field soil but could include rotted plants and animals, as well as living things, such as worms and insects.

### BUILD ON WHAT YOU KNOW

Students' responses to the Build On What You Know questions throughout the unit will help them with the end-of-unit Design Project. Part of the project involves identifying the type of soil in their schoolyard soil sample and deciding what their sample needs to grow healthy plants. The first step is to identify what is in their schoolyard that helps make the soil. If the schoolyard is a grassy area, they will likely determine that the soil there has more humus in it than other samples. If the schoolyard includes sandy areas for play, they might also say that their sample will have lots of rocks in it as well.

## DI Differentiating Instruction

### *For EAL/ELL*

Create a graphic representation of the information in this lesson to help EAL/ELL students understand the text. Make a visual flow chart or a web with words and diagrams to illustrate the meaning of the words.

### *For Reteaching*

If students are having difficulty identifying whether the soil in each photo will have more rocks, air, water, or humus, ask them to identify what they see more of in the photo: rocks, air, water, or plants and animals. Prompt them to infer that if they see more plants, such as in a forest, the soil will contain more humus. If they see more water, such as in a wetland, there will be more water in the soil.

## Assessment *for* Learning

| What to Look for in Student Work | What to Do |
|---|---|
| Students can identify what is in soil. | • Observe students as they read and discuss the text and photos in this lesson.<br>• Observe students as you create a visual representation of what is in soil. |
| Students can infer what will be in soil based on location. | • Observe students as they view photos and infer what will make the soil in each location.<br>• Check students' responses to Communicate questions 1–3. |

# 3 How Do Indigenous Peoples Understand Soil?

Page 132

| Time |
| --- |
| 80–120 min |
| **Line Masters** |
| • LM 4-6 |

## Indicator Assessment Chart

| Indicator | Assessment Opportunities |
| --- | --- |
| **ES3.2 a.** Suggest ways in which individuals and communities value and use soil, including the importance of Mother Earth for First Nations and Métis peoples. | • Work On It, p. 133<br>• Communicate, p. 133, q. 1, 2 |

## Lesson Goal

To find out how First Nations and Métis peoples think about soil

traditional ***KNOWLEDGE***

### Background Information

First Nations and Métis peoples used observation to learn about the natural world. By closely watching their natural environment, they learned how to survive. Elders taught children about their natural environment by taking them with them as they went to check snares or to pick berries and sharing stories and wisdom about what they observed (e.g., a bird in the sky or a particular plant on the ground).

Although the *Pearson Saskatchewan Science Program* often refers to First Nations and Métis peoples in the same cultural context, it is important to note that First Nations and Métis peoples form very distinct cultural groups. However, in most instances where the textbook refers to First Nations and Métis peoples together, it is because they share similar cultural practices. In this lesson, the narrative of Mia and her Grandmother, which concerns the teaching of traditional First Nations tobacco offerings, could easily be a story between a Métis Grandmother and granddaughter.

At first glance, tobacco offerings may not seem synonymous with Métis cultural practices, but many Métis Elders, Traditional Knowledge Keepers, and people have adopted this practice and Métis Elders and Knowledge Keepers derive these teachings from their First Nations ancestry. Thus, such teachings that apply to First Nations people also apply to Métis people, though it is important not to over generalize. Differences that may arise between the two cultural groups often come from the European heritage of Métis people, which has introduced more recent European practices and cultural customs into their traditional teaching.

## *Mia's Story*

As Mia's story unfolds over several lessons in the unit, Mia's understanding of soil evolves. In the Unit Opener on page 125 of the student book, Mia and her friend Jay try to understand and define soil from a western view. In Lesson 3 on page 132, we learn that Mia is First Nations, and her Grandmother uses the oral tradition to teach her about the traditional First Nations view of soil. Later, in Lesson 15 on page 158, Mia tells her friend Jay all about composting and how it helps us take care of the soil.

In the narrative of Lesson 3, Mia's Grandmother teaches Mia how First Nations people offer tobacco to Mother Earth to show their great reverence and thankfulness for her gifts. Mia's Grandmother also imparts several key traditional First Nations teachings:

- **Connectedness and humility:** Through Spirit all things are connected. First Nations and Métis peoples strongly believe that all things created on Earth have Spirit that originates from Creator. Because all things are created and have Spirit, they believe that all things are equal, but that each one has different needs and different ways of relying on the others. Thus, they have a distinct awareness of the importance of humility. For example, humans who were created with great intelligence and imagination, lacked the claws, teeth, and fur to survive cold nights and long winters. Creator had pity for humans and gathered the animal spirits together. "Who will help our poor brother?" Creator challenged. The spirits of the bison, the elk, the deer, the moose and the birds then came forward, offering their bodies for food, their fur and feathers for warmth, and their hides for shelter.
- Through this story, First Nations people illustrate how dependent people are on the natural world and how animals, such as the bison and the elk, have little dependence on us. People rely on plants for food, medicines, and shelter. However, plants exist and thrive without our assistance. The First Nations elements of air, fire, water, and rock exist to sustain people with the breath we breathe, the heat we need to keep warm and to cook, the materials we use to build homes, and the tools we use for ceremonies. Yet, these elements have no need of us. This deep value and appreciation of human mortality and dependence on the natural world makes First Nations people thankful and thus, gives rise to the next important protocol and teaching—the value of thankfulness.
- **Thankfulness and the tobacco offering:** In offering tobacco to Mother Earth for the plant she picks, Mia's Grandmother expresses the gratitude that First Nations people give through ritual, when they harvest plants, hunt, trap, or fish. For more information on tobacco offerings see Unit 2 of this Teacher's Resource.

## Curriculum Connections

In this lesson, students have the opportunity to develop skills and concepts in these areas:

### *English Language Arts*

CR3.4 d. Ask questions and support answers by connecting prior knowledge with literal information found in, and inferred from, texts including First Nations and Métis resources.
CR3.4 e. Identify the main idea and supporting details in informational text and extract appropriate and significant information.
CC3.1 a. Use words, symbols, and other forms, including appropriate technology, to express understanding of topics, themes, and issues and make connections to learning in other areas of study.
CC3.1 b. Communicate thoughts, feelings, and ideas clearly and, when appropriate, artistically.

### *Social Studies*

IN3.1 a. Describe characteristics of daily life in communities studied, and compare the ways in which the needs are met by individuals in diverse communities (e.g., housing, tools, work, use of the land, games, education).
IN3.1 b. Give examples of how culture is reflected in daily life in various communities, and examine why these cultural elements are important (e.g., language, stories, cultural traditions, religious traditions, recreation, art, architecture, clothing).

## Get Started ▶

- Review what students learned about how scientists understand soil in the previous lesson. Then, ask, *What do you know about First Nations and Métis ways of knowing? How do you think First Nations and Métis peoples might understand soil differently?* Record students' suggestions and revisit them after reading the text to correct any misinformation, and add new understandings.

traditional ***KNOWLEDGE***

- As you read the text with students, discuss how the way they understand the word *gift* (e.g., as a birthday or Christmas present) may be different from the way First Nations and Métis peoples understand the word *gift*. Explain that Mother Earth and all living things are sacred because they are gifts from Creator. Creator offers us all the living things of Mother Earth, so that we have everything we need to survive. As human beings, we are nothing without these gifts.

| Time |
| --- |
| 60–120 min |
| **Learning Context** |
| inquiry<br>cultural perspectives |
| **Level of Inquiry** |
| guided |
| **Skills** |
| • observing |
| **Grouping** |
| class/small groups |
| **Materials and Equipment** |
| (per group)<br>• clipboard<br>• paper and pencils for sketching<br>• camera (optional) |
| **Line Masters** |
| • LM 4-6 |

traditional ***KNOWLEDGE***

## Work On It

### Purpose

To observe the natural world as First Nations and Métis peoples do

### Activity Notes

- You may wish to invite an Elder to take the class on a nature walk so that students can experience the way in which Elders traditionally taught children (see *"Protocol for Contacting Elders and Traditional Knowledge Keepers"* in the Program Overview of this Teacher's Resource).
- This activity emphasizes the value of observation shared by scientists and First Nations and Métis peoples. While both observe the world carefully to understand nature, how they use observation differs vastly. Many scientists use observation to help confirm or verify hypotheses, provide new insights, generate new models, and provide evidence for existing ideas. Historically, First Nations and Métis peoples have used observation to gain a better understanding of their environment and to determine animal behaviours, characteristics of plants, and changes in season for survival.
- In this activity, it is important for you to help students appreciate the value of observation and the variety of reasons for it. Have students brainstorm a list of reasons for observation (e.g., to understand nature, to learn about the world, to marvel, to appreciate aesthetics or beauty).
- As a class, develop a list of observation guidelines or rules that include the following and ensure students understand them:
  - **Take only observations:** Do not take any animals or plants. Leave them in their native habitat and draw or take pictures only.
  - **Leave only footprints:** Do not disturb plants or animals. Respect the land and do not litter.
- Provide copies of LM 4-6 Nature Walk for students to record their observations along with clipboards or pieces of strong cardboard with clips to hold the line master, so students have a firm surface for writing or sketching their observations. Students may also wish to record observations by taking photos with digital cameras.
- Ensure that you provide time for students to look closely at the natural environment and share what they notice. Students should identify everything they see in the natural environment as gifts of Mother Earth.

## Additional Activity

traditional ***KNOWLEDGE***

- The Get Started text also provides an important teaching opportunity about the portrayal of stereotypes. Throughout the textbook, the *Pearson Saskatchewan Science Program* attempts to present a balanced view of First Nations and Métis peoples in both traditional roles and modern contemporary contexts. For example, profiles of First Nations and Métis people in various careers attempt to illustrate ways First Nations and Métis people may use their cultural values to shape their contemporary lives.
- In this lesson, although Mia and her Grandmother are fictitious characters, teachers can help students see that they are modern First Nations people who retain their traditional values. Teachers may also wish to use the following imagery activity to help students understand stereotypes that they may have of other cultures.

- **Imagery activity:** Read the first part of Mia's story on page 125 of the student book and invite students to imagine what Mia looks like. Have them record their ideas in a description or picture. Read the second part of Mia's story on page 132 and repeat the activity. Then ask students to compare their images of Mia before and after they realized she is First Nations. Helping students see the images they form as they read may help them understand the kinds of stereotypes they form in real life. Then have students reread the two parts of Mia's story together and pose questions, such as:
  - *How did you imagine Mia before you learned she was First Nations?*
  - *How did you feel when you learned that Mia was First Nations?*
  - *What clues in the story on page 132, gave you the impression that Mia is First Nations?*
  - *How did you imagine Mia when you learned she was First Nations? What clothing did she wear?*
- If students imagined Mia or her Grandmother wearing traditional First Nations clothing, you may wish to explore why. Explain that traditional practices and values live on in First Nations communities, but that First Nations people live, work, and thrive as modern peoples—not as cultures of the past (e.g., Elders may share their ways of tanning hides and how these practices have changed over the years, but they do not walk around in buckskin clothing). You may wish to discuss other stereotypes students know and how these images do not reflect the real people of the culture or the community.

## Communicate

When you return to the classroom, provide an opportunity for students to share what they observed on their nature walk. Students can choose to tell, write about, or show what they observed.

1. Students' answers may vary but could include trees, rocks, soil, flowers, insects, and so on. Every natural thing they see on their nature walk is a gift from Mother Earth.
2. Students' answers may vary, but they could include:
   - Leave only footprints when you are in the natural environment. Keep any litter to throw away in the proper place.
   - Give thanks to Mother Earth for the gifts she provides.
   - Take care not to harm or kill any living thing.
   - Observe living things without interfering with them.
   - Do not break branches or rip bark from trees or shrubs (First Nations and Métis peoples see trees as living and something to be honoured).

### BUILD ON WHAT YOU KNOW

Have students record how they will show respect for the gifts of Mother Earth they use to make healthy soil for their school vegetable garden. Ensure they understand that whatever they add to make the soil healthier will come from Mother Earth and, therefore, is a gift from Creator. They will not offer tobacco to give thanks, but encourage them to think of another way to give thanks.

## DI Differentiating Instruction

### *For EAL/ELL*

To enhance comprehension of the information in this lesson, make sure the text is read aloud for EAL/ELL students. Use visuals (e.g., the photo in the student book and diagrams to illustrate the content) and dramatizations of the narrative to enhance understanding.

### *For Enrichment*

Challenge students to brainstorm for ways they could increase the respect shown by other students in the school for living things in the schoolyard. Consider how effective each idea would be and choose the idea that students think would be most effective. Create an action plan for implementing the idea and carry it out.

## Assessment *for* Learning

| What to Look for in Student Work | What to Do |
|---|---|
| Students can suggest ways in which individuals, communities, and First Nations and Métis peoples value and use soil. | • Observe students during the nature walk and check the observations they record.<br>• Observe or check students' responses to Communicate questions 1 and 2. |
| Students can suggest ways that they can show respect for soil and all living things. | • Check students' responses to Communicate question 2. |

# 4 What Makes Soils Different? *Page 134*

| Time |
|---|
| 40–80 min |
| **Line Masters** |
| • LM 4-7 |

## Indicator Assessment Chart

| Indicator | Assessment Opportunities |
|---|---|
| **ES3.1 b.** Examine physical characteristics (e.g., particle size, texture, moisture, particle size distribution, colour, and ability to hold together) of soils from different locations (e.g., garden, flower pot, river bed, slough, hill top, grassy field, lawn, ditch, and forest) in their environment. | • Work On It, p. 134<br>• Communicate, p. 135, q. 1, 2 |
| **ES3.1 d.** Analyze soil samples using tools such as spoons, hand lenses, jars, and filters appropriately and safely. | • Work On It, p. 134 |
| **ES3.1 e.** Make and record observations and measurements in investigations related to soil composition using techniques such as notes in point form, diagrams, tables, bar graphs, photographs, and video. | • Work On It, p. 134 |
| **ES3.1 h.** Sort soil samples according to one or more physical characteristics such as texture, ability to absorb water, particle size, and colour. | • Work On It, p. 134 |
| **ES3.1 j.** Propose answers to initial questions related to soil composition based on the results of personal investigations. | • Communicate, p. 135, q. 4 |

## Lesson Goal

To find out what makes one soil sample different from another

## Background Information

Soils vary because of the great variety of rocks, plants, and animals from which they are composed. Soils also vary because the percentages of rock fragments, mineral grains, organic matter, air, and water can differ considerably from sample to sample. Soil can be classified by considering the texture, the size of the grains, the size of the pores, how much air and water it contains, the type and amount of nutrients, and how deep the soil is (that is, the distance to the rock on which the soil is found).

## Curriculum Connections

In this lesson, students have the opportunity to develop skills and concepts in these areas:

### *English Language Arts*

CC3.1 a. Use words, symbols, and other forms, including appropriate technology, to express understanding of topics, themes, and issues and make connections to learning in other areas of study.

## Get Started ▶

- Ask students to predict what might make one soil sample different from another. Record their ideas on chart paper or the board so that you can revisit them when students complete the activity in this lesson.
- As you read the text with students, pause and reflect on the ideas they shared before reading about how one soil sample might be different from another. Confirm those ideas that were correct and adjust or correct the others.
- Examine and describe the soil samples in the photo on page 134 of the student book. Identify ways in which these soil samples are different from one another. Ask questions to promote observations.
- After reading the text, create a web with students to identify the ways in which one soil sample might be different from another.
- Students need three different soil samples for the Work On It. They can use the samples from Lesson 1 as one soil type. Involve students in a discussion about how to add different soil samples to the ones already in the classroom. Ideas may include another outing to a nearby location, students bringing more samples from home, or going to a nursery to buy different types of garden soil. Collect soil samples through the plan you establish together.

**Time**

30 min

**Learning Context**

inquiry

**Level of Inquiry**

structured

**Skills**

- observing
- classifying
- inferring
- comparing
- communicating

**Grouping**

pairs

**Materials and Equipment**

(per group)
- newspaper
- marker
- spoons
- 3 different soil samples
- magnifying lens
- pencils

**Line Masters**

- LM 4-7

## Work On It

### Purpose

To investigate and determine that colour, texture, particle size, and the ability of soil particles to stick together make soils different

### Activity Notes

- Before students begin the activity, distribute and discuss how to use LM 4-7 What Makes Soils Different? to record their observations.
- To support students in recording their observations, brainstorm with the class a list of words students may need to use. Ask, *What words could you use to describe the texture, or the way the soil feels?* As students suggest words, record them on chart paper.

*continued*→

**SAFETY CAUTION!**

Never put soil in your mouth. Always wash your hands after handling soil. You may also wish to provide rubber gloves for students to use to handle soil.

- Review the steps in What You Will Do with students before they begin their investigations. Make sure that tabletop surfaces are covered with newspaper. Discuss with students the safety precaution of washing hands carefully after handling the soil.
- Observing and comparing are process skills core to most science investigations. Ensure that students are following the procedure correctly and recording their observations as they work. Consider whether both students in each pair have a role, and whether students are listening to one another's ideas.
- Explain how to use one characteristic for sorting. If students choose colour, they could sort their soil samples from darkest to lightest colour. If students choose texture, they could sort their samples from softest to roughest. If students choose particle size, they could sort their samples from smallest to largest, or largest to smallest. If they choose whether the soil particles stick together, they can sort their samples from most sticky to least sticky.

## Communicate

Meet as a class and have pairs present their observations and the way in which they sorted their soil samples. Next, use the Communicate questions to engage students in making inferences about the contents and quality of the soil samples.

1. Students' answers may vary depending on the samples compared but could include sorting the soils by colour, texture, particle size, or ability to stick (or hold) together.
2. Students' answers may vary but could include that all the soils are a type of brown colour and all the soils are made of small things. The texture and colours of the soils vary. The main ingredient of samples also varies. One sample may have a lot of humus, while another may be composed almost entirely of rock particles.
3. Students' answers may vary but should identify the soil sample with the most humus as good for growing things. Later in the unit, students will consider which types of soil hold water and which do not. In this question, you can see if students have begun to consider water retention as a useful characteristic of soil. Students who choose one specific type of soil will likely think that the chosen sample contains nutrients for plants or that it looks the most like the type of soil they see in gardens.
4. Students' answers may vary but could include that they can now answer questions, such as what is in soil and what makes soils different.

## DI Differentiating Instruction

### *For Reteaching*

Students can select one soil sample. Provide a magnifying lens and encourage them to observe the sample "to get to know it well." Next, give students a different sample and ask them to tell one way it is different from the one they have just examined closely. Then have them tell one way it is the same.

### *For Enrichment*

Ask students to predict what might be different about soil from their backyard, their local park, a field, a forest, their garden, a ditch, and so on. Have them gather soil from different areas and test it. Invite students to add their results to the chart they began in the Work On It.

## Assessment *for* Learning

| What to Look for in Student Work | What to Do |
|---|---|
| Students can identify colour, texture, particle size, and ability to hold together of soils from different locations in their environment. | • Observe students during the Work On It activity.<br>• Check the observations students record.<br>• Check students' responses to Communicate questions 1 and 2. |
| Students can analyze soil samples using spoons and magnifying lenses appropriately and safely. | • Observe students during the Work On It activity. |
| Students can record observations related to soil composition in a table. | • Observe students as they record their observations during the Work On It activity.<br>• Check to see that they are using appropriate descriptive vocabulary. |
| Students can sort soil samples according to texture, particle size, colour, or whether the particles stick together. | • Observe students as they identify one characteristic from the table and use it to sort their soil sample.<br>• Watch to see that they understand how to sort by one attribute. |
| Students can suggest answers to questions they posed about what is in soil at the beginning of the unit. | • Check students' responses to Communicate question 4.<br>• Check students' responses on their individual KWL charts, if applicable. |

# 5 What Is in Soil?

Page 136

**Time**

80 min

**Vocabulary**

- sand
- silt
- clay
- loams

**Line Masters**

- LM 4-8
- LM 4-9

## Indicator Assessment Chart

| Indicator | Assessment Opportunities |
|---|---|
| **ES3.1 b.** Examine physical characteristics (e.g., particle size, texture, moisture, particle size distribution, colour, and ability to hold together) of soils from different locations (e.g., garden, flower pot, river bed, slough, hill top, grassy field, lawn, ditch, and forest) in their environment. | • Work On It, p. 136<br>• Communicate, p. 137, q. 1, 2 |
| **ES3.1 c.** Classify soils in their environment according to location and type (e.g., clay, sand, silt, and loam). | • Work On It, p. 136<br>• Communicate, p. 137, q. 1, 2 |
| **ES3.1 e.** Make and record observations and measurements in investigations related to soil composition using techniques such as notes in point form, diagrams, tables, bar graphs, photographs, and video. | • Work On It, p. 136 |

## Lesson Goal

To find out if a loam is mostly sand, silt, or clay

### Background Information

The different types of rock pieces found in soil vary in size. The coarsest particles are sand measuring from 0.05 mm to 2.0 mm. Sand particles are the largest and heaviest soil particles. They feel gritty to the touch. When squeezed, moist sand particles will fall apart—they will not form a ball. Sandy soils are porous (there are larger spaces between sand particles than between silt or clay particles), and they usually hold less water than other types of soils, because the large spaces make it easier for gravity to pull the water down through the particles. Because of this, soil with large amounts of sand is not useful for growing most plants.

Silt particles measure from 0.002 mm to 0.05 mm—smaller than sand particles but larger than clay particles. They are too small to see with the naked eye. Silt particles are often found in places that have flooded and dried out again. They feel smooth and slippery like baby powder. Silt particles are more easily eroded by water than clay particles, because they do not stick, or bond, together as well as clay particles. The smaller spaces between particles mean that silty soils hold nutrients and water well. This can make them good soils for growing plants.

Clay particles measure less than 0.002 mm in diameter. They are the smallest and lightest soil particles. Like silt particles, they cannot be seen with the naked eye. Clay particles stick, or bond, together when wet, and they dry smooth and hard, which is why potters use clay to make pottery. Plants have a difficult time growing in soil that is high in clay, because there is little space between clay particles for roots to grow and for the air and nutrients that growing plants need. Soils that are high in clay tend to hold water, because the particles fit together so closely that it is difficult for water to flow through. Soils that are high in clay can become waterlogged.

Loam soils are soils with a fairly even mixture of sand, silt, and clay. A loam with slightly more sand in the mixture is called a sandy loam. A loam with slightly more silt is called a silty loam, and a loam with slightly more clay is called a loam high in clay. Farmers prefer loam soils for growing plants and crops because they are the most fertile soils. A good loam soil contains 40 percent sand, 40 percent silt, and 20 percent clay. It also contains humus. This balance holds the amount of water and air plants need to thrive. Sand particles create larger pores that allow more air and water to move in the soil. Clay particles, along with organic matter, help bind the soil particles together and hold water. Silt helps to hold the nutrients that plants and animals need. Humus soaks up water and helps soil hold moisture.

## Curriculum Connections

In this lesson, students have the opportunity to develop skills and concepts in these areas:

### *English Language Arts*

CC3.1 a. Use words, symbols, and other forms, including appropriate technology, to express understanding of topics, themes, and issues and make connections to learning in other areas of study.

## Focus on Literacy

### *After Reading: 3-2-1 Summary*

Hand out LM 4-8 3-2-1 Summary Organizer. Say, *Today we read about the three different kinds of particles found in soil and their physical characteristics. When we learn something new, it can helpful to make notes on what we have read in order to help us recall and summarize this information. However, notes do not always have to take the form of written sentences. We can use graphic organizers like the* 3-2-1 Summary *one on the handout to help us summarize information. Organizers make it easier to recall information because of the visual cues they offer.*

Prompt students to complete each of the three sections of the graphic organizer based on what they have read in the text. Have students share their work to ensure the accuracy of the information they have recorded in their organizers. Invite students to share their questions and record them on the class or individual KWL charts.

### *Before Writing: 3-2-1 Summary*

Inform students that a graphic organizer is a useful tool for recording information and recalling the information as they study. Say, *Writers often use graphic organizers to record their ideas and then convert this information into another form to present it to their audience. For example, the author of this lesson presented the information on "What is in soil?" in paragraph form in our grade 3 textbook.*

Ask, *How might this information have been presented differently if the audience was a group of grade 1 students?* Have students discuss this with a partner (e.g., fewer words, simple close-up pictures with labels). Then explain that the physical presentation of writing is called "format."

Ask, *Who else might be interested in learning more about soil? How would you present this information to them? What format would you use?* Students can then work in pairs to identify an audience and choose a format in which to present the information from their graphic organizers.

**Get Started ▶**

- Review with students the ways in which they compared the soil samples in the previous lesson (e.g., by colour, texture, particle size, and ability of soil particles to hold together).
- Explain that the purpose for reading the text in this lesson is to find out more about the main kinds of rock particles in soil and how to identify different types of soil.
- As you read the text with students, use questions such as the following to help them make connections with their previous experiences with soil:
  - *Think about when you have played in sand at the beach or in a sandbox. How did the sand feel?*
  - *Have you ever played in mud that has washed out of a field or mud at the edge of a creek bank? This is mostly silt. How did it feel between your fingers or toes?*
  - *Have you ever made something out of clay? How did the clay feel?*
- Ask students to reread the text in the Get Started and the introductory text in the Work On It. Create a web with three main branches for the three main kinds of rock particles like the one on the next page.

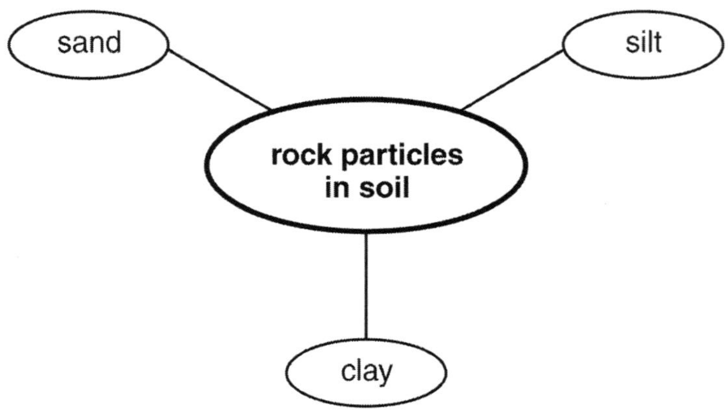

- Add details about each kind of rock particle to the web as shown below.

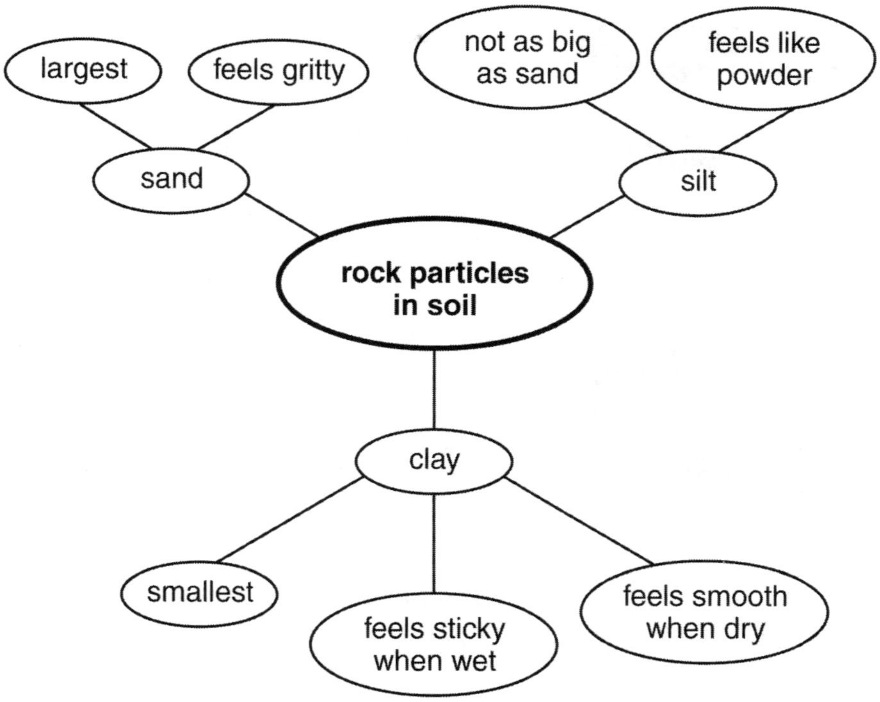


- Have samples of salt or sugar, baby powder or flour, and clay available for students to touch so that they understand how something feels when it is gritty, like powder, and sticky.
- Students will need soil samples from three different places (e.g., garden, flower pot, river bed, slough, hill top, grassy field, lawn, ditch, and forest) for the Work On It. Have students accompany you to get the soil samples, so they can observe the locations and the plants growing in each to answer the Communicate questions. Alternatively, note the location where you collect each sample and take photos or videos of it and the plants growing in it that students can examine.
- As students gather the soil samples, ensure that they label each sample with its location and note the surroundings and type of plants growing in each location. You may wish to have them record their observations by writing or sketching, or by taking digital photos or videos at each location.

**Time**

30 min

**Learning Context**

inquiry

**Level of Inquiry**

structured

**Skills**

- observing
- interpreting
- classifying
- inferring
- communicating

**Grouping**

pairs

**Materials and Equipment**

(per group)

- soil samples from 3 different places
- paper towel
- marker
- spray bottle of water
- spoons
- pencils

*Note: Keep the soil samples for use in Lesson 7.*

**Line Masters**

- LM 4-9

## Work On It

### Purpose

To perform texture and rolling tests to determine if soil samples are mostly sand, silt, or clay

### Activity Notes

- Read the first paragraph and share with students that a mixture of sand, silt, clay, and humus is good for growing plants and crops. A good loam soil for growing plants contains humus, equal amounts of sand and silt, and half as much clay as silt or sand (40 percent sand, 40 percent silt, and 20 percent clay). Tell students that they will find out why in the lessons that follow.
- Review the steps in What You Will Do with students before they begin their investigations. Ensure that students label each soil sample with its location as they place the samples on paper towel.
- Distribute and discuss how to use LM 4-9 What Is in Soil? to record their observations. Observe students as they test their soil samples and ensure that they are following the steps in the procedure and recording their results correctly.
- Students should be able to identify whether each sample is mostly sand, silt, or clay by the way the soil feels. If the sample feels gritty, it is high in sand. If it feels smooth and slippery and not sticky between their fingers, it is high in silt. If it feels sticky and can be rolled into a worm shape that does not fall apart when dry, the sample is high in clay.
- If students cannot identify a predominant texture, the soil sample is likely a combination of sand, silt, and clay, and will therefore be a loam. In this case, they can enter the word "*loam*" in the column "*High in sand, silt, or clay.*"

## Communicate

1. Students' answers may vary but could include connections, such as:
   - If the soil sample comes from a place where there are lots of rocks, there is probably more sand in the soil.
   - If the soil sample comes from a place where lots of plants grow, there is probably more humus in the soil and a mixture of sand, silt, and clay.
   - If the soil sample comes from a location where water runs or sits, there is probably more silt or clay in the sample.
2. Students' answers may vary depending on where the soil samples were collected. If the soil sample was collected in a grassy field, they might have seen plants such as grasses and dandelions. If it was collected from a creek bank or a slough, they might have seen plants such as willows and cattails. If it was collected from a forest, they might have seen plants such as trees, shrubs, and wild roses. Connections students might see could include:
   - Tall plants grow in soil that has lots of humus and is a fairly equal mix of sand, silt, and clay. Forests with lots of undergrowth need soil rich in nutrients that holds air and water for growing plants.
   - Certain plants such as cattails and willows will grow in soil that is high in silt and clay that holds water well.

## DI Differentiating Instruction

### *For EAL/ELL*

After reading the text, create a web as outlined in the Get Started of this lesson to help EAL/ELL students understand the content. Use visual/graphic representations as often as possible to enhance understanding for these students. Ensure that EAL/ELL students are paired with students who are proficient English speakers and writers.

### *For Reteaching*

Review the textures of salt or sugar, baby powder or flour, and clay. Label each as gritty, slippery, or sticky. Students can select one soil sample, feel it, and compare the texture of it to the known samples of salt/sugar, baby powder/flour, and clay. They can then identify which it feels closest to, record the texture from the appropriate label, and do the same with the other soil samples. Providing the labelled texture samples for direct comparison will help students identify the texture of the soil in each sample.

## Assessment *for* Learning

| What to Look for in Student Work | What to Do |
|---|---|
| Students can examine the texture and ability to hold together of soils from different locations in their environment. | • Observe students carry out the texture and worm shape tests on soil samples in the Work On It activity.<br>• Check students' responses to Communicate questions 1 and 2. |
| Students can make connections between the location of soil and the type of soil they will find there. | • Check students' responses to Communicate questions 1 and 2. |
| Students can make and record observations about soil composition. | • Observe students as they complete the Work On It activity.<br>• Check students' recorded observations. |

# 6 Separating Soil

Page 138

| Time |
| --- |
| 80–120 min |
| **Line Masters** |
| • LM 4-10 |

## Indicator Assessment Chart

| Indicator | Assessment Opportunities |
| --- | --- |
| **ES3.1 c.** Classify soils in their environment according to location and type (e.g., clay, sand, silt, and loam). | • Work On It, p. 138<br>• Communicate, p. 139, q. 1, 2 |
| **ES3.1 d.** Analyze soil samples using tools such as spoons, hand lenses, jars, and filters appropriately and safely. | • Work On It, p. 138 |
| **ES3.1 e.** Make and record observations and measurements in investigations related to soil composition using techniques such as notes in point form, diagrams, tables, bar graphs, photographs, and video. | • Work On It, p. 138<br>• Communicate, p. 139, q. 2 |

## Lesson Goal

To investigate how to separate the sand, silt, and clay in a soil sample

## Background Information

Students place a soil sample in a jar, add water, shake it up, and then observe over 24 hours to see how the soil resettles in the jar. This process of sedimentation demonstrates how soil can be separated into a continuum of its different components. Students observe that larger particles (e.g., sand) settle first and smaller pieces (e.g., silt and, lastly, clay) take longer to settle. Depending on the soil they test, students may observe up to three layers of soil. The thickness of the layers will depend on how much sand, silt, and clay is in the soil sample.

When students separate soil this way, they will get a continuum of the largest particles on the bottom to the finest particles on top. Scientists split this continuum into three distinct groups (e.g., sand, silt, and clay), and students may expect to see three distinct layers with boundaries between the layers. However, soil is generally a very heterogeneous mixture that contains more than three distinct sizes of particles; therefore, separating it through this sedimentation process will produce a number of layers, from the largest particles on the bottom to the smallest particles on the top. The only way to get three layers with distinct boundaries is to make a soil mixture that starts with three pure samples of sand, silt, and clay so that there are three distinct sizes of particles in the soil mixture.

## Curriculum Connections

In this lesson, students have the opportunity to develop skills and concepts in these areas:

### *Mathematics*

SS3.1 a. Observe and describe activities relevant to self, family, and community that would involve the measurement of time.

### *English Language Arts*

CC3.1 a. Use words, symbols, and other forms, including appropriate technology, to express understanding of topics, themes, and issues and make connections to learning in other areas of study.
CC3.1 b. Communicate thoughts, feelings, and ideas clearly and, when appropriate, artistically.

## Focus on Literacy

### *During Reading: Think Aloud*

Use the think aloud strategy to help students recall, paraphrase, summarize, and synthesize information as you model the reading of photograph captions. Read the first caption on page 138 of the student book and say, *The writer of this caption has given us two pieces of information about sandy soil. She tells us that this soil does not hold water well and does not allow plants to grow well. I've noticed that the other photos on this page focus on the different soil types we learned about in Lesson 5. I wonder if the other captions will focus on these same two pieces of information?*

Read the next caption and confirm that there does appear to be a pattern in the type of information given in the captions. Continue the think aloud by saying, *I always find it easier to use some type of graphic organizer to make notes than simply writing out the important information. I'm thinking that we can set up a chart to record whether each type of soil holds water well and allows plants to grow well.*

On the board or chart paper, create an organizer, such as a matrix like the one below, to recall and summarize what students learn from the captions about the types of soil.

| Type of Soil | Holds Water Well | Plants Grow Well in This Soil |
|---|---|---|
| Sandy soil | X | X |
| Silty soil | √ | X |
| Soil with a lot of clay | √ | X |
| Loamy soil | √ | √ |

Reread the first caption and mark the appropriate boxes with a check mark or "x." Have students work with a partner to read the next caption and record information in the chart. Students can work in pairs or individually to continue reading and recording information in the appropriate boxes for each type of soil.

## Get Started ▶

- Review what students learned in Lesson 5 about the size and texture of sand, silt, and clay particles. Explain that they will use what they learned about these particles to develop deeper understandings about soils that have different amounts of sand, silt, and clay.
- With students, examine each photo and read its caption. Help students make connections between this information and what they know about the types of particles shown by asking questions such as:

**Photo of sandy soil**

- *Why do you think sandy soil is loose? Think about the size and texture of sand particles. If sand particles are the largest particles and they feel gritty, would they have smooth or rough edges? If they have rough edges, would they fit together tightly?*
- *If sand particles do not fit together tightly, could the particles hold water in the spaces between them?*

**Photo of soil high in silt**

- *If silt particles are smaller than sand particles and they feel smooth, would they have smooth or rough edges? If they have smooth edges, would they fit together more closely than sand particles? If so, would they hold water in the spaces between them better than sand?*
- *Think about what you know about the size of silt particles. Why do you think the wind can blow silty soil away?*
- *If wind can blow silty soil away, would plants grow well in it?*

**Photo of soil high in clay**

- *Think about the size and texture of clay particles. What does this tell you about how the particles would fit together and how the particles would hold water in the spaces between them?*
- *This type of soil holds water very well and yet plants do not grow very well in it. What might be the reasons?*

**Photo of loam**

- *Think about the sizes of the different soil particles and how they would fit together when they are mixed. Why might a mixture of these particles hold water well?*

**Time**

60 min over 2 days

**Learning Context**

inquiry

**Level of Inquiry**

structured

**Skills**

- observing
- comparing
- interpreting
- inferring
- communicating

**Grouping**

pairs

**Materials and Equipment**

(per group)
- glass jar with a lid
- soil sample
- container of water
- marker
- spoon
- paper towel
- magnifying lens
- pencils

**Line Masters**

- LM 4-10

## Work On It

### Purpose

To use the process of sedimentation to separate the layers in a soil sample and identify them as sand, silt, and clay

### Activity Notes

- Since students need to mark the sedimentation that occurs after three to four hours, it is important to do the first part of this activity in the morning.
- You may wish to provide soil samples taken from different locations and varying depths so that all soil samples are not the same and students can compare their samples. Or, instead of using straight soil samples, you may wish to add different amounts of humus, white or coloured sand, pebbles, and clay to the samples before handing them out. This will ensure more recognizable and visible sedimentation layers.
- Shaking the jar of soil and water for two minutes can feel like a long time for students. You may wish to put some music on and encourage them to dance and shake the jar until the music stops.
- Students may want to check their jars frequently during the wait times. Remind them to look only and not to move the jars so that the soil particles do not mix with the water again.
- Provide LM 4-10 Separating Soil for students to record their observations. Encourage them to take time and try to capture their observations in their drawings as accurately as possible. Have students use LM 4-10 Separating Soil to record their findings in step 8.
- You will need to prepare space where students can place their jars until the next day. If you do not have enough jars, or are concerned about students handling glass and pouring water in the classroom, you might decide to demonstrate the activity. Choose three different samples of soil and set up three jars for students to observe and compare.

## Communicate

Students will use question 1 to summarize their findings from step 8 of the Work On It. In answering question 2, students will use what they discovered in step 8 to identify each layer that settled in the jar.

1. Note that the jars may not have distinct layers of soil visible. Instead, expect to see a gradated layer of soil, with larger particles visible at the bottom and smaller ones at the top. The humus will either float in the water or settle on top of the soil in a separate layer. By looking closely, students will see that larger soil particles are at the bottom of the jar and smaller ones are at the top.

   After rubbing the particles from each layer between their fingers, students should find that the particles feel gritty at the bottom as the sand particles settle out first. The particles in the middle layer should feel smooth and slippery as they are the silt particles, and the particles in the top layer should feel sticky as they are the clay particles.
2. Students should infer that sand is at the bottom and clay is at the top. To test this observation, you could do a demonstration in which you add white or coloured sand and pure clay to the soil beforehand.

*continued→*

If you provided soil samples from different locations and varying depths, meet as a class so that students can observe and compare jars. Place the jars so that they are close together and students can see them easily. Have each pair of students present their jar and labelled drawings and ask the class whether they agree with the pair's labels. Then ask students to consider which of the other jars is most like the one being presented, and which resembles it the least. Put the jars that appear similar in one group. Through discussion, establish a second and, if possible, a third group.

Revisit the KWL chart from the beginning of this unit. Ask:

- *Is there anything in the "What I Know About Soil" column that needs correcting?*
- *What have you learned?* Record responses in the "What I Learned About Soil" column.
- *What else do you want to know about soil?* Record these questions in the "What I Want to Know About Soil" column.

## DI Differentiating Instruction

### *For Reteaching*

To show the connections between the size and texture of different types of soil particles and their ability to hold water and grow plants well, use rocks to symbolize sand particles, small smooth stones to symbolize silt particles, and tiny pebbles to symbolize clay particles. When the rocks are together, the "particles" cannot hold water in the spaces between them very well. When the small stones are together, the spaces between the "particles" are smaller because the small stones fit more closely together. When the tiny pebbles are together, the spaces between the "particles" are even smaller because the pebbles fit even more closely together.

### *For Enrichment*

Explain that loam is a fertile soil in which plants grow well. Have students investigate another soil sample by following the same steps of this activity. Students can examine the jar and predict the percentages of sand, silt, and clay. Students can then add material to change the sample to loam (40 percent sand, 40 percent silt, and 20 percent clay).

## Assessment *for* Learning

| What to Look for in Student Work | What to Do |
|---|---|
| Students can use what they know about the size, texture, and ability to hold water and grow plants well of different types of soil particles to classify and analyze soils. | • Observe students discussing the text and photos in the Get Started.<br>• Observe students during the Work On It activity.<br>• Check students' responses to Communicate questions 1 and 2. |
| Students can use spoons and magnifying lenses appropriately and safely. | • Observe students during the Work On It activity. |
| Students can record their observations after specified time intervals using diagrams. | • Check students' drawings and responses to Communicate question 2. |

# 7 How Much Water?

Page 140

| Time |
| --- |
| 80 min |

| Line Masters |
| --- |
| • LM 4-11<br>• LM 4-12 |

## Indicator Assessment Chart

| Indicator | Assessment Opportunities |
| --- | --- |
| **ES3.1 f.** Make predictions about the capability of different types of soil to absorb water and test these predictions through exploration and investigation. | • Work On It, p. 140 |
| **ES3.1 g.** Collect and display data, using tables and bar graphs, to show the amount of water absorbed by different types of soil. | • Work On It, p. 140 |
| **ES3.1 h.** Sort soil samples according to one or more physical characteristics such as texture, ability to absorb water, particle size, and colour. | • Communicate, p. 141, q. 2 |
| **ES3.1 i.** Communicate procedures and results of investigations related to the testing of water absorption of soils using drawings, demonstrations, and oral and written descriptions. | • Communicate, p. 141, q. 1–3 |

## Lesson Goal

To find out if sand, silt, clay, or loam holds the most water

### Background Information

Water soaks into some soils faster than others due to soil porosity (the size of the pores or the spaces between the soil particles). The size of the pores will determine how fast the water will move through the soil. Gravity is the biggest force pulling the water down into the soil. The larger the spaces between the soil particles, the easier it is for gravity to pull the water down and the faster the water will soak in. Sand has larger spaces between the particles than soil high in clay or silt, so water soaks in and drains through it rapidly and little is stored. Silt and clay have small pores or spaces between the particles. As a result, water pools on the surface and soaks in more slowly than when water falls on sand. Because the pores are small, water does not drain through silt and clay quickly and they hold more water than sand.

The amount of water soil holds is also affected by the amount of humus in the soil. Loam (garden soil) has a mixture of sand, clay, silt, and humus. The spaces between the particles are a mixture of large and small. Hence, water will not easily pool on the surface as it does on clay or silty soil, but it will not drain as fast as through sandy soil. Loam should be the "happy medium"—it should allow water to drain easily, yet still hold plenty of water needed for growing plants.

## Curriculum Connections

In this lesson, students have the opportunity to develop skills and concepts in these areas:

***Mathematics***

SP3.1 a. Observe and describe situations relevant to self, family, or community in which a particular type of data recording or organizing strategy might be used, including tally marks, charts, lists, and knots on a sash.

***English Language Arts***

CC3.2 a. Demonstrate understanding of the topic, problem, question, or issue in a variety of ways (e.g., dance pieces, visual representations, drama in context, diagram, demonstration, chart).

**Time**

40 min

**Learning Context**

inquiry

**Level of Inquiry**

structured or guided

**Skills**

- experimenting
- observing
- inferring
- interpreting
- comparing
- measuring
- communicating
- predicting

**Grouping**

pairs

**Materials and Equipment**

(per group)
- equal amounts of dry sand, silt, clay, loam
- 7 paper cups
- 7 pieces of fabric
- nail or skewer
- 2 measuring cups
- water
- soil samples from Lesson 5
- pencils

**Line Masters**

- LM 4-11
- LM 4-12

## Get Started ▶

- Before reading the Get Started together, ask: *What do plants need to grow? Do all plants need the same things? Do you have plants growing indoors at home? Do you give them all the same amount of water?*
- After discussing students' responses, read the text and look at the photos together. Talk about whether students have ever seen plants similar to those shown.
- Read the introductory text in the Work On It with students as an overview of what they will be doing.

## Work On It

### Purpose

To investigate and determine if sand, silt, clay, or loam holds the most water

### Activity Notes

- Beforehand, contact a local landscaping company about obtaining free or inexpensive samples of the soils students investigate (dry sand, silt, clay, and loam) or order samples from a science supply house. Alternatively, you can obtain sand from beaches, playgrounds, roadside ditches, sand and gravel suppliers, hardware stores, or garden supply stores. Silt can be found at the bottom or edge of a stream, river, pond, or a lake, the exit end of a culvert, the lower end of a washout in a farmer's field, on the delta of a river, or an area that has been flooded. Clay can be found where a basement is being dug, at the bottom of a washout where the topsoil has been eroded away, on the banks of a river, or in art supply stores. You can find loam in a farmer's field, garden, forest, meadow, or garden supply store.
- The structured inquiry approach of this activity provides the question and procedure. Students follow the procedure, and observe and record data on LM 4-11 How Much Water? Table and Bar Graph. Then, based on evidence, they predict which soil sample from Lesson 5 will hold the most water and conclude which soil sample is best for growing plants.

**SAFETY CAUTION!**

Take care when you handle the nail or skewer. It has a very sharp end, and it should only be used to poke holes in the paper cup.

- If you feel that some or all of your students are ready for a higher level of inquiry, you may wish to have them plan the investigation to find out which soil sample will hold the most water. If so, provide LM 4-12 How Much Water? to help students plan and carry out their investigations. Meet as a class or with this group of students to talk about planning the investigation before they begin work with their partners.
- Discuss with students steps 1 to 6 that are outlined on LM 4-12 How Much Water? to ensure they understand what each step involves.
- Discuss the predictions students make in step 1 and record them on the chalkboard. Ask, *How many of us think the sand will hold the most water? How many think the silt will hold the most water? How many think the clay will hold the most water? How many think the loam will hold the most water?*
- Before students begin to plan their investigation in step 3, have a discussion to exchange ideas and consider whether they want to use additional materials. For many students, this may be the first time they have planned an investigation. To guide this discussion, ask questions such as:
  - *Why is it important that you use the same amount of water for each soil sample?*
  - *What can you put the soil sample in so that water can flow out of it?*
- Have students present their plans to the class. Encourage students to ask one another questions about the plans. Have students consider making revisions to their plans before they go on to step 4.
- Help students collect the materials they need. Encourage students to help other groups find the things that they need. You may wish to have some students use pure sand and pure or near pure clay along with bought garden soil to ensure distinctly different results.
- As students carry out their investigations, some groups may find that they need to revise their plan. Encourage groups who encounter challenges to meet with you. They can explain what they think needs to change in order for their investigation to be successful. Record their comments for student assessment.
- Be prepared for groups to reach different conclusions, and set aside time to discuss why this may have happened. This discussion may lead to repeating the investigation as a demonstration. Some students will see the value of repeating an investigation, and others will want to see which result is correct.
- Depending on the soils tested, there may not be much difference in water retention. If so, use a graduated cylinder to measure the water. This will allow you to notice small variations.
- Before students predict which soil sample from Lesson 5 will hold the most water, you may wish to gather students together to share and discuss their findings thus far. Help them to connect what they discovered about the types of soil from each location in Lesson 5 to their results from this investigation. (e.g., If loam held the most water in their investigation, which soil sample from Lesson 5 had a mixture of clay, silt, and sand? If clay held the most water in their investigation, which soil sample from Lesson 5 had the most clay?)
- As students plan and carry out their investigations, visit all groups to see how members are participating. Some students will naturally take a passive role and let others carry out the bulk of the work. Encourage these students to become more involved by giving them specific tasks.

This feature suggests that students use a bar graph to show their results. Before completing the bar graph, have students record their data in a table such as the one below, which is provided on the line masters suggested for use with this activity.

| | Sand | Silt | Clay | Loam |
|---|---|---|---|---|
| mL of water drained | | | | |

## Additional Activity

You may wish to have a few plants that need little watering and others that need a great deal of water in the classroom for students to take care of. Usually plants come with care instructions and suggested watering schedules. Students can also do their own research to find out how much water the different plants need. You may wish to visit a nursery or florist to buy the plants as a class. While there, students could ask nursery employees for information about the soil plants grow in and the amount of water they need.

## Communicate

If all students followed the steps in the student book, bring the class together and have the groups present their results. If some or all of your students planned their investigation, ask these students to explain the materials they used and the steps they followed. If more than one group planned their investigations, after the first group presents, ask: *Did any other group follow a similar plan? How was your plan similar? How was it different?* Continue to have all groups share the materials they used and the procedures they followed. Draw comparisons whenever possible.

1. Sandy soil let the most water drain through. Expect students to have discovered that the loam holds the most water, yet allows water to drain quickly; that the sandy soil drains quickly but holds little water; and that the silt and clay soil drain very slowly and hold a lot of water. Results may vary widely depending on the type of soil tested and on the amounts of sand, silt, and clay in the soils.
2. Students' answers may vary, depending on the type of soil tested and on the amounts of sand, silt, and clay in the soils, but should include that loam holds the most water. Silt and clay soil hold a lot of water, and sandy soil holds little water.
3. Students should accept that loam is the best for growing things. Their choice of loam should be based on the results of their investigation. They should discover that sandy soil did not hold enough water and that silt and clay held the water for too long a period of time.

After completing this investigation, look back at the KWL chart from the start of the unit. Ask students what they learned about soil and record their responses in the corresponding column of the chart. Ask them if they have other questions about soil and record them on the chart.

### BUILD ON WHAT YOU KNOW

Students should choose loam for their school vegetable garden because it holds the most water, yet allows water to drain quickly.

## DI Differentiating Instruction

### *For EAL/ELL*

Pair EAL/ELL students with partners who read and speak English very well. Encourage these students to read each step aloud for their EAL/ELL partner and to follow the text with their finger so their partner can associate the written and spoken words. Then, demonstrate with the materials what the step in the procedure asked them to do.

### *For Reteaching*

If students got confusing results in their investigations, you may wish to redo the investigation as a demonstration.

### *For Enrichment*

Challenge students to plan an investigation in which they measure exactly the same amount of different types of soil and time how long it takes for a certain amount of water to drain through. Results should vary widely between samples. Good garden soil will probably drain fastest, yet hold the most water. Sandy soil will drain fairly quickly but hold less water, and silt and clay soil (depending on the amount of clay) will drain slowly or not at all.

## Assessment *for* Learning

| What to Look for in Student Work | What to Do |
|---|---|
| Students can make predictions about the capability of different types of soil to absorb water and they can test these predictions through exploration and investigation. | • Observe students during the Work On It activity.<br>• Check students' recorded predictions. |
| Students can collect and display data on a bar graph to show the amount of water absorbed by different types of soil. | • Observe students as they transfer their results to a bar graph during the Work On It activity.<br>• Check students' completed bar graphs. |
| Students can sort soil samples according to ability to absorb water. | • Check students' responses to Communicate, question 2. |
| Students can communicate procedures and results of investigations related to the testing of water absorption of soils using oral and written descriptions. | • Observe students as they explain the steps of the procedure in their own words to a partner.<br>• Observe students as they conduct the investigation and record their results in chart from and then on a bar graph.<br>• Check students' responses to Communicate, questions 1–3. |

# 8 What Lives in Soil?

Page 142

| Time |
|---|
| 120–160 min |
| **Line Masters** |
| • LM 4-13 |

## Indicator Assessment Chart

| Indicator | Assessment Opportunities |
|---|---|
| **ES3.2 b.** Examine the interdependence between animals and soils (e.g., insects and grubs live in soil, soil provides shelter for some animals, and earthworms aerate soil). | • Work On It, p. 142<br>• Communicate, p. 143, q. 1 |
| **ES3.2 c.** Examine the interdependence between plants and soils (e.g., soils provide nutrients for plant growth, plant leaves die and fall onto the ground, and plant roots spread throughout soil). | • Work On It, p. 142<br>• Communicate, p. 143, q. 1 |

## Lesson Goal

To find out how plants, animals, and soil depend on each other

### Background Information

Humus is home to millions of tiny creatures called *nematodes*. In one cubic centimetre, there are thousands of them. Usually, you can only see these creatures with a strong magnifying lens. You may see them at the top of a soil sample, but they will quickly move deeper into the soil as they do not tolerate either light or dryness.

Topsoil contains plant roots, fungi, and insects of many types. Mining bees and wasps lay their eggs in topsoil. Ant nests are made up of a network of tunnels that are often underground. As ants work, they bring soil particles to the surface and carry their food down into the soil. This mixes the soil particles and adds new nutrients.

June beetle grubs also live in the soil. These beetle larvae feed on living plant roots for two to three years until they are ready to emerge as adults. The illustration on pages 142–143 of the student book identifies mites, springtails, and spiders that live in moist topsoil and eat rotting plants and animals. Their stomachs break these pieces of rotting plants and animals down into smaller pieces. When these tiny creatures pass waste, nutrients are added to the soil. Nutrients feed plants so the plants grow. Some mites are predators and eat smaller mites, springtails, and insect eggs.

Some creatures burrow deeper into the soil. Earthworms burrow through the soil by relaxing and contracting muscles along their bodies. During the day, slugs and snails burrow down into the soil where it is moist and cool. Larger animals like gophers, badgers, and groundhogs also burrow into the soil.

traditional ***KNOWLEDGE***

Plants depend on the soil for nutrients, air, and water. Plant roots take in air, water, and nutrients from the soil. When plants and animals die, their decomposing parts add nutrients to the soil, which new and growing plants take in through their roots. Plant nutrients move through the food chain. When animals, such as rabbits or deer, eat leafy plants on top of the soil, they get the nutrients they need from these plants. When animals, such as wolves or coyotes, kill and eat plant-eating animals, such as rabbits or deer, plant nutrients are passed on to them through the meat of the animals they eat. When animals die, their bodies decay and add nutrients to the soil. New and growing plants use these nutrients.

Soil needs space for air and water, because plants need air and water to grow. Animals, insects, and bacteria that live in the soil also need air and water to survive. Air spaces give plants and animals room to grow.

First Nations and Métis peoples believe that soil is part of Mother Earth and that Mother Earth and all living things are gifts from Creator and, therefore, they are sacred. In this lesson, teachers need to help students appreciate that many First Nations and Métis peoples have strong spiritual beliefs. Chief among these is the belief that many beings (e.g., plants, animals) and the elements (e.g., air, water, fire, rock) have Spirit. The spirit of Creator, which connects all of us, is believed to live in these beings and the elements.

While some teachers and students may have differing views on this topic, teachers need to help all students learn to respect the beliefs of others. Teachers must emphasize the diversity of worldviews—the ways that people of different cultures reference, understand, live, experience, and make meaning of the world around them. Students bring a host of cultural references into the classroom, and emphasizing diversity helps them understand the value of having a multitude of perspectives and beliefs, especially ones that may differ from the dominant worldview. In this way, First Nations and Métis students and students of other cultures and/or with differing beliefs may feel respected and welcome in the classroom.

## Curriculum Connections

In this lesson, students have the opportunity to develop skills and concepts in these areas:

### *English Language Arts*

CC3.1 a. Use words, symbols, and other forms, including appropriate technology, to express understanding of topics, themes, and issues and make connections to learning in other areas of study.

CC3.1 b. Communicate thoughts, feelings, and ideas clearly and, when appropriate, artistically.

CC3.2 a. Demonstrate understanding of the topic, problem, question, or issue in a variety of ways (e.g., dance pieces, visual representations, drama in context, diagram, demonstration, chart).

## Get Started ▶

**SAFETY CAUTION!**
If you look for living things in the soil outdoors, always put back logs and rocks quickly where you found them.

- Before reading the text with students, begin a discussion by saying, *The soil is home to many different living things. What can you think of that lives in the soil?* Record students' responses on the board or chart paper. You may wish to categorize their responses into animal and plant life. Once you have listed all their ideas, invite students to look at the illustration on pages 142–143 of the student book to try to find some of the living things they have mentioned.
- Read the captions and identify the corresponding parts of the illustration with students. Share information from Background Information with students. Note the living things that live on top of the soil, in the top layer of soil, and deep in the ground.

| **Time** |
|---|
| 30 min |
| **Learning Context** |
| inquiry |
| **Level of Inquiry** |
| confirmation |
| **Skills** |
| • observing<br>• classifying<br>• interpreting<br>• communicating |
| **Grouping** |
| pairs |
| **Materials and Equipment** |
| (per group)<br>• pencils |
| **Line Masters** |
| • LM 4-13 |

## Work On It

### Purpose

To identify ways in which plants, animals, and soil depend on each other

### Activity Notes

- Have students work in pairs to find as many ways that plants, animals, and soil depend on each other as they can in the illustration on pages 142–143 of the student book. Provide LM 4-13 What Lives in Soil? for students to record their findings. Students should be able to identify the following interdependencies from the captions and the illustration:

| How Soil Depends on Plants | How Plants Depend on Soil |
|---|---|
| • Plant roots spread through soil and keep it from blowing or washing away.<br>• Plant leaves die, fall to the ground, rot and add nutrients to the soil. | • Plant roots take in air, water, and nutrients from the soil that plants need to grow. |
| **How Soil Depends on Animals** | **How Animals Depend on Soil** |
| • Tiny creatures such as bacteria, mites, springtails, and spiders eat rotting plants and animals.<br>• Tiny creatures, such as mites, springtails, and spiders, loosen the soil, which makes more space for air and water to get into the soil.<br>• When groundhogs, ants, June beetles, dung beetles, ground squirrels, badgers, moles, and rabbits dig in the soil, this loosens the soil and makes spaces for air and water to get into the soil. | • Insects like grasshoppers lay their eggs in soil.<br>• Grubs, which are young beetles, live in the soil and eat plant roots.<br>• Groundhogs hibernate in burrows deep in the soil during the winter.<br>• Anthills can be seen above the soil, but they have many tunnels and burrows in the soil.<br>• June bugs and dung beetles dig their nests in soil to lay their eggs.<br>• Tiny creatures (e.g., bacteria, mites, springtails, spiders) live in soil and eat rotting plants and animals.<br>• Ground squirrels, badgers, moles, and rabbits dig deep tunnels and burrows in the soil. |

## Additional Activity

Take students outside to find living things in the soil. Go to a nearby garden and have students crouch low on the ground, sit silently, and simply observe. Students can look for ants and other small creatures, and search for signs that living things may have dug into the soil. Try to find rocks or small logs to lift so that students can observe the living things that may be underneath. You may wish to have students draw pictures of what they find. Discuss how these living things help the soil and how the soil helps them. Because they help each other, these living things and soil are interdependent. Make sure that students know not to touch the living things they find. Also, make sure students realize that the area must look undisturbed when they leave. Be sure that they return rocks and logs to the place they found them.

## Communicate

- The Communicate question asks students to create a representation (e.g., story, illustrations, comic strip, model, computer slide presentation) to illustrate their understanding of how plants, animals, and soil depend on each other. As students decide which product they will create, ensure that they understand what is involved. Also ask them to consider these questions:
  - *Who is my audience for this information?*
  - *What ideas are most important to my audience?*
  - *What method is best for sharing the important ideas?*
  - *What materials and how much time do I have?*
  - *Which option matches my strengths and interests best?*
- Work with students to develop an assessment checklist of criteria for their finished products. Post the checklist in the classroom so students can refer to it as they work.
- Provide time for students to plan and create their stories, illustrations, comic strips, models, and computer slide presentations. Circulate among students as they work and provide assistance as needed.
- Invite students to present their finished work to the class. After each student presents his/her product, give students an opportunity to provide oral feedback to one another. Ask students to comment on what each student did well and suggest one thing they could do to improve their product or presentation next time. Help students to express their comments using positive language.

1. Students' responses will vary, depending on their choice of product, but should include all the ways in which plants, animals, and soil depend on each other that they identified in the Work On It activity.

## DI Differentiating Instruction

### *For Reteaching*

Students can draw and cut out pictures of plants and animals that live in soil. Use these pictures to create a bulletin board display that illustrates the ways in which plants and animals depend on soil and the ways in which soil depends on plants and animals. Visit the library for books students can use as drawing references.

### *For Enrichment*

Challenge students to go beyond the content that is presented on pages 142–143 of the student book and research to find more information on ways in which plants, animals, and soil depend on each other.

## Assessment *for* Learning

| What to Look for in Student Work | What to Do |
|---|---|
| Students can identify ways in which animals and soil are interdependent (e.g., insects and grubs live in soil, soil provides shelter for some animals, and earthworms aerate soil). | • Observe students during the Work On It activity.<br>• Check students' responses to Communicate question 1. |
| Students can identify ways in which plants and soil are interdependent (e.g., soil provides nutrients for plant growth, plant leaves die and fall onto the ground, and plant roots spread throughout soil). | • Observe students during the Work On It activity.<br>• Check students' responses to Communicate question 1. |

# 9 Meet the Earthworms!

Page 144

| Time |
|---|
| 80 min |

| Line Masters |
|---|
| • LM 4-14<br>• LM 4-15 |

## Indicator Assessment Chart

| Indicator | Assessment Opportunities |
|---|---|
| **ES3.2 b.** Examine the interdependence between animals and soils (e.g., insects and grubs live in soil, soil provides shelter for some animals, and earthworms aerate soil). | • Work On It, p. 144<br>• Communicate, p. 145, q. 1, 2 |

## Lesson Goal

To find out how earthworms help provide what plants need to grow

## Background Information

Earthworms are bisexual. They have no legs, and move using *setae* (hair-like structures on their undersides) and motions of extending and contracting. Earthworms breathe through their skin and must remain moist. If they dry out, they will die.

The earthworm is a segmented animal. All segments are the same except for the head, which has a mouth but no eyes, and the *clitellum*, a flat section located somewhere between the 31$^{st}$ and the 37$^{th}$ segments. The clitellum contains many glands. Although they have no eyes, earthworms can sense light through their skin.

Earthworms prefer darkness, and they will move away from light and burrow into the soil. As they burrow into the ground, they eat soil and dead leaves, and deposit their waste as nutrient-rich *castings* on the surface. This process produces humus, mixes soil, and creates holes in soil where air and water can penetrate (i.e., *aerates* soil). Earthworms survive the winter by burrowing deep in the soil.

## Curriculum Connections

In this lesson, students have the opportunity to develop skills and concepts in these areas:

### *English Language Arts*

CR3.2 d. Record facts and ideas from grade-appropriate visual and multimedia texts including DVD, television program, magazine, and reference resources.
CR3.4 d. Ask questions and support answers by connecting prior knowledge with literal information found in, and inferred from, texts including First Nations and Métis resources.
CC3.1 a. Use words, symbols, and other forms, including appropriate technology, to express understanding of topics, themes, and issues and make connections to learning in other areas of study.

## Focus on Literacy

### *After Reading: Cause and Effect*

Tell students, *Writers have many different ways to organize their ideas. Sometimes, if writers simply want to tell us about something, they might use lots of adjectives and descriptive language. If writers want to answer certain questions for readers, they might use a question and answer pattern to organize their information. We've seen this in the "Ask ..." feature in our textbook. In this lesson on earthworms, the writer wants to tell us how earthworms help plants get what they need from the soil. The second paragraph gives us lots of information about how earthworms cause certain events to happen in the soil so that plants can grow. This type of relationship is called a "cause-and-effect" relationship. Let's reread this paragraph to get a better sense of how an earthworm's actions can affect plant growth.*

Read the first few sentences aloud and pause to think aloud, tracing how plants get the air and water they need from the soil. On the board or chart paper, record the following events:

earthworms eat soil → soil loosens → space in soil now has room for air and water → air and water enters soil → plants grow

Draw boxes around each event, or piece of information, and use arrows as shown above so that students can see how one event causes the next to occur.

Read the next few sentences aloud and pause again to think aloud. Trace how plants get the food or nutrients they need to grow from the soil. Start by recording "earthworms eat soil" in the first box and invite students to help you complete the chain of events:

earthworms eat soil → soil not used by earthworms passes out of their bodies back into soil → droppings are good nutrients / food for plants → plants grow

Consolidate learning by having students turn to a partner and answer the following questions:

- *What are the three things plants need to grow?* (air, water, food/nutrients)
- *What helps provide these things?* (earthworms)
- *How do earthworms help?* (Students should be able to retrace or summarize the cause-and-effect sequences above.)

## Get Started ▶

- Invite students to look at the photo of an earthworm on page 144 of the student book and read the text with students.
- Use the Focus on Literacy activity on the previous page to help students understand the relationship between earthworms and soil.
- Explain that one way to find out more about earthworms is to observe them over time. The class will work together to build a home for earthworms in the classroom.

**!** Earthworms need air to breathe. Earthworms breathe air through their skin. When it rains, air holes in the soil fill with water. This makes earthworms come up to the surface so they can breathe. The next time it rains, have students look out for earthworms. Invite students to share where they spotted earthworms and how many they saw.

**Time**

60–90 minutes

**Learning Context**

inquiry

**Level of Inquiry**

confirmation

**Skills**

- observing
- inferring
- experimenting

**Grouping**

pairs

**Materials and Equipment**

(per group)

- large, clear jar
- small rocks or pebbles
- sand
- soil
- spoon
- water
- earthworms
- worm food such as leaves
- aluminum foil
- tape
- pencils

**Line Masters**

- LM 4-14

## Work On It

### Purpose

To conduct an investigation to observe how earthworms mix soil

### Activity Notes

- Some students may be reluctant to handle earthworms. This is natural. Do not push them. Encourage students who are comfortable with worms to do the collecting. Others can watch and offer suggestions. Observe to make sure that students treat the living things with respect and that they replace earth and rocks that have been disturbed.
- As a class, make a plan to collect earthworms. Some students will recall that after it rains earthworms can be seen on the ground and on sidewalks. Discuss why this is so (see ! feature above).
- The class may decide to wait for a good rainfall before going on an earthworm collecting expedition. Alternately, try hosing down an area or pouring buckets of water over a section of lawn or garden. Digging in garden soil with a trowel will probably turn up some earthworms as well. You may wish to simply buy earthworms from a fishing store instead.
- Keep in mind that the earthworm home should be completed before embarking on an earthworm collecting expedition. Earthworms need to be in moist soil so their skin does not dry out. Mix some leaves and grass into the soil because earthworms like to eat soil and dead plant matter.
- Distribute copies of LM 4-14 Meet the Earthworms! for students to record their observations.

Earthworms need air and a moist skin. Add a few drops of water to the soil every day. Earthworms breathe through their skin and must remain moist. If they dry out, they will die.

**SAFETY CAUTION!**

Remind students to be careful when picking up earthworms. Earthworms are living creatures and must be treated with care and respect. Make sure that all students involved in collecting the worms wash their hands well afterward.

## Communicate

Encourage students to share what they have learned about earthworms.

1. Expect students to observe that the soil appears to have been loosened and mixed.
2. Earthworms are good for the soil because they eat soil. This loosens the soil and makes room for water and air. Earthworms also produce droppings that are good for plants. The soil is good for earthworms because they live in soil. It provides their food, air, moisture, and shelter.

### BUILD ON WHAT YOU KNOW

Review with students what they learned about how plants, animals, and soil depend on each other in Lessons 8 and 9. In particular, identify ways in which plants and animals help soil. Ask students to think about the soil they will make for their vegetable garden. How will they use plants and animals to make their soil healthy? Have them record their ideas (e.g., add humus, or decayed plant and animal matter, to the soil; add earthworms to the soil to aerate and add nutrients to the soil).

## DI Differentiating Instruction

### *For EAL/ELL*

The visual nature of this lesson will help EAL/ELL students understand how earthworms benefit soil. You may wish to have them draw pictures in boxes to illustrate the cause-and-effect relationship between earthworms in soil as in the Focus on Literacy activity.

### *For Reteaching*

Students can prepare a newsletter to send home to their parents, explaining how useful earthworms can be. The newsletter could include drawings, written information, and extra information that students have researched.

### *For Enrichment*

Students can use LM 4-15 What Type of Environment Do Earthworms Like? to learn more about earthworms. Students can also research to find answers to the questions they still have about earthworms. As they find answers to their questions, they can share what they learn with the class.

## Assessment *for* Learning

| What to Look for in Student Work | What to Do |
|---|---|
| Students can identify ways in which earthworms and soil benefit each other. | • Observe students during the Work On It activity.<br>• Check students' responses to Communicate questions 1 and 2. |

# 10 How Does Moving Water Affect Soil?

Page 146

| Time |
| --- |
| 120 min |
| **Line Masters** |
| • LM 4-16 |

## Indicator Assessment Chart

| Indicator | Assessment Opportunities |
| --- | --- |
| **ES3.2 f.** Collaboratively design and safely carry out procedures to determine the effects of moving water on different types of soils. | • Work On It, p. 146<br>• Communicate, p. 147, q. 1–3 |

## Lesson Goal

To find out what happens when water moves over different types of soil

## Background Information

Two basic factors lead to soil erosion by water. Water must pool on the surface and then it must start to move. When water falls on soil, it soaks in. If more water falls than the ground can absorb over any given period of time, then the water will build up on the surface. If the surface of the ground is perfectly level, the water will remain where it builds up. However, the ground surface usually has a slope, and gravity causes the water to move in the direction of the slope.

Water soaks into some soils faster than others due to soil porosity (the spaces between the soil particles). Gravity is the biggest force pulling the water down into the soil. The size of the spaces between the soil particles will determine how fast the water will move through the soil. The larger the spaces between the soil particles, the easier it is for gravity to pull the water down and the faster the water will soak in. The faster it soaks in, the less chance it will have to pool on the surface and cause erosion. Sandy soil has larger spaces between the particles than soil high in silt or clay, and it is less likely to erode given the same rainfall.

In soil high in silt or clay, water pools on the surface much more easily than on sandy soil, because the spaces between the soil particles are smaller. In soil high in clay, the individual particles are smaller than silt or sand particles, but they may be harder to move than silt particles, because clay particles stick together when they are wet much more than sand or silt particles. In this case, the size of the raindrops may be important, because the impact of raindrops will dislodge the clay particles.

*continued→*

In loamy soil with humus, the spaces between the particles are a mixture of large and small. Hence, water does not pool easily on the surface as it does on a clay or silty soil, but it will not drain as fast as in sandy soil. The humus in loam acts like a sponge to absorb water and helps soil hold moisture. Loamy soil with humus takes in water faster and holds more water than soil with smaller or fewer air spaces. Because loamy soil has both sand and clay in nearly equal proportions, as the soil forms the clay and sand combine to form aggregates, or a mixture of particles. Aggregates give it more stability and resistance to erosion than individual particles of the same type.

Texture is the principal factor affecting soil erosion by water, but structure, organic matter, and permeability also contribute. Moving water easily transports **very fine** sand, silt, clay, and loam particles even at low speeds. Greater amounts of water or faster moving water are required to move larger, heavier sand and gravel particles. Sand, sandy loam, and loamy soils tend to be less susceptible to erosion by moving water than silt, very fine sand, and certain clay textured soils. The steeper the slope of a field, the more soil particles will be carried by moving water.

## Curriculum Connections

In this lesson, students have the opportunity to develop skills and concepts in these areas:

### *English Language Arts*

CC3.1 a. Use words, symbols, and other forms, including appropriate technology, to express understanding of topics, themes, and issues and make connections to learning in other areas of study.

CC3.1 d. Communicate ideas, findings, and information pertaining to topics, problems, questions, or issues by creating easy-to-follow visual, oral, and written formats with a clear purpose (e.g., short report, explanation of a procedure).

## Get Started ▶

- Before reading the text, have students brainstorm ways in which water moves in natural and human-built environments. Record their suggestions on the board or chart paper.
- After discussing students' suggestions, read the text in the Get Started and look at the photos together. Ask whether students have seen water moving in the ways shown in the photos.
- Discuss where students can see water moving where they live.
- Review with students what they know about the size, weight, and texture of particles in sand, silt, clay, and loam. Elicit what they learned about how different types of soil absorb water. Prompt them to consider what might happen when water moves over different kinds of soil. Ask, *Would water move some soil particles? In which soil type would water move the most particles?*

| Time |
| --- |
| 60–80 min |
| **Learning Context** |
| inquiry |
| **Level of Inquiry** |
| guided |
| **Skills** |
| • experimenting<br>• observing<br>• inferring<br>• comparing<br>• communicating<br>• controlling variables<br>• predicting |
| **Grouping** |
| pairs |
| **Materials and Equipment** |
| (per group)<br>• equal amounts of sandy soil, silty soil, soil high in clay, and loamy soil high in humus<br>• 4 cookie sheets or baking pans<br>• 8 blocks or books<br>• measuring cups<br>• water<br>• camera (optional)<br>• pencils |
| **Line Masters** |
| • LM 4-16 |

## Work On It

### Purpose

To plan an investigation to find out if water moves the most soil particles in sandy soil, silty soil, soil high in clay, or loamy soil high in humus

### Activity Notes

- Beforehand, contact a local landscaping company about obtaining free or inexpensive samples of the soils students investigate or order samples from a science supply house. Alternatively, you can get sandy soil from roadside ditches, farmers' fields west of Saskatoon, or a garden supply store or greenhouse (horticultural sand). Silt can be found at the bottom or edge of a stream, river, pond, or a lake, the exit end of a culvert, the lower end of a washout in a farmer's field, on the delta of a river, an area that has been flooded, or farmers' fields east of Saskatoon. Soil high in clay can be found where a basement is being dug, at the bottom of a washout where the topsoil has been eroded away, on the banks of a river, and in farmers' fields around Regina. You can find loamy soil high in humus in a farmer's field, garden, forest, meadow, or garden supply store.
- This activity has been set up with a guided inquiry approach so that only the question and a list of materials are provided. The students will decide how to use the suggested materials, consider the use of other materials, develop the steps in the procedure, and observe and record the results of their investigation. Then, based on the evidence, they will make conclusions about why water moves more of one kind of soil particles than the soil particles in the other samples.
- If you feel that some or all of your students need a lower level of inquiry, you may wish to provide them with the steps of the procedure on LM 4-16 How Does Moving Water Affect Soil? for their investigation.
- Help students plan and carry out their investigations. Discuss the predictions students make in step 1 and record them on the board.
- Help students collect the soil samples and other materials they need. You may wish to have some students use pure sand and pure clay along with purchased garden soil to ensure distinctly different results.
- Before students decide which materials to use and begin to plan how they will use these materials, have a discussion to exchange ideas and consider which variables must be controlled as well as other materials they could use. Ask questions such as:
    - *What can you put the soil samples in so water can move over them? Why do you need to put them in the same kinds of containers?*
- After discussing all the variables to be considered, provide an opportunity for student pairs to meet, decide which additional materials they wish to use in step 2, and plan their investigations for step 3. Have students present their plans to the class. Encourage students to ask one another questions about the plans. Have students consider making revisions to their plans before they go on to step 4.
- In step 4, pairs carry out their investigation. At this point, some pairs may find that they need to make revisions to their plan. Encourage pairs who encounter challenges to meet with you. They can explain what they think needs to change in order for their investigation to be successful.
- In step 5, students make a conclusion based on their investigation. Groups may reach different conclusions. Discuss why this may have happened. This discussion may lead to repeating the investigation as a demonstration.

Students could draw diagrams or use a digital camera to record what happens when water runs over each soil sample. Diagrams, photos, and videos all provide a visual representation of the results, which can be discussed and compared following the investigation. They can also be used to display the results of the investigation.

## Communicate

If your students planned their investigations, ask each pair of students to explain the materials they used and the steps they followed. After the first pair presents, ask, *Did any other pair follow a similar plan? How was your plan similar? How was it different?* Continue to have all pairs share and draw comparisons whenever possible. If some or all of your students followed the steps as outlined on LM 4-16 How Does Moving Water Affect Soil?, bring the class together and have the groups present their results.

1. Students' answers may vary, but expect students to discover that the water moved the most soil particles in the sample that is high in silt.
2. Although silt particles are heavier than clay particles, which are the smallest particles, they are more easily eroded by water because silt particles do not stick together as much as clay particles do when the particles are wet. That means that water may not move clay particles as easily as silt particles.
3. The moving water deposits the soil particles at the lowest end of the cookie sheet or baking pan.

After completing this lesson, look back at the KWL chart from the start of the unit. Ask students what they learned about soil and record their responses in the "*What I learned about soil*" column of the chart. Ask them if they have other questions about soil and record them in the appropriate column.

## DI Differentiating Instruction

### *For Reteaching*

If students got mixed results in their investigations and came to different conclusions, you may wish to repeat the investigation as a demonstration.

### *For Enrichment*

Challenge students to repeat the investigation to find out what happens if they:

- increase the amount of water on the soil samples
- increase or decrease the force of the water as it hits the soil particles in each soil sample
- increase or decrease the slope of the soil sample

## Assessment *for* Learning

| What to Look for in Student Work | What to Do |
|---|---|
| Students can design and safely carry out procedures to determine the effects of moving water on different types of soils. | • Observe students as they design and carry out their investigations.<br>• Check students' responses to Communicate questions 1 to 3. |
| Students can determine which types of soils are affected most by moving water. | • Check students' responses to Communicate questions 1 and 2. |

# 11 Erosion Changes Soil

Page 148

| Time |
| --- |
| 40 min |
| **Vocabulary** |
| • soil erosion |
| **Line Masters** |
| • LM 4-17 |

## Indicator Assessment Chart

| Indicator | Assessment Opportunities |
| --- | --- |
| **ES3.2 e.** Observe the effects of moving water on soils in different environments (e.g., beneath an eavestrough downspout, along a stream bank, down a slope, and under a sprinkler). | • Work On It, p. 148<br>• Communicate, p. 149, q. 1, 2 |

## Lesson Goal

To find out how moving water causes soil erosion

## Background Information

During erosion, soil or rock is worn down and/or carried away to a new location. Water and wind cause soil erosion to occur naturally on all land. Erosion carries away huge amounts of fertile topsoil in Canada each year and decreases crop productivity. Some soil erosion occurs slowly, and other forms of soil erosion, such as landslides and flooding, occur quickly and dramatically. The following factors affect how quickly and severely soil erosion occurs:

- **Rainfall intensity and runoff**

Raindrop splash is the first part of erosion. The size and the force of the drops can cause soil particles to dislodge and move in the direction of the surface slope due to gravity. Raindrop splash and runoff water can easily move fine sand, silt, clay, and organic particles. Larger sand and gravel particles need greater raindrop energy or runoff amounts to move. Raindrop splash causes the most noticeable soil movement during short, severe thunderstorms. Significant soil loss can also occur during less-intense rainstorms that last longer than thunderstorms. For runoff to occur, water must pool on the surface and then start to move. If soil is compacted, has a hard crust, or is frozen, runoff increases. Runoff from farmlands is greatest in the spring when the soil is full of water, snow is melting, and new plant growth has not yet begun.

- **Soil erodibility** (the ability of soils to resist erosion)

Soils that absorb water more quickly and have more organic matter have better resistance to erosion. Sand, sandy loam, and loamy soils are less erodible than silt and very fine sand, and soils high in clay.

- **Length and angle of the surface slope**

The steeper the surface slope, the more soil loss there is from erosion. There is also more soil erosion as the length of the slope increases, because greater length allows for more runoff to accumulate.

*continued*→

- **Plant life**

Plants, fallen leaves, and decaying plant matter on the surface protect the soil from the effects of raindrop splash. Plants also help slow runoff and as water slows down, it has more time to be absorbed by the soil. Plants also provide channels for water to find its way into the soil. Therefore, if the ground has a surface slope and little to no plant life on it, it will easily erode.

## Curriculum Connections

In this lesson, students have the opportunity to develop skills and concepts in these areas:

### *English Language Arts*

CR3.1 a. View, listen to, read, and respond to a variety of texts that reflect the issues related to identity, community, and social responsibility and connect to personal experiences, other texts, and other areas of study.
CC3.1 a. Use words, symbols, and other forms, including appropriate technology, to express understanding of topics, themes, and issues and make connections to learning in other areas of study.
CC3.4 e. Identify the main idea and supporting details in informational text and extract appropriate and significant information.

### *Social Studies*

DR 3.3 b. Identify ways in which people in communities studied interact with the land (e.g., meeting needs and wants, how land is protected or neglected).
DR 3.3 c. Identify local environmental issues that affect life in communities studied.
DR 3.3 d. Compare environmental concerns (e.g., air quality, soil conservation, water availability and quality) common to both the local community and communities studied.

## Get Started ▶

- Review with students what they learned about what happens when water moves over different types of soil in Lesson 10.
- Ask students to share what they think they know about the word *erosion*. Tell students that in this lesson they will learn how erosion changes soil.
- Read the Get Started text on page 148 with students and examine the photos.
- To demonstrate what happens when water causes rocks to rub against each other, you may wish to conduct the Additional Activity that is outlined on the next page.

- Ask, *How does moving water change rocks?* Display a group of rocks that includes some rocks that are smooth and ask: *Which of these rocks do you think may have been in moving water for a long time? What makes you think so?* Encourage students to look for rocks in the environment that seem to have been changed by moving water.

| Time |
| --- |
| 20 min |
| **Learning Context** |
| inquiry |
| **Level of Inquiry** |
| confirmation |
| **Skills** |
| • observing<br>• interpreting<br>• communicating |
| **Grouping** |
| pairs |
| **Materials and Equipment** |
| (per pair)<br>• pencils |
| **Line Masters** |
| • LM 4-17 |

## Work On It

### Purpose

To examine photos and identify how moving water causes soil erosion

### Activity Notes

- Have students examine the photos in the Work On It in pairs and identify how moving water is moving soil particles and causing soil erosion in each one. Distribute LM 4-17 Erosion Changes Soil for students to record their observations. Then, provide an opportunity for students to share their observations.
- Invite students to describe a time or a place where they saw moving water cause erosion in similar ways to those shown in the photos. Ask: *Have you ever seen soil moving from one place to another? Where could you walk outside to see signs of erosion? Can you think of a photo that you could add to this page about erosion?*

## Additional Activity

Collect 3 to 5 jagged rocks, a can with a lid, water, a strainer, and an empty container. Have students examine the jagged rocks carefully before starting. Put the rocks in a can filled halfway with water. Have students shake the can vigorously for several minutes, passing it on as they get tired. Encourage them to predict what is happening to the rocks inside the can. After several minutes of active shaking, open the can. Hold a strainer over the empty container and pour the water through it. Ask students to examine the rocks again and describe any changes they see. Look in the strainer at the water that has been poured out. What has changed? Place the rocks and water back in the can and continue the process. Check again after some time to see how the rocks have changed.

## Communicate

You may wish to provide an opportunity for students to refer to the KWL chart started at the beginning of this unit. Pose questions such as:

- *What have you learned about soil that we can add to the chart?*
- *Is there anything in the "What I Know About Soil" column that needs to be changed?*
- *What new questions do you have about soil to add to the chart?*

1. Moving water picks up soil particles and transports them from one location to another.
2. Students' answers may vary, but should include that they would see more erosion from moving water on the clay banks of a river, because of the volume and force of the moving water over an extended period of time.

## Differentiating Instruction

### *For EAL/ELL*

Utilize the visual demonstrations described in this lesson (see Get Started and Additional Activity) to help EAL/ELL students understand what is meant by soil erosion.

### *For Reteaching*

Go outside and have students pour water on different surfaces (e.g., grass, a garden bed, asphalt, pavement, and a leaf-covered area). Encourage them to observe how the water hits the surface and what happens to the earth material it hits. Ask questions such as:

- *When does the water move soil?*
- *Does the water run away from where it hits the surface?*
- *Does the water travel or does it seem to be absorbed?*

Encourage students to identify places where water will cause soil to move, and other places where water will not affect the soil.

### *For Enrichment*

Challenge students to search for photos on the Internet that illustrate soil erosion. Provide an opportunity for students to share the photos they find and explain how moving water is causing soil erosion in each one.

## Assessment *for* Learning

| What to Look for in Student Work | What to Do |
|---|---|
| Students can observe and identify the effects of moving water on soils in different environments (e.g., beneath an eavestrough downspout, along a stream bank, down a slope, and under a sprinkler). | • Observe students during the Work On It activity.<br>• Check students' responses to Communicate questions 1 and 2. |

# 12 How Can We Prevent Soil Erosion?

Page 150

**Time**

120 min

**Line Masters**

- LM 4-18

## Indicator Assessment Chart

| Indicator | Assessment Opportunities |
|---|---|
| **ES3.2 g.** Propose practices that individuals and communities can take to reduce the effects of erosion on a small-scale (e.g., vegetable garden and flower pot) and large-scale (e.g., agricultural field, sports field, river bank, and road ditch). | • Work On It, p. 151<br>• Communicate, p. 151, q. 1–3 |

## Lesson Goal

To investigate how to prevent water from eroding soil

## Background Information

Planting grasses, bushes, and trees helps hold soil in place, protects the soil from raindrop impact and splash, slows down the movement of surface runoff, and allows surface water to move into the soil, all of which prevent soil erosion. The most effective vegetation covers for preventing erosion are forests and permanent grasses, which completely cover the soil. Plant roots and rotting organic waste provide channels that allow surface water into the soil.

Crops, such as alfalfa, or winter cover crops, such as winter wheat or winter rye, can help reduce erosion more than crops that are planted in the spring and harvested in the fall, because they cover soil for a longer period. Farmers can protect their soil from erosion by leaving stubble untilled after harvest and over the winter months. Many farmers in Saskatchewan utilize zero-till farming, which means they seed directly into the stubble and straw cover from the previous year's crop. The less the soil surface is disturbed by tilling, the more the vegetation and residue cover at or near the surface protects the soil from erosion.

When trees and grass are left to grow on steep hillsides and not cleared for cropland, these hillsides will be more resistant to erosion. Farmers can also conserve soil and help prevent soil erosion by planting grass and not plowing low areas in a field where water usually runs and collects.

Farmers can use measures such as contour plowing (working the soil around the curve of a hill), contour planting (planting crops around the curve of a hill rather than up and down a hill), strip cropping (planting row crops in strips across a slope and alternating grain and forage crops in the strips), and terracing (creating wide ridges that go around a hill to slow the movement of water down the hill) to control erosion on a field.

## Curriculum Connections

In this lesson, students have the opportunity to develop skills and concepts in these areas:

### *English Language Arts*

CC3.1 a. Use words, symbols, and other forms, including appropriate technology, to express understanding of topics, themes, and issues and make connections to learning in other areas of study.

### *Social Studies*

DR 3.3 b. Identify ways in which people in communities studied interact with the land (e.g., meeting needs and wants, how land is protected or neglected).
DR 3.3 c. Identify local environmental issues that affect life in communities studied.

**Time**

60–80 min

**Learning Context**

inquiry
problem solving

**Level of Inquiry**

guided

**Skills**

- inferring
- observing
- interpreting
- experimenting
- hypothesizing
- comparing
- communicating
- controlling variables
- predicting

**Grouping**

pairs

**Materials and Equipment**

(per group)
- loam
- 2 cookie sheets or baking pans
- water
- other materials students choose
- camera (optional)
- pencils

**Line Masters**

- LM 4-18

## Get Started ▶

- Review how moving water erodes soil. Brainstorm ways in which soil erosion could be prevented with students. Ask, *How could soil be held in place so that moving water cannot move soil particles?* Record students' suggestions so they can compare their ideas with those they encounter in the Get Started in the student book.
- Have students examine the photos and read the captions in the Get Started on page 150 with a partner and be ready to compare and contrast the illustrated ways of preventing soil erosion with the list of brainstormed ideas.
- Instruct students to work with their partner to sketch and label how each photo illustrates a way of preventing erosion. Ask, *How does each way help soil stay in place and take in water?* Then, provide an opportunity for pairs to share their sketches and explain how each way holds soil in place and helps soil take in water.

## Work On It

### Purpose

To plan an investigation to prevent water from eroding loamy soil

### Activity Notes

- This activity has been set up with a guided inquiry approach so that only the question and a list of materials are provided. Students will decide how to use the suggested materials, consider the use of other materials, develop the steps in the procedure, and observe and record the results of their investigation. Then, based on the evidence, they will make conclusions about how they can prevent water from eroding the soil.
- If you feel that some or all of your students need a lower level of inquiry, you may wish to provide the steps of the procedure to find out how to prevent water from eroding the soil. If so, provide copies of LM 4-18 How Can We Prevent Soil Erosion? for these students.

- Talk about students' ideas for preventing water from eroding soil and record their ideas on the chalkboard.
- Before students begin to plan their investigations, hold a discussion to exchange ideas and consider which variables must be controlled as well as other materials they could use. To guide this discussion, ask questions such as:
- *Why do you need to set up the two soil samples exactly the same and try your idea on one soil sample, but not the other?*
- *Should the soil sample in each container be level? Should it be packed down?*
- After discussing all the variables to be considered, provide an opportunity for student pairs to meet and decide which additional materials they wish to use in step 3. Help students collect the soil samples and other materials they need to conduct their investigation.
- Have students present their plans to the class. Encourage students to ask one another questions about the plans. Have students consider making revisions to their plans before they go on to step 4.
- Students can draw diagrams or use a digital or video camera to record what happens when water runs over each soil sample.
- In step 4, pairs carry out their investigation. At this point, some pairs may find that they need to make revisions in their plan. Encourage pairs who encounter challenges to meet with you. They can explain what they think needs to change in order for their investigation to be successful. Record their comments for student assessment.
- In step 5, students make a conclusion based on their investigation. Be prepared for groups to reach different conclusions, and set aside time to discuss why this may have happened. This discussion may lead to repeating the investigation as a demonstration.

## Communicate

1. Students' answers may vary but could include:
   - Adding humus to the soil helps the soil take in more water. When the soil can take in more water, less soil can be carried away by moving water.
   - Planting seeds so that plants can grow and root in the soil helps keep soil in place.
   - Contour planting or cultivation across the slope helps soil take in more water and hold it in place.
   - Building ridges of soil across the slope will help slow the runoff of water.
2. Students' answers may vary but could include trying a different idea to prevent water from eroding the soil, using different materials, controlling more variables, or recording the results differently.
3. Students' answers may vary but could include planting seeds, adding humus to the soil, adding a straw cover, making holes in the surface of the soil, or contour planting or cultivation.

### BUILD ON WHAT YOU KNOW

Students' plans may include using loam (e.g., a fairly equal mixture of sand, silt, and clay), humus, and growing plants in their soil to prevent water from eroding the soil in their school vegetable garden.

## DI Differentiating Instruction

### *For EAL/ELL*

It may help EAL/ELL students to follow the procedure as outlined on LM 4-18 How Can We Prevent Soil Erosion? Pair EAL/ELL students with partners who read and speak English very well. Encourage these students to read each step aloud for their EAL/ELL partner and to follow the text with their finger so their partner can associate the written and spoken words. Then, demonstrate with the materials what each step in the procedure asks them to do.

### *For Reteaching*

Use the structured inquiry approach that is provided on LM 4-18 How Can We Prevent Soil Erosion? You may also wish to redo the investigation as a demonstration.

### *For Enrichment*

Challenge students to repeat the investigation to find out what happens if they:

- place a straw covering on the soil
- plant seeds in the soil and allow them to begin growing before adding water
- dig a drainage ditch down the slope of one soil sample
- dig a drainage ditch down the slope of one soil sample, plant seeds along its length, and allow the seeds to begin to grow before adding water
- create ridges across the slope of one soil sample to slow the movement of the water

## Assessment *for* Learning

| What to Look for in Student Work | What to Do |
| --- | --- |
| Students can propose practices that individuals and communities can take to reduce the effects of erosion on a small-scale (e.g., vegetable garden and flower pot) and large-scale (e.g., agricultural field, sports field, river bank, and road ditch). | • Observe students as they plan and carry out their investigations.<br>• Check students' responses to Communicate questions 1–3. |

# 13 Using Earth's Soils

Page 152

**Time**

120 min

**Vocabulary**

- berms

**Line Masters**

- LM 4-19

## Indicator Assessment Chart

| Indicator | Assessment Opportunities |
|---|---|
| **ES3.2 a.** Suggest ways in which individuals and communities value and use soil, including the importance of Mother Earth for First Nations and Métis peoples. | • Work On It, p. 153<br>• Communicate, p. 153, q. 1–3 |
| **ES3.2 d.** Relate the characteristics (e.g., composition, colour, texture, and ability to absorb water) of soils to their uses (e.g., agriculture, berms, pottery, earth shelters, road building, habitats, landscaping, and purifying water). | • Work On It, p. 153<br>• Communicate, p. 153, q. 1–3 |

## Lesson Goal

To learn how people use different soils and clay

## Background Information

Farmers need soil that holds nutrients and water for plants. Loam is used for growing crops. It is a fairly equal mixture of sand, silt, and clay with humus. The sand particles create spaces for more water and air. The clay and humus help to keep the soil particles together and hold water. The silt helps to hold the nutrients and water that growing plants need. The humus provides the nutrients that plants need to grow.

A berm is an earth mound or wall. People build berms to prevent erosion or to reduce traffic noise. Berms are also used to landscape yards. A large berm might be made of a gravel and sand base topped with a layer of clay and then loam. The sand and gravel provide a strong base. The clay holds the berm together, and plants can grow in the loam.

Soil provides a surface for building roads, buildings, and sidewalks. Humans have also found ways to use soil to build strong and stable shelters. In fact, soil has been used as a building material for thousands of years, and it is still an important building material. Native Americans in the Great Plains built lodges with logs and covered them with grass and dirt. Some settlers cut large blocks of sod to build their homes. Houses made of sandy clay, water, and straw are known as *adobe* homes and are found in warm climates, such as the southwestern United States. In dry regions, houses made of adobe bricks last hundreds of years. These homes keep out heat and cold.

*continued*→

Brick construction is common in eastern Canada because of the demands of the climate. Bricks are made from shale and clay, which are mixed with water until a thick paste is formed. This mixture is poured into machines that create the brick shapes. Concrete is an important building material that is common everywhere. Concrete is made from gravel, fine sand, cement (ash and limestone), and water.

Our fuel comes indirectly from the soil. Coal is made from plants that grew in the soil long ago. Oil and gas are also made from organic materials (decayed plants and animals). Some of these things grew in the soil at one time or lived on things that grew in the soil. Coal, oil, and gas are extracted from under layers of rock and soil.

Wetlands act like sponges to store water during wet times of the year. Then, they release water into aquifers and underground streams where we get most of our drinking water. Plants that grow in the wetlands hold the soil and help keep it from getting washed away. Wetlands also purify the water. They filter out harmful chemicals and waste materials. When dirty water flows through a wetland, the soil cleans it.

Soil acts as a filter to purify water. It helps to filter out pollutants and clean up water before it flows through to lakes, rivers, and other sources of drinking water. In the alternate activity provided with this lesson, layers of soil act like strainers or filters to clean the dirty water. Only particles in the dirty water that are smaller than the spaces between the particles in each layer in the cup can pass through with the water. The pebbles strain out the larger particles in the water. As the dirty water passes through the next layer, the spaces between the sand particles are smaller. Only dirty particles that are smaller than these spaces can pass through with the water. As the dirty water passes through the clay, the spaces between the soil particles are very tiny. Very small particles in the dirty water get trapped in the clay. The water that drips from the clay layer at the bottom of the cup is cleaner. The pebbles, sand, and clay filter out many of the particles that made the water dirty.

## Curriculum Connections

In this lesson, students have the opportunity to develop skills and concepts in these areas:

### *Social Studies*

IN3.1 a. Describe characteristics of daily life in communities studied, and compare the ways in which the needs are met by individuals in diverse communities (e.g., housing, tools, work, use of the land, games, education).

### *English Language Arts*

CR3.1 a. View, listen to, read, and respond to a variety of texts that reflect the issues related to identity, community, and social responsibility and connect to personal experiences, other texts, and other areas of study.

## Get Started ▶

- What a soil is used for depends on its characteristics (e.g., type of soil particles, particle size, texture, ability to hold water). Review the characteristics of different kinds of soil—sand, silt, clay, and loam—and have students predict what these soils might be used for. Record students' suggestions so they can compare the uses they suggest with those they learn about in the text.
- Have students work in pairs to examine the photos and read the captions in the Get Started on page 152 of the student book.
- Guide students to compare and contrast the illustrated ways of using Earth's soils in the student book with their list of suggested uses.
- Have students work with a partner to sketch the ways in which different soils are used in each of the photos. Instruct them to be ready to explain in their own words how the characteristics of each type of soil match its use. Then, provide an opportunity for pairs to share their sketches with another pair and explain how each way of using soil matches its characteristics.

**Time**

40–60 min

**Learning Context**

inquiry

**Level of Inquiry**

guided

**Skills**

- making models
- observing
- communicating
- predicting

**Grouping**

individuals

**Materials and Equipment**

(per student)
- clay
- water
- plastic or wood board
- tools for cutting and shaping clay
- pencils

**Line Masters**

- LM 4-19

## Work On It

### Purpose

To use clay to make something useful and then test the object to see if it fulfills its purpose

### Activity Notes

- Air-hardening clay will be the easiest to work with in this activity. This type of clay is readily available in art supply stores and does not require firing in a kiln. If you have access to a kiln at your school, ask the art teacher to assist you in firing student projects.
- Before you introduce the clay to students, ask if any of them have worked with clay before. Encourage these students to share their experiences and to offer tips and advice on working with clay. Explain that it is important to keep clay moist while you are working with it. If students do not complete their objects in one class period, make sure that the clay is wrapped well with damp paper towels and covered with plastic. This will ensure that it does not begin to dry and harden before the next working session.
- Allow time for students to manipulate and experiment with the clay before they build their objects. Students can explore rolling, pinching, and using tools to shape the clay. If possible, invite an experienced potter to introduce clay and some clay-working techniques to the class.
- Although students are asked to plan what they want to create, it is likely that their plans will change as they work. This is part of the natural creative process and should be accepted. Visit students as they work and encourage them to describe the texture of the clay and the challenges they are facing.
- Tools for cutting and shaping clay could include plastic knives, pizza cutters, and rolling pins.
- You may wish to use LM 4-19 How Soil Purifies Water as an alternate or additional activity.

## Additional Activity

Present the class with two groups of objects: one group made of manufactured materials (e.g., markers, pens, Lego® blocks, and a plastic comb) and another group made of natural materials (e.g., a clay pot, pencil, chalk, stone jewellery, and ceramic beads). Invite students to tell how the items in each group are alike. After discovering that the items in one group are all made from manufactured materials and the items in the other group are made of natural materials, challenge students to think of other items to add to each group. Keep the groups on display and encourage students to add items as they are found.

## Communicate

Provide an opportunity for students to show their completed work to the class. They can explain what they tried to create, the challenges they faced in working with clay, and the results they observed when they tested their object to see if it did what it was supposed to do. As students share their work and challenges, discuss what they could do differently next time.

1. Clay is good for making something useful because the particles are sticky when they are wet. When clay dries, it is smooth and hard.
2. Students' answers may vary but could include a clay pitcher, cup, plate, bowl, beads, plant pot, brick for building, and so on.
3. Students' answers may vary but could include clay because the particles stick together when wet and dry smooth and hard, or sod (grass and the layer of soil held together by the roots) as the roots hold soil together and it can be cut into blocks for building.

## DI Differentiating Instruction

### *For Enrichment*

- Students can use earth materials to build a bird's nest. They will need small twigs, straw, grass, string, cardboard, mud, and water. Enlist students' help in collecting these materials. Once the materials are collected, give students a piece of cardboard on which to build. They will begin by using handfuls of twigs and straw to form a circle. Next, students will use the string and long pieces of grass to try to weave and tie the twigs and straw into a nest-like shape. Finally, they will add wet mud to the materials in order to cover and shape them into a nest.
- Students could research to find out how people from various cultures use earth materials to build their homes and other useful objects.

## Assessment *for* Learning

| What to Look for in Student Work | What to Do |
| --- | --- |
| Students can relate the characteristics of soils (e.g., composition, colour, texture, and ability to absorb water) to their uses (e.g., agriculture, berms, fuel, pottery, earth shelters, road building, habitats, landscaping, and purifying water). | • Observe students as they read and discuss the Get Started and complete the Work On It activity.<br>• Check students' responses to Communicate questions 1–3. |

# 14 Preventing Harm to Our Soil

Page 154

**Time**

80–120 min

**Vocabulary**

- compacted

**Line Masters**

- LM 4-20

## Indicator Assessment Chart

| Indicator | Assessment Opportunities |
|---|---|
| **ES3.2 h.** Suggest sustainable practices (e.g., composting and fertilizing) that can affect soils positively and reduce or prevent harmful effects such as compaction and contamination of soils. | • Work On It, p. 155<br>• Communicate, p. 155, q. 1–3 |

## Lesson Goal

To find out how people can prevent harm to soil

## Background Information

As farm tractors and field equipment have become larger and heavier, soil compaction has become a greater concern. When farmers use heavy equipment on soil, especially when the soil is wet, compaction can result. This means that the soil particles are pressed together and the space between the particles, or pore space, is reduced. When compaction happens, less water is absorbed into the soil and more runoff results. Thus, soil becomes more erodible. It is also more difficult for plant roots to penetrate compacted soil and absorb needed nutrients and water. There is also less space for the air needed by plants. To solve the problem of compaction, soil particles need to be loosened so that there is greater space between the particles, and humus needs to be added to the soil so it can take in more water. The best way to control compaction is to reduce the number of times farmers move heavy equipment across a field, especially when soils are wet.

Contamination of soils, or soil pollution, results from a build-up of chemicals, contaminants, toxic waste, and salts. Agriculture is one cause of soil pollution. Chemicals that are sprayed on crops to control weeds and insects can seep into the ground and pollute the soil. The application of mineral fertilizers to soil can result in the build-up of heavy metals in soil. Industry is another cause of soil pollution. Some iron, steel, power, and chemical manufacturing plants dump their waste in the ground, which results in a build-up of heavy metals and other contaminants in the soil. Other plants burn their waste. Heavy metals are released into the atmosphere and eventually settle on the ground and seep into the soil. Still other companies try to dispose of their waste in landfills and underground bins, but when toxins leach out of these disposal sites, they pollute the soil.

*continued→*

Polluted soil can kill plants and destroy crops. Chemicals can be absorbed into plants that are used as food (e.g., lettuce). Animals that feed on micro-organisms and worms in the polluted soil are also affected, because they ingest contaminants from the bodies of their prey. Polluted soil can contaminate water supplies if contaminants leach into water that moves through the soil.

Polluted soil can be treated in the following ways:

- excavate it and transport it to a landfill if it affects people's health
- excavate it and send it to a treatment facility, which burns soil to get rid of the chemicals in it
- excavate it and send it to a landfarm to be spread out, tilled, and aired out (as it is exposed to air, pollutants such as gas air out)
- inject into it microbes that can digest organic pollutants

## Curriculum Connections

In this lesson, students have the opportunity to develop skills and concepts in these areas:

### *Social Studies*

DR3.3 b. Identify ways in which people in communities studied interact with the land (e.g., meeting needs and wants, how land is protected or neglected).

### *English Language Arts*

CC3.1 d. Communicate ideas, findings, and information pertaining to topics, problems, questions, or issues by creating easy-to-follow visual, oral, and written formats with a clear purpose (e.g., short report, explanation of a procedure).

## Get Started ▶

- Invite students to share what they know about what makes healthy soil (e.g., spaces between soil particles for air and water; a mixture of clay, silt, sand, and humus).
- Ask students what people might do to make soil unhealthy. Record their ideas.
- Read the text about compacted soil with students. Compare the information in the text to students' ideas. If students did not suggest compacted soil, add it to the list of ideas. Examine the photo of water gathering in the tracks of heavy equipment in fields. Discuss with students where they have seen water gathering on compacted soil and how farmers might reduce compacting in their fields.
- Read the text about polluted soil with students. Compare the information to the list of students' ideas of what people might do to make soil unhealthy. If polluted soil was not suggested, add it to the list. Examine the photo of polluted soil. Discuss with students where they have seen soil being polluted and reasons why contaminated soil would have to be removed.

- Organize students in pairs and have them view the photos and read the text on page 154 of the student book again. You may wish to have them choose one way that people make soil unhealthy, such as compaction or contamination, and create a poster that informs other students in the school about this issue.

| Time |
| --- |
| 40–60 min |
| **Learning Context** |
| inquiry |
| **Level of Inquiry** |
| guided |
| **Skills** |
| • inferring<br>• observing<br>• interpreting<br>• experimenting<br>• hypothesizing<br>• comparing<br>• communicating<br>• controlling variables |
| **Grouping** |
| groups |
| **Materials and Equipment** |
| (per group)<br>• loam (enough to fill 2 baking pans of cookie sheets ¾ full)<br>• 2 cookie sheets or baking pans<br>• 6 books<br>• watering can<br>• water<br>• camera (optional)<br>• pencils |
| **Line Masters** |
| • LM 4-20 |

## Work On It

### Purpose

To observe what happens when water falls on compacted soil and investigate how to help compacted soil take in more water

### Activity Notes

- Provide materials for each group and have group members complete steps 1 to 5. Have students record the results from step 5 on LM 4-20 What Happens When It Rains on Compacted Soil? Students can describe what happened with words, draw a diagram to show what happened in each pan, or take a digital photo or video to record what happened.
- Provide an opportunity for groups to meet and discuss ideas to help compacted soil take in more water before they decide on the plan they want to try. Discuss questions such as the following:
  - *How can soil be loosened to increase the space between soil particles so the soil can take in more water? Should you loosen it all or poke holes into it?*
  - *What can be added to the loam to increase channels for water to enter the soil?*
- After discussing students' ideas, ask students to decide on a plan, record it in their notebooks, and then try it. Students can describe what happened with words, draw a diagram to show what happened in each pan, or take a digital photo or video to record what happened.

## Communicate

Provide an opportunity for students to share what happened in their investigations. Identify different ideas that students used to help compacted soil take in more water.

1. Students' answers may vary but should include that loosening the packed loam to increase the size of the spaces between soil particles helped the packed soil take in more water.
2. Students' answers may vary but could include poking holes into the packed loam to provide channels for water to enter the soil and adding organic material to the packed loam to increase the porosity and absorption of the soil and add channels for water to enter the soil.
3. If soil can take in more water, plant roots can absorb water that the plants need to grow. If soil can take in more water, it also has more space for air. Plant roots also absorb air that is needed for plant growth from the soil.

## DI Differentiating Instruction

### *For EAL/ELL*

Pair EAL/ELL students with partners who read and speak English very well. Encourage these students to read each step aloud for their EAL/ELL partner and to follow the text with their finger so their partner can associate the written and spoken words. Then, demonstrate with the materials what each step in the procedure asks them to do.

### *For Reteaching*

If students experience varying results in their investigations, you may wish to redo the Work On It activity on page 155 of the student book as a demonstration.

### *For Enrichment*

Have students prepare a pamphlet or poster to help farmers who are having problems with runoff and poor plant growth because of compacted soil.

## Assessment *for* Learning

| What to Look for in Student Work | What to Do |
|---|---|
| Students can suggest ways to reduce or prevent harmful effects, such as compaction and contamination of soils. | • Observe students as they read and discuss the Get Started text.<br>• Observe students as they complete the Work On It activity.<br>• Check students' responses to Communicate questions 1–3. |

# Ask … Why is it important to understand soil?

Page 156

| Time |
| --- |
| 80–120 min |
| **Line Masters** |
| • LM 4-21 |

## Indicator Assessment Chart

| Indicator | Assessment Opportunities |
| --- | --- |
| **ES3.2 i.** Research careers that involve an understanding of soils. | • Research, p. 157 |

traditional ***KNOWLEDGE***

## Background Information

Each First Nation in Saskatchewan has its own healers, medicines, medicinal uses of plants, local knowledge, and healing ceremonies. However, most uses of plants, ceremonies, and medicines are common to all. A strong commitment to traditional life and ceremony is the means through which one becomes a traditional herb gatherer and healer. This journey involves many years of apprenticeship, acting as a helper to a healer or Elder. The helper receives information and knowledge about medicines from the Elder through the oral tradition like all other traditional teachings. Healers may pass along their knowledge to family members. Elders and Knowledge Keepers believe that all medicines have a spiritual nature and derive their potency through Creator; sometimes knowledge and usage of medicines are given to them through powerful visions and dreams or in ceremonies, such as fasts.

Although traditional practices and values live on in First Nations and Métis communities, it is important that students do not have the stereotype that all First Nations and Métis people still live in tipis on reserves. As the career profile of forester Bill Murray in this section illustrates, First Nations and Métis people live, work, and thrive as modern people in the contemporary world. Teachers need to help paint a picture of First Nations and Métis people as professionals, such as doctors, lawyers, and teachers, who may retain their cultural values and traditional languages.

## A Forester

- Read the text with students to find out how soil is important in Bill Murray's work. Use the following questions to guide a class discussion:
  - *Why does Bill Murray have to think about soil types when he plans where to begin harvesting trees in the spring?*
  - *Based on what you know about soil types, why do you suppose frost comes out of sandy soil sooner than loam or clay soil?*
  - *Why do you think harvesters cannot leave deep ruts when they harvest trees?*

- Guide students to record notes about how understanding soil is important to Bill Murray's work. Students' notes should include the following points:
  - Understanding how long frost stays in different types of soil helps Bill Murray decide where to begin harvesting trees.
  - Understanding how water moves through different types of soil helps Bill Murray decide where skidders can work to harvest trees.

## An Applied Science Technologist

- Read the profile with students to find out how soil is important in Stephanie Langevin's work. Use the following questions and additional information as a guide to students' discussion:
  - *How do you suppose Stephanie Langevin checks the soil to see if it is healthy? What signs might she see that would tell her that soil is healthy or polluted?*
  - *What businesses or activities might pollute the soil with chemicals? (For example, was there a gas station or a dry cleaner on the site in the past? Did anyone recycle batteries or manufacture goods there?)*
- Ask students how they think polluted soil might be cleaned and explain that polluted soil is dug out if it affects people's health. Where polluted soil is sent depends on the chemicals in the soil. It might be sent to a landfill or a treatment facility, which burns soil to get rid of the chemicals. Or, it might be sent to a landfarm to be aired out. If gas had leaked into the soil from a gas station on the site, the soil would be sent to a landfarm. There, the soil is spread out and tilled. As it is exposed to the air, the gas evaporates.
- Guide students to record notes about how understanding soil is important to Stephanie Langevin's work. Students' notes should address the following points:
  - Understanding the importance of healthy soil guides Stephanie Langevin's work for the City of Saskatoon.
  - Understanding what makes soil healthy and what pollutes soils helps Stephanie Langevin decide how to clean it up.
  - Researching how people have used the soil in the past helps Stephanie Langevin understand what might have polluted the soil.

traditional **KNOWLEDGE**

## A Traditional Herb Gatherer

- Read the profile with students to find out how soil is important to Yvonne Morin's work. Use the following questions and additional information as a guide for a class discussion:
  - *How might Yvonne Morin's traditional medicines differ from medicines your doctor prescribes for you?*
  - *Why is it so important for Yvonne Morin to find earth and plants that are untouched by pollution? How does pollution hurt soil and plants?*
  - *Why is it so important that we show respect for Earth and its soil?*

- Guide students to record notes about how understanding soil is important to Yvonne Morin's work. Students' notes should include the following points:
  - Understanding how healthy soil provides essential nutrients for healthy plants helps Yvonne Morin locate the best plants for her medicines.
  - Understanding how pollution hurts Earth's soil and its plants shows Yvonne Morin how important it is to have respect for Earth and its soil.

## Research

- Have students gather and synthesize information about other careers related to soil (e.g., farmer, gardener, potter, landscaper, geologist, engineer, builder, construction worker, and conservation officer). Guide students to use what they know about soil to infer how understanding soil is important to each job and record notes to summarize their inferences.
- Use LM 4-21 Why Is It Important for a University Teacher to Understand Soil? as an additional profile or resource for the Research activity.
- You may wish to use a jigsaw approach for this research activity. Assign student pairs one of the jobs listed on page 157 of the student book and ask them to find out about the work in this job, using the recommended websites listed below. Then, provide an opportunity for pairs to share what they learned and record notes about what the job involves.
- Suggested websites for student research include the following:
  - National Occupational Classification Profiles: www5.hrsdc.gc.ca/NOC/English/NOC/2006/SearchAlphabetical.aspx
  - Saskatchewan JobFutures: Careers in Saskatchewan: www.saskjobfutures.ca/index.cfm?event=page.careers

| What to Look for in Student Work | What to Do |
| --- | --- |
| Students can research careers that involve an understanding of soil. | • As students research the suggested careers, observe whether they can identify how understanding soil is important to the work in the careers. |

# 15 Taking Care of Our Soil

Page 158

| Time |
| --- |
| 120 min |

| Vocabulary |
| --- |
| • compost<br>• composter |

| Line Masters |
| --- |
| • LM 4-22<br>• LM 4-23 |

## Indicator Assessment Chart

| Indicator | Assessment Opportunities |
| --- | --- |
| **ES3.2 h.** Suggest sustainable practices (e.g., composting and fertilizing) that can affect soils positively and reduce or prevent harmful effects such as compaction and contamination of soils. | • Work On It, p. 159<br>• Communicate, p. 159, q. 1, 2 |

## Lesson Goal

To find out how to keep soil healthy

## Background Information

Humus forms naturally as dead plants and animals decay. These organic materials provide nutrients for plants and help produce fertile soil. Composting is a way to mimic the process of creating humus in the natural environment. Bacteria, fungi, and other microscopic organisms live in soil, air, and water and turn dead plants and animals into nutrients that can be used again. These decomposers produce special enzymes that allow them to break down dead plants and animals and use them as food.

You may wish to access further information on composting provided by the Saskatchewan Waste Reduction Council at www.saskwastereduction.ca/resources/Composting/composting-index.html.

## Curriculum Connections

In this lesson, students have the opportunity to develop skills and concepts in these areas:

### *Mathematics*

SP3.1 g. Pose and solve situational questions related to self, family, or community by collecting and organizing data, representing the data using a bar graph or line plot, and interpreting the data display.

### *Social Studies*

DR3.3 b. Identify ways in which people in communities studied interact with the land (e.g., meeting needs and wants, how land is protected or neglected).

### *English Language Arts*

CC3.3 a. Use oral language to clarify and extend personal understanding, interact courteously with others (e.g., share ideas and opinions, complete tasks, discuss concerns or problems), and sustain conversations by extending others' contributions.

## Get Started ▶

- Invite students to read the text on page 158 of the student book with a partner to find out what compost is and how it helps keep soil healthy.
- In a journal entry, have students explain in their own words what compost and composters are. Also, have students share any personal knowledge or experience with compost and composters.

Adding compost to soil adds nutrients to soil. Gardeners and farmers may also use rotted manure or peat moss to enrich soil. Draw students' attention to these ways of enriching soil as they design their surveys to determine how people take care of soil.

**Time**

60–80 min

**Learning Context**

decision making

**Level of Inquiry**

structured

**Skills**

- communicating

**Grouping**

groups

**Materials and Equipment**

(per group)
- pencils

**Line Masters**

- LM 4-22

## Work On It

### Purpose

To conduct a survey about how people in the community take care of soil

### Activity Notes

- Meet with students to decide the following points:
  - what questions to ask in their survey—questions are suggested in the student book, but feel free to expand or change them
  - how to record people's answers to the survey questions—if students use the suggested questions, provide LM 4-22 Taking Care of Our Soil Survey Questions to record people's answers
  - how many people to survey—LM 4-22 Taking Care of Our Soil Survey Questions provides for three people, but this can be adjusted
  - how they will share their survey results—students may wish to compile their results on a bar graph such as the following:

**How People in Our Community Take Care of Soil**

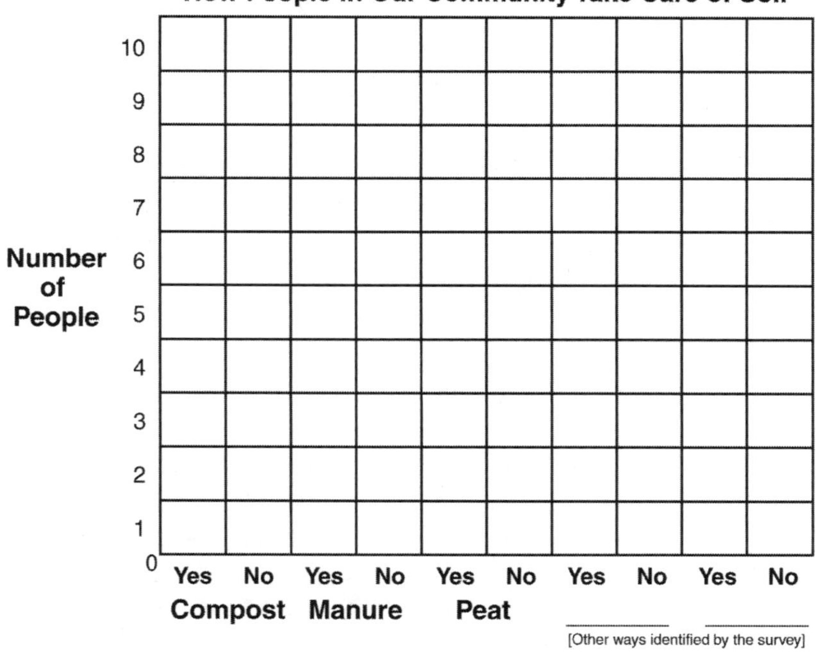


*continued*→

- When students' bar graphs are completed, use questions such as the following to help them interpret the results of their survey:
  - *How does the number of people who care for soil compare to the number of people who do not care for soil?*
  - *Which ways of caring for the soil are most popular in your survey?*

## Additional Activity

Have students make their own compost with the step-by-step recipe on LM 4-23 Can You Compost?

### Communicate

1. Set a due date for students to complete their surveys and bring their results to class. Help students to compile their results and create a class bar graph to show the results of their survey. Provide an opportunity for students to examine the graph and discuss the results.
2. This question asks students to create an action plan to help take care of soil in their community. Begin by asking students to brainstorm for ideas. List students' ideas, examine each, and discuss what they would have to do to put each into action. Record key points for each idea. Then, create a shortlist of ideas that are the most doable by students. Examine these ideas again—consider practicality, time involved, any needed materials, resources, or help. Hold a class vote to determine which idea students will put into action to help take care of soil in their community. Then, work with students to create and record a step-by-step action plan (e.g., how we will care for soil, what we will need, what we need to do, who will do each step, when each step will be completed, how we will know our action plan is a success).

## DI Differentiating Instruction

### *For EAL/ELL*

Pair EAL/ELL students with students who are proficient in English for conducting the survey.

### *For Enrichment*

If your school has no composting program, consider starting one. Students can research, collect materials, post signs, and write letters to parents explaining why composting is helpful. Explain that there will be two benefits to the school's composting project: waste will be diverted from landfill sites, and the school garden will benefit from receiving nutrients from the compost. Have students make a simple composter with the step-by-step procedure on LM 4-23 Can You Compost?

## Assessment *for* Learning

| What to Look for in Student Work | What to Do |
|---|---|
| Students can suggest sustainable practices (e.g., composting and fertilizing) that can affect soils positively and reduce or prevent harmful effects such as compaction and contamination of soils. | • Observe students during the Work On It and check their survey results.<br>• Check students' responses to Communicate questions 1 and 2. |

**DESIGN PROJECT**

# Create Soil for a Garden

*Page 160*

**Time**

160–240 min

**Learning Context**

inquiry

**Level of Inquiry**

structured

**Skills**

- making models
- observing
- interpreting
- communicating
- predicting

**Grouping**

groups

**Materials and Equipment**

(for whole class)

- soil samples from your schoolyard (one for each group)
- humus or compost
- earthworms
- silt
- sand
- clay
- hand lenses
- water
- glass jars with lids
- watering cans
- spray bottles
- containers or pans for healthy soil (one for each group)
- vegetable seeds
- pencils

**Line Masters**

- LM 4-24
- LM 4-25

## Curriculum Indicators

| Indicators Met in Design Project |
| --- |
| **ES3.1 b.** Examine physical characteristics (e.g., particle size, texture, moisture, particle size distribution, colour, and ability to hold together) of soils from different locations (e.g., garden, flower pot, river bed, slough, hill top, grassy field, lawn, ditch, and forest) in their environment. |
| **ES3.1 c.** Classify soils in their environment according to location and type (e.g., clay, sand, silt, and loam). |
| **ES3.1 d.** Analyze soil samples using tools such as spoons, hand lenses, jars, and filters appropriately and safely. |
| **ES3.1 e.** Make and record observations and measurements in investigations related to soil composition using techniques such as notes in point form, diagrams, tables, bar graphs, photographs, and video. |
| **ES3.2. a.** Suggest ways in which individuals and communities value and use soil, including the importance of Mother Earth for First Nations and Métis peoples. |
| **ES3.2 b.** Examine the interdependence between animals and soils (e.g., insects and grubs live in soil, soil provides shelter for some animals, and earthworms aerate soil). |
| **ES3.2 c.** Examine the interdependence between plants and soils (e.g., soils provide nutrients for plant growth, plant leaves die and fall onto the ground, and plant roots spread throughout the soil). |
| **ES3.2 g.** Propose practices that individuals and communities can take to reduce the effects of erosion on a small-scale (e.g., vegetable garden and flower pot) and large-scale (e.g., agricultural field, sports field, river bank, and road ditch). |
| **ES3.2 h.** Suggest sustainable practices (e.g., composting and fertilizing) that can affect soils positively and reduce or prevent harmful effects such as compaction and contamination of soils. |

## Background Information

Students will use a soil sample from their schoolyard to create healthy soil for their vegetable garden. Part of the project involves identifying the type of soil in their sample and deciding what their soil sample needs to grow healthy plants. The first step will be identifying what is in their schoolyard that helps make the soil. If their schoolyard is a grassy area, they will probably determine that their schoolyard soil will have more humus in it. If there are sandy areas for play, they might also say that their schoolyard soil will have more rocks in it as well. They will then determine what they must add to the schoolyard soil to make it healthy for growing vegetables.

*continued→*

**traditional KNOWLEDGE**

As students have learned in the unit, many First Nations and Métis peoples believe that soil is part of Mother Earth. Students should record how they will show respect for the gifts of Mother Earth that they use to make healthy soil for their vegetable garden. Whatever they add to make the soil healthier will come from Mother Earth and, therefore, is a gift from Creator. They will not offer tobacco to give thanks, but encourage them to think of another way to give thanks. They should treat the soil sample and everything they add to it with respect. Soil is not just dirt. The spirit of Creator is alive in Mother Earth, and soil is a part of Mother Earth. That means that the soil and all things that depend on the soil to live are sacred.

## Curriculum Connections

In this lesson, students have the opportunity to develop skills and concepts in these areas:

### *English Language Arts*

CC3.1 b. Communicate thoughts, feelings, and ideas clearly and, when appropriate, artistically.
CC3.2 a. Demonstrate understanding of the topic, problem, question, or issue in a variety of ways (e.g., dance pieces, visual representations, drama in context, diagram, demonstration, chart).
AR3.1 f. Apply criteria to judge the quality of their viewing, listening, reading, representing, speaking, and writing.

## Get Started ▶

- Throughout the unit, students have learned what makes soil healthy for growing plants and ways to care for soil and keep it healthy. In the Build on What You Know activities, they recorded what they needed to know about healthy soil. Have students review these notes.

## Work On It

### Purpose

To have students use what they have learned about soil to create healthy soil for a class vegetable garden

### Activity Notes

- Read the description of the design project on page 161 of the student book. Ask students the following questions:
  - *What do you need to do?* (Students need to work in small groups to make a plan to create healthy soil for a school vegetable garden.)
  - *What will you use to put your plan into action?* (Students will use a soil sample from the schoolyard to put their plan for healthy soil into action.)

- *How will you use a soil sample from the schoolyard to create healthy soil for a school vegetable garden?* (Students will have to identify the type of soil in their sample, decide what their soil sample needs to grow healthy plants, make the soil as healthy as possible, plant vegetable seeds, and keep the soil healthy and free from harm after planting.)

- Tell students that they will record their plans to keep track of their thinking. Provide copies of LM 4-24 Design Project Planner for this purpose.
- Display the suggested materials. Ask students if they can think of other things that they may need to figure out what to add to a sample of schoolyard soil to make it healthy soil for a vegetable garden and then to keep it healthy after they plant vegetable seeds. Collect as many materials as possible. Give students time to bring materials from home.
- Place students in small groups of three or four students or allow students to choose their group members. Then instruct group members to meet and work through the steps below on LM 4-24 Design Project Planner:

1. Brainstorm ideas for how you will:
   - identify the type of soil in your sample
   - decide what your soil sample needs to grow healthy plants
   - make the soil as healthy as possible
   - keep the soil healthy after you plant vegetable seeds
   - prevent harm to your soil
   - show respect to Mother Earth and give thanks for the plants
2. Decide which ideas you want to use. Make sure you know why you are using each idea.
3. Use the ideas to make an action plan. Decide on the steps you need to take and put them in the order they need to happen.
4. Think about the materials and equipment you need and list them.
5. Decide how you will know the soil you create is healthy for growing vegetables and what you will use as evidence for this.
6. Follow the steps in your plan to create healthy soil.

- Provide copies of LM 4-25 Design Project Rubric for students to use for self-assessment. You may also wish to use the rubric to assess students' performance during the project and their presentations.

## Communicate

Meet with students to review what is required for Communicate questions 1 and 2.

1. Students can be expected to describe and/or demonstrate the steps of their action plan and present evidence that their plan was a success.
2. Students can be expected to present the soil they made and explain the steps they took to make it healthy soil for growing vegetables from the schoolyard sample they were given.

- Brainstorm with students for effective ways that they might present the required elements of the Communicate questions (e.g., using a poster or a computer slide presentation to show their action plan, demonstrating or showing videos of the steps they took to make healthy soil, showing plants or videos of the plants growing in the soil they made as evidence that their plan was a success).

*continued→*

- Students can meet with their group members to decide and record how they plan to present the required parts of their design project for Communicate questions 1 and 2.
- Before students present their projects, meet with them to review the elements of an effective presentation such as:
  - deciding how to present each part of their design project
  - deciding on the order in which each part will be presented
  - deciding what each group member will do during the presentation and ensuring that each group member has an equal part
  - practising the presentation so that each group member knows what to say and do
  - making eye contact with the audience
  - pointing out important aspects of the design project as they are being presented
  - speaking clearly with a strong voice
  - being excited and interested in their own presentation because this will cause the audience to be excited and interested in what they did
  - inviting questions from the audience at the end of the presentation
- Provide an opportunity for students to practise their presentations.

## DI Differentiating Instruction

### *For EAL/ELL*

Ensure that EAL/ELL students are placed in groups with students who read and speak English very well. Encourage these students to read each step aloud and to demonstrate with the materials what each step in the procedure asks them to do.

### *For Enrichment*

Challenge students to make their own soil. What will the ingredients be? What tools will they need? Students can begin by creating a recipe card for soil. They can collect the needed ingredients and tools, and then try to follow their recipe. Successful recipes can be exchanged and tested.

## Assessment for Learning

| What to Look for in Student Work | What to Do |
|---|---|
| Students can examine physical characteristics, classify, and analyze soil samples from their environment. | • Observe students as they work to test their soil sample and determine what it needs to be healthy soil. |
| Students can make and record observations in investigations related to soil composition. | • Observe students as they work with group members to create healthy soil. |
| Students can prove that their soil is healthy for growing vegetables. | • Check students' responses to Communicate questions 1 and 2. |
| Students can examine the interdependence between plants and soils and animals and soils and suggest sustainable practices that can affect soils positively. | • Observe students as they work on the project.<br>• Check students' responses to Communicate questions 1 and 2. |

# UNIT 4 SUMMARY

**Page 162**

Students may wish to use this unit summary as a study guide. The Unit 4 Summary is available as a line master (LM 4-1 Unit 4 Summary).

# Show What You Know

**Page 164**

You may wish to use the review questions in one or more of the following ways:

- Use the questions as a guide to an oral class discussion and review.
- Use a jigsaw approach to review the unit. Organize students in small groups and assign each group a selection of questions (e.g., Group 1—questions 1, 6, and 11; Group 2—questions 2, 7, and 12) to discuss and answer on LM 4-26 Show What You Know. Each group can present their responses during a sharing session. Provide an opportunity for students from other groups to add to or comment on the group's responses to each question.
- Use a game show format to add an element of fun to students' review of soil. Organize students in teams and provide each team with chart paper and markers. Present one question at a time and have each team discuss their answer, and nominate a recorder to record it on chart paper within a time limit (e.g., 30 seconds to 1 minute for knowledge-based questions and 2 to 3 minutes for questions that require group discussion and deeper thought). After each question, have teams share their responses. Teams can earn a point for each important point they make in each response. Thus, each team can earn points for each question, and teams can earn more points by being thorough and providing complete responses. Keep track of teams' points in a score box on the board.

**1.** Students' answers will vary but could include that most soils are a mixture of sand, silt, and clay, and that plant roots take in air, water, and nutrients from the soil.

**2.** The four parts of soil that scientist say are non-living are rocks, air, water, and humus.

**3.** First Nations and Métis peoples understand that Mother Earth is made of four parts—rock, air, water, and fire. Soil is part of Mother Earth. The spirit of Creator is alive in Mother Earth. Spirit connects everything and everyone as one. It makes everything alive.

**4.** Students' answers may vary but could include:

- Soils have different-sized particles.
- Soils are different colours.
- Soils can have different textures.
- Some soil crumbles when you squeeze it in your hand. Other soil is sticky and holds together.
- Different types of soil can have different amounts of sand, silt, clay, and humus.

5. Students' pictures and labelling may vary, but could include the following details:
   - Plants grow in soil. Plant roots take in air, water, and nutrients from soil. Plant roots also keep soil from blowing or washing away. Plant leaves die and fall to the ground. They rot and add nutrients to the soil.
   - Animals that live in soil loosen it. This makes more space for air and water. Some animals also eat rotting plants and animals. Their waste adds nutrients to the soil that plants need.
   - Insects like grasshoppers, June bugs, and dung beetles lay their eggs in soil. Anthills can be seen above the soil, but they have many tunnels and burrows in the soil. Grubs, which are young beetles, live in the soil and eat plant roots. Ground squirrels, badgers, moles, and rabbits dig deep tunnels and burrows in the soil. Groundhogs hibernate in burrows deep in the soil during the winter.
6. Ground squirrels loosen the soil when they make tunnels. This makes more space for air and water in the soil. Growing plants need to take in air and water from the soil.
7. Students' answers will vary depending on where they live, but could include humus from dead plants and animals, bits of dead leaves and twigs from vegetation in the area, the presence of broken rock or sand, water, and air.
8. Students' answers may vary but could include references to feeling the texture of the soil particles, squeezing moist soil particles to see if they stick together, using a magnifying lens to examine the sizes of the soil particles, separating the layers of soil by shaking a soil sample in water and letting the particles settle.
9. Students' answers may vary but could include measures such as the following:
   - Adding humus to the soil helps the soil take in more water. When the soil can take in more water, less soil can be carried away by moving water.
   - Planting seeds so that plants can grow and root in the soil helps keep soil in place.
   - Contour planting or cultivation across the slope helps soil take in more water and hold it in place.
   - Building ridges of soil across the slope will help slow the runoff of water.
   - Making holes in the surface of the soil to allow more water to be absorbed by the soil.
10. Students' answers will vary depending on the questions that were not answered in the KWL chart and the new questions that students have about soil. Provide an opportunity for students to access print, non-print, and online resources to find answers to their questions.

11. Students' responses will vary depending on the community in which they live, but could include:

   - Farmers use loam for their crops and people use loam to plant vegetable gardens, flower beds, and lawns because it holds nutrients and water for plants. The sand particles create spaces for more water and air. The clay and humus help to keep the soil particles together and hold water. The silt helps to hold the nutrients and water that growing plants need. The humus provides the nutrients that plants need to grow.
   - Construction workers pack layers of sand and gravel on soil to build roads. As the particles pack together, they make a solid base.
   - People build berms to prevent erosion, to reduce traffic noise, or to landscape yards. A large berm might be made of a gravel-and-sand base topped with a layer of clay and then loam. The sand and gravel provide a strong base. The clay holds the berm together, and plants can grow in the loam.
   - Potters use clay to make pottery. When wet clay particles are pressed together, they stick. They dry smooth and hard.
   - People make structures out of concrete. Concrete is made from gravel, fine sand, cement (ash and limestone), and water.

12. Students' responses will vary, but could include that soil must be honoured and respected as a part of Mother Earth, which provides all that humans need to survive. Whenever people take from Mother Earth, they should offer thanks for the gifts she provides. Therefore, whenever people use soil or take something from soil, they should offer thanks for this gift from Creator. Because Mother Earth and all living things are sacred, students' responses should also include reference to observing living things without interfering with them and taking care not to harm or kill any living thing.

13. Students' responses will vary but could include that soil is much more than just dirt. Soil is an essential natural resource on which all living things depend.

## Looking Back

Self-evaluation allows students to communicate their learning and their feelings about it. Seeing how students view their learning can give you insight and information on which to base your programming decisions.

Ask students to answer these questions individually, then to share their answers with the class. Some students will likely find some areas of this unit easier than other areas. This exercise may help students identify who can give them assistance to understand difficult concepts.

# Unit 4 Line Masters

## Table of Contents

## Table of Contents *(continued)*

Name: ____________________________

# Unit 4 Summary

| Scientists and First Nations and Métis peoples understand soil in similar and different ways. | |
|---|---|
| **SUMMARY**<br>□ Scientists say that soil has four non-living parts: rocks, air, water, and humus.<br><br>□ First Nations and Métis peoples say that Mother Earth is made up of four parts—rock, air, water, and fire. | **MY STUDY NOTES** |

| Soils are different. | |
|---|---|
| **SUMMARY**<br>□ Different types of soil have different amounts of sand, silt, and clay. | **MY STUDY NOTES** |

| Plants, animals, and soil depend on each other. | |
|---|---|
| **SUMMARY**<br>□ Plants grow in soil. Plant roots take in nutrients, water, and air from soil and keep soil in place.<br><br>□ Animals that live in soil loosen it. This makes more space for air and water. Their waste adds nutrients to the soil that plants need. | **MY STUDY NOTES** |

| People use soil in different ways. | |
|---|---|
| **SUMMARY**<br>□ People use different types of soil for different tasks. | **MY STUDY NOTES** |

| People can affect soil. | |
|---|---|
| **SUMMARY**<br>□ People can pollute soil with chemicals and compact soil with heavy equipment.<br><br>□ People can add nutrients to soil by adding humus, compost, or rotted manure. | **MY STUDY NOTES** |

**Name:** ______________________________

# Unit 4 Vocabulary

Check off each vocabulary term below as you learn it in this unit.

After you check off all the terms, make a concept map using as many terms as you can. Start your concept map with this word in the centre: "soil". Use the back of this page or a separate page for your concept map.

- ☐ berms, p. 152
- ☐ clay, p. 136
- ☐ compacted, p. 154
- ☐ compost p. 158
- ☐ composter, p. 158
- ☐ humus, p. 130
- ☐ loams, p. 136
- ☐ particles, p. 130
- ☐ sand, p. 136
- ☐ silt, p. 136
- ☐ soil erosion, p. 149

Name: ______________________________

# Soil KWL Chart

| What I KNOW About Soil | What I WANT to Know About Soil | What I LEARNED About Soil |
|---|---|---|
| | | |

Name: ______________________________

# OWL Chart

| What I OBSERVED | What I WONDER | What I LEARNED |
| --- | --- | --- |
| | | |

Name: ______________________________

# Is There Air in Soil?

You cannot see air. So how do you know if there is air in soil? Try this experiment to find out.

## What You Need

- soil
- clear jar
- water

## What You Will Do

1. Fill the jar half full with soil.

2. Pour water into the jar so it is almost full.

3. Look carefully at the water. Do you see bubbles of air?

## What Did You Find Out?

1. Draw a picture to show what you saw form in the water. Where do you think the air in the bubbles comes from?

Name: ______________________________

# Nature Walk

Go for a walk outdoors in nature and observe the world around you. What gifts of Mother Earth can you see? Write notes and make sketches in the table below.

| Gifts of Mother Earth | What I Observed About Mother Earth's Gifts |
|---|---|
| | |

Name: ________________________________

# What Makes Soils Different?

Use touch and sight to describe the soil samples. Squeeze the soil to see if sticks together. Record your findings in the table below.

| Soil Sample | Colour | Texture (How It Feels) | Particle Size | Sticks Together? |
|---|---|---|---|---|
| 1 | | | | |
| 2 | | | | |
| 3 | | | | |

Name: ______________________________

# 3-2-1 Summary Organizer

| | |
|---|---|
| 3 | **Main kinds of rock particles found in soil:** |
| 2 | **Examples of ways particles are different from each other:** |
| 1 | **Questions I have:** |

Name: ______________________________

# What Is in Soil?

Rub each soil sample between your fingers. Record the texture in the table below.

| Where Did I Get the Soil Sample? | Gritty, Slippery, or Sticky? | High in Sand, Silt, or Clay? |
|---|---|---|
| | | |
| | | |
| | | |

**Worm Shape Test:**

| Where Did I Get the Soil Sample? | Did the Particles Fall Apart Right Away?<br><br>Yes or No? | Did the Particles Stick Together When Damp, but Fall Apart When Dry?<br>Yes or No? | Did the Particles Stick Together When Dry?<br><br>Yes or No? | High in Sand, Silt, or Clay? |
|---|---|---|---|---|
| | | | | |
| | | | | |
| | | | | |

Name: ______________________________

# Separating Soil

Draw pictures to record your observations in the chart below.

**Before shaking the jar:**

Date: ______________ Time: __________

**After shaking the jar and waiting for 5 minutes:**

Date: ______________ Time: __________

**After waiting for 3 to 4 hours:**

Date: ______________ Time: __________

**The next day:**

Date: ______________ Time: __________

Record your findings in the table below.

| Layer | Particle Size (Smallest, Largest) | Texture (How the Particles Feel) | Sand, Silt, or Clay? |
|---|---|---|---|
| Bottom | | | |
| Middle | | | |
| Top | | | |

Name: ______________________________

# How Much Water?
# Table and Bar Graph

Record your results on the table below.

| | Sand | Silt | Clay | Loam |
|---|---|---|---|---|
| mL of water drained | | | | |

Then, transfer your results to the bar graph:

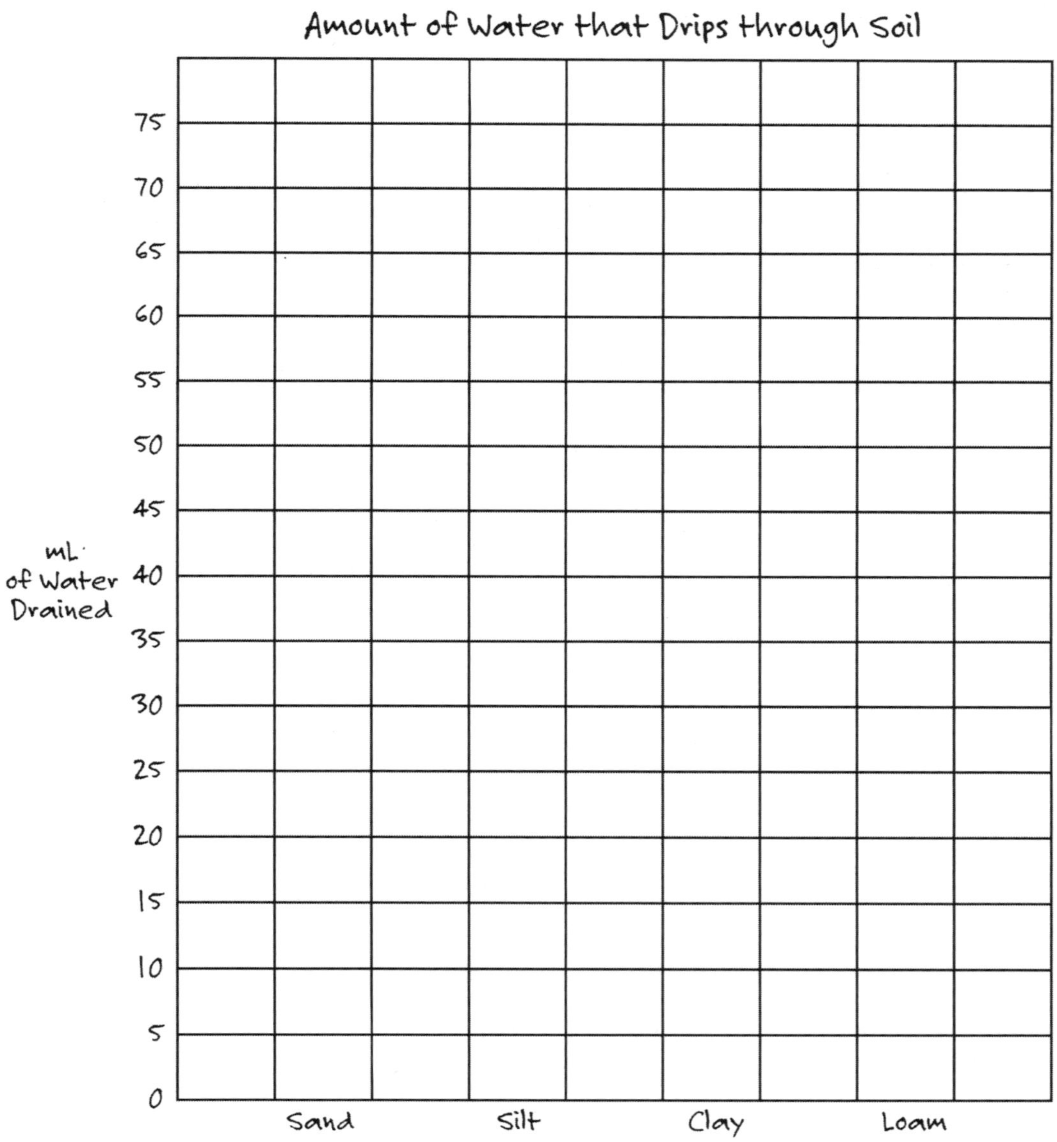

Name: ______________________________

# How Much Water?

**Step 1:**
I predict this soil will hold the most water: ______________________

**Step 2:**
I need these materials:
- equal amounts of dry sand, silt, clay and loam
- 7 paper cups
- 7 pieces of fabric
- nail or skewer
- 2 measuring cups
- water
- soil samples from Lesson 5
- __________
- __________

**Step 3:**
This is my diagram to show how we will set up our investigation:

**Step 4:**
Record your results on the following table:

| | Sand | Silt | Clay | Loam |
|---|---|---|---|---|
| mL of water drained | | | | |

Then, transfer your results to the bar graph on the next page.

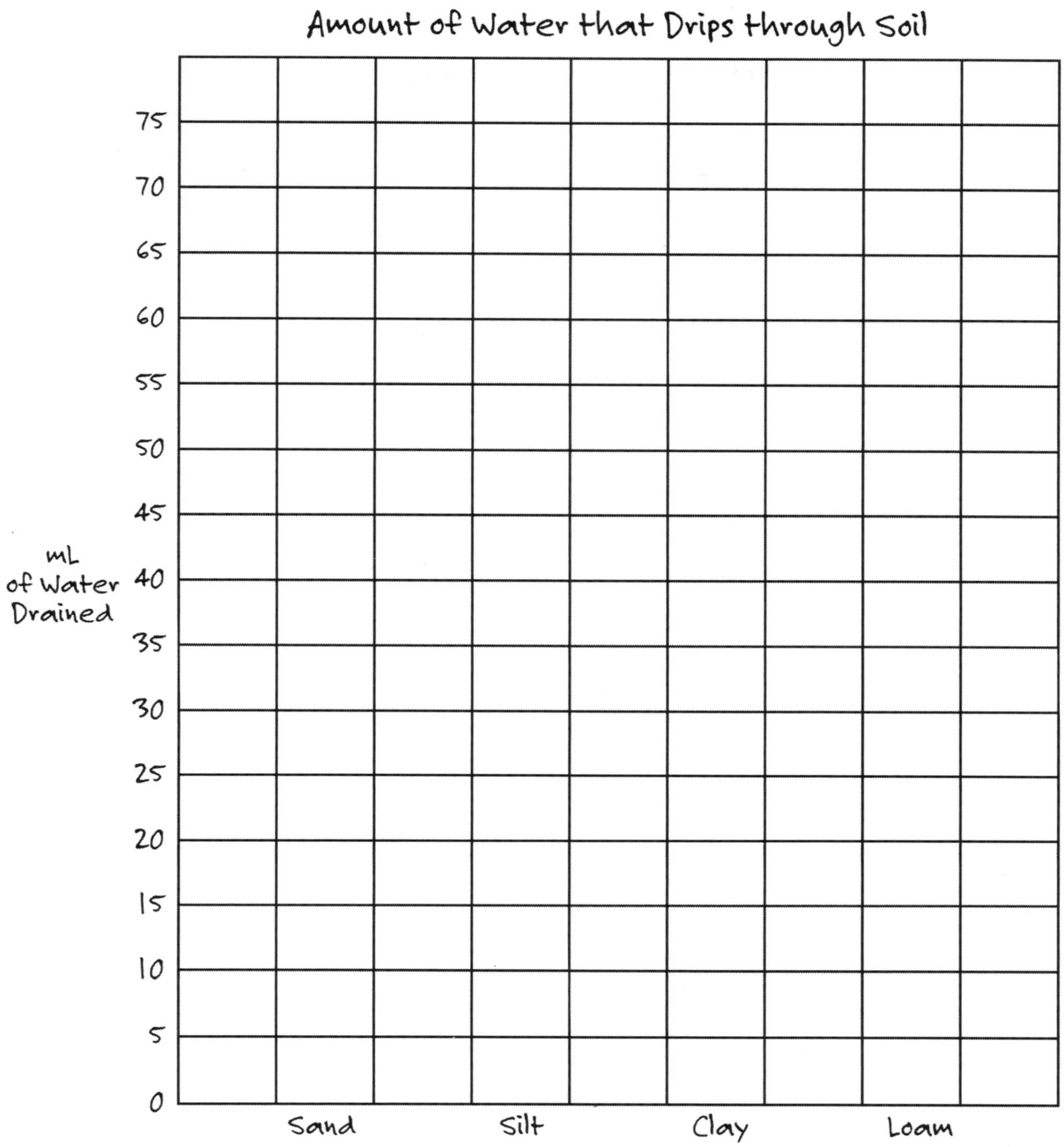


**Step 5:**

Which soil sample held the most water? ______________________________

Why do you think this soil sample hold the most water?

________________________________________________________________________________

________________________________________________________________________________

**Step 6:**

I predict this soil sample from Lesson 5 will hold the most water:

_______________________________________________

Which soil sample from Lesson 5 held the most water? ____________________

Why do you think this soil sample hold the most water?

_______________________________________________

_______________________________________________

Name: ______________________________

# What Lives in Soil?

Look at the picture on pages 142 and 143 of the student book to find the ways that plants, animals, and soil depend on each other. Record your findings in the table below.

| How Soil Depends on Plants | How Plants Depend on Soil |
|---|---|
| | |

| How Soil Depends on Animals | How Animals Depend on Soil |
|---|---|
| | |

Name: ______________________________

## Meet the Earthworms!

After one week, the earthworm jar looked like this:

Name: ______________________________

# What Type of Environment Do Earthworms Like?

## What You Need

- 3 or 4 earthworms
- 2 paper towels
- box with a lid
- water

**SAFETY CAUTTION!**
Wash your hands after handling earthworms.

## What You Will Do

1. Line half of the box with a dry paper towel.
2. Line the other half of the box with a wet paper towel. Make sure the wet and dry paper towels do not touch.

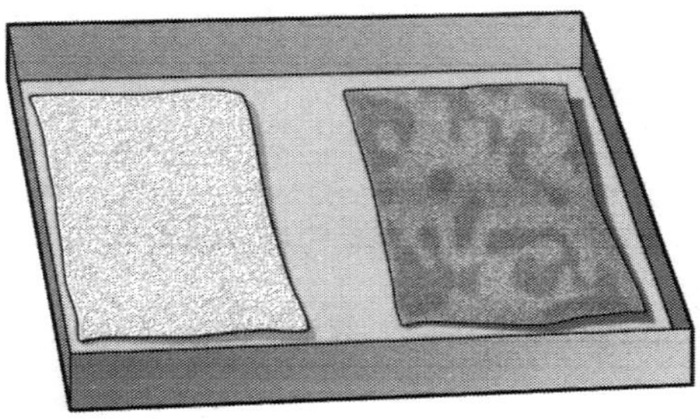

3. Put the earthworms in the middle of the box.

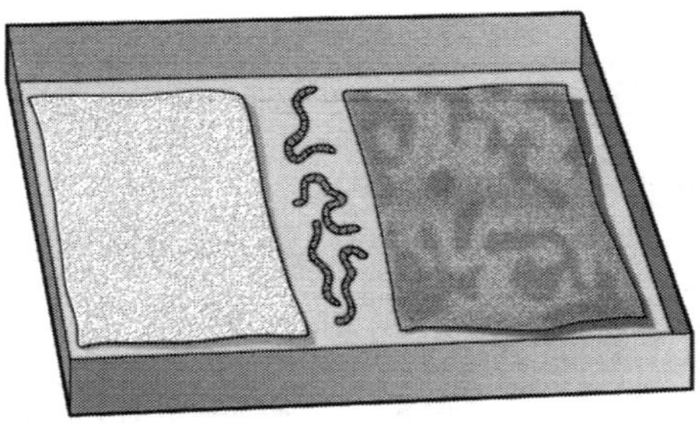

4. Put the lid on the box to make it dark inside.
5. After 5 minutes lift the cover. Where are the earthworms?

## What Did You Find Out?

1. Where did the earthworms go? What does this tell you? Think of a question about earthworms you would like to answer. Write your answers on the back of this page.

Name: ___________________________________

# How Does Moving Water Affect Soil?

## What You Need

- equal amounts of sandy soil, silty soil, soil high in clay, and loamy soil high in humus
- 4 cookie sheets or baking pans
- 8 blocks or books
- measuring cups
- water
- spray bottle or foam cup and a nail or skewer
- camera (optional)

## What You Will Do

1. Place each soil sample in a cookie sheet or baking pan. Smooth out each soil sample so that it is level in the pan.

2. Place blocks or books under one end of each pan to lift it. Make sure all these ends are lifted to the same level so that all the pans sit at the same angle.

3. Predict in which soil sample water will move the most soil particles.

4. If you do not have a spray bottle, prepare the foam cup. Poke 12 to 14 holes in the bottom of the cup with a nail or a skewer. Take care not to poke yourself or anyone else with the sharp end.

5. Measure 125 mL of water and put it in the spray bottle. Spray the lifted end of one soil sample until you use all the water. If you are using a foam cup, hold the cup above the lifted end of one soil sample. Pour the water from the measuring cup into the foam cup and let the water sprinkle onto the soil sample until all of it runs through the holes in the bottom of the cup.

6. Record what happens to the soil particles in the sample by drawing a diagram or taking digital photos or recording a video.

7. Repeat steps 5 and 6 with the other soil samples.

Name: ______________________________

# Erosion Changes Soil

1. Look at the photos on page 149 of the student book. Discuss how moving water is causing erosion in each photo. Record your ideas in the table below.

| | |
|---|---|
| **Photo: Water pouring out of a downspout** | **Photo: Moving water in a stream or river** |
| **Photo: Moving water cutting a channel in the soil** | **Photo: Moving water under a sprinkler** |

2. Discuss places where have you seen moving water cause erosion. Record your ideas below.

______________________________

______________________________

______________________________

______________________________

Name: ________________________________

# How Can We Prevent Soil Erosion?

**What You Need**

- loam
- 2 cookie sheets or baking pans
- blocks or books
- measuring cup
- water
- spray bottle or foam cup and a nail or skewer
- straw (dried grain stalk), cut in 1–2 cm lengths
- grass clippings
- grass, wheat, or oat seeds
- camera (optional)

**What You Will Do**

1. Place one soil sample in each cookie sheet or baking pan. Smooth out each soil sample so that it is level in the pan.

2. Place blocks or books under one end of each pan to lift it. One end of each pan should be lifted to the same level so that each pan sits at the same angle.

3. Cover the surface of one soil sample with straw.

4. If you do not have a spray bottle, poke 12 holes in the bottom of the foam cup with a nail or a skewer.

**SAFETY CAUTTION!**
Handle sharp objects, such as a nail or skewer, with care.

5. Measure 125 mL of water and put it in the spray bottle. Spray the lifted end of one soil sample until you use all the water. If you are using a foam cup, hold the cup above the lifted end of one soil sample. Pour the water from the measuring cup into the foam cup and let the water sprinkle onto the soil sample until all of it runs through the holes in the bottom of the cup.

6. Record what happens to the soil particles in the sample by drawing a diagram or taking digital photos or recording a video.

7. Repeat steps 5 and 6 with the other soil sample.

8. Repeat this experiment with two more samples of loam, but in step 3, mix grass clippings into one sample of loam.

9. Repeat this experiment with two more samples of loam, but in step 3, plant seeds into one sample of loam. When the young plants are 3 to 4 centimetres high, continue with steps 4 to 7.

Name: ______________________________

# How Soil Purifies Water

## What You Need

- clay
- sand
- pebbles
- foam cup
- clear plastic glass that is smaller than the foam cup
- toothpicks
- dirty water in a measuring cup (make it as dirty and mucky as you want)

## What You Will Do

1. Place a layer of clay inside the foam cup, so that it covers the bottom of the cup.

2. Add a layer of sand on top of the clay.

3. Add a layer of pebbles on top of the sand and clay.

4. Use a toothpick to poke 8 to 10 holes in the bottom of the foam cup.

5. Place the foam cup into a smaller plastic glass. Place toothpicks between the cups to allow air to escape from the bottom glass.

6. Pour 50 to 75 mL dirty water into the top cup.

7. Observe the water that drips from the bottom of the top cup.

## What Did You Find Out?

1. How does the water appear different from the water you poured into the top cup?

______________________________________________________________________

2. How do the spaces between the particles in each layer of the cup change?

______________________________________________________________________

3. As the size of the spaces between the particles in each layer changes, what filters out of the dirty water?

______________________________________________________________________

Name: ______________________________

# What Happens When It Rains on Compacted Soil?

What happened when we sprinkled equal amounts of water on each pan of loam:

| **Pan with unpacked loam** | **Pan with packed loam** |
| --- | --- |
| | |

What we plan to do to the compacted soil to help it take in more water:

______________________________

______________________________

______________________________

______________________________

What happened after we changed the compacted soil and sprinkled water on it:

______________________________

______________________________

______________________________

______________________________

Name: ______________________________

# Why Is It Important for a University Teacher to Understand Soil?

**A University Teacher**

My name is Tom Yates. I am a teacher in the Department of Soil Sciences at the University of Saskatchewan.

I teach students how to describe and name soils. To do this, we look at how the soil formed and how much clay, sand, silt, and humus is in the soil. Knowing this, we can decide how the soil should be used. For example, is it good for growing food?

I teach students to understand soil. Then they can help others decide how to use and care for soil. Some students help farmers decide what to grow on their land. Other students work in the forestry industry. They help companies decide which trees to replant in areas where trees have been cut down. Others work on projects to clean up polluted soil.

**What Did You Find Out?**

**1.** In your own words, explain why it is important for Tom Yates to understand soil.

**Name:** ______________________________

# Taking Care of Our Soil
# Survey Questions

| Questions | Person 1 | Person 2 | Person 3 |
|---|---|---|---|
| Do you compost plant waste and add it to soil? | Yes No | Yes No | Yes No |
| Do you spread manure on soil? | Yes No | Yes No | Yes No |
| Do you add peat moss to soil? | Yes No | Yes No | Yes No |
| What other ways do you care for soil? | | | |

Name: ______________________________

# Can You Compost?

**Ingredients**
- A large container
- Vegetable and fruit peelings
- Other organic waste like leaves, grass clippings, eggshells, tea leaves, and coffee grounds
- Water
- Soil
- A long stick for stirring

Soil with humus is good for growing many types of plants. Gardeners and farmers add humus to soil to make it better for growing things. Humus is made from decaying plant matter. This process is called composting. Gather the ingredients listed at the left. Then follow the steps below to make your own compost.

1. Take the container outside. Put soil in the bottom.
2. Add vegetable and fruit peelings and other waste.
3. Add water to make everything damp.

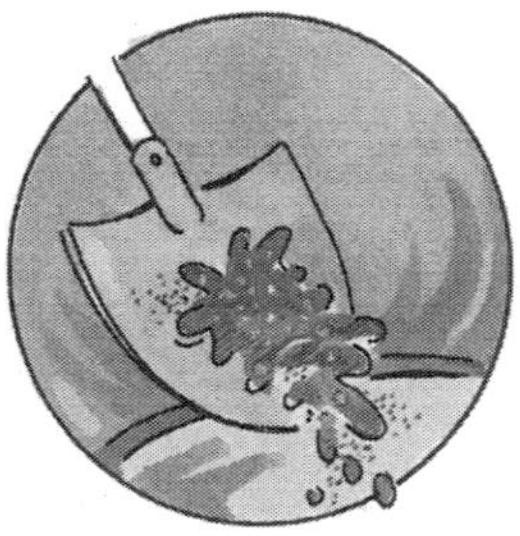

4. Put another layer of soil on top.
5. Repeat the layers.
6. Every week, stir well with the long stick.
7. After about two months, you will have humus! It is ready to add to your garden.

Name: ______________________________

# Design Project Planner: Create Soil for a Garden

| Brainstorming Ideas | Best Idea (or Ideas) | Why We Chose This Idea (or Ideas) |
|---|---|---|
| **How can we decide what our schoolyard soil sample needs to grow healthy plants?** (Review Lessons 5, 6, and 7) ⇨ | ⇨ | |
| **What will we add to our schoolyard soil sample to make it as healthy as possible?** (Review Lessons 5, 6, 8, and 9) ⇨ | ⇨ | |
| **How will we keep our soil healthy after we plant vegetable seeds?** (Review Lessons 12, 14, and 15) ⇨ | ⇨ | |
| **How will we prevent harm to our soil?** (Review Lessons 12 and 14) ⇨ | ⇨ | |
| **How will we show respect to Mother Earth and give thanks for the plants?** (Review Lesson 3) ⇨ | ⇨ | |

**Steps we need to take to test our schoolyard soil sample and then make healthy soil from it:**

**Step 1:** ______________________________

______________________________

**Step 2:** ______________________________

______________________________

**Step 3:** ______________________________

______________________________

**Step 4:** ______________________________

______________________________

**Step 5:** ______________________________

______________________________

**Step 6:** ______________________________

______________________________

**Materials and equipment we will need:**

**How we will know that the soil we create is healthy for growing vegetables:**

**1.** ______________________________

______________________________

**2.** ______________________________

______________________________

**3.** ______________________________

______________________________

| |
|---|
| **Problems we faced as we tested our schoolyard soil sample and created healthy soil:** |
| **What we did to solve our problems:** |

| **How we will present our Design Project:** | |
|---|---|
| **Our action plan** | |
| **Evidence that our action plan was a success** | |
| **The healthy soil we made from the sample of schoolyard soil we were given** | |
| **The steps we took to make healthy soil from the sample of schoolyard soil we were given** | |

**Name:** ______________________________

# Design Project Rubric: Create Soil for a Garden

| | 1 Star<br>★ | 2 Stars<br>★★ | 3 Stars<br>★★★ | 4 Stars<br>★★★★ |
|---|---|---|---|---|
| **Testing your schoolyard soil sample** | You needed help to test your schoolyard soil sample to find out what was in it. | You used one way to test your schoolyard soil sample to find out what was in it. | You used two ways to test your schoolyard soil sample to find out what was in it. | You used three or more ways to test your schoolyard soil sample to find out what was in it. |
| **Designing your action plan** | You needed help to discuss ideas and make decisions for your action plan. | You discussed ideas and made decisions but you did not record them all. | You discussed and recorded some of your ideas and decisions to create your action plan. | You discussed and recorded all of your ideas and decisions to create a complete action plan. |
| **Putting your plan into action to create healthy soil from your schoolyard soil sample** | You needed help to put the steps in your plan into action to create healthy soil from your schoolyard soil sample. | You put some of the steps in your plan into action in the order you planned them to create healthy soil from your schoolyard soil sample. | You put most of the steps in your plan into action in the order you planned them to create healthy soil from your schoolyard soil sample. | You put all of the steps in your plan into action in the order you planned them to create healthy soil from your schoolyard soil sample. |
| **Showing respect for Mother Earth** | You had to be reminded to show respect for Mother Earth in the way you handled the materials and cared for the soil and growing plants. | You showed respect for Mother Earth in the way you handled the materials and cared for the soil and growing plants some of the time. | You showed respect for Mother Earth in the way you handled the materials and cared for the soil and growing plants most of the time. | You showed respect for Mother Earth in the way you handled the materials and cared for the soil and growing plants all of the time. |
| **Working with group members** | You needed help to co-operate and work with your group members. | You worked co-operatively and usefully with group members some of the time. | You worked co-operatively and usefully with group members most of the time. | You worked co-operatively and usefully with group members all of the time. |
| **Group presentation**<br>Required parts:<br>- action plan<br>- evidence that your action plan was a success<br>- the healthy soil you made<br>- the steps you took to make healthy soil | Your presentation did not include the required parts of your Design Project. | You presented some of the required parts of your Design Project. | You presented the required parts of your Design Project. | You presented all parts of your Design Project clearly and completely. |

Name: ______________________________

# Show What You Know

1. Look at the KWL chart you made at the start of this unit. Record what you learned about soil.

______________________________________________________________________

______________________________________________________________________

______________________________________________________________________

______________________________________________________________________

2. Name the four parts of soil that scientists say are non-living.

______________________________________________________________________

______________________________________________________________________

3. Explain how First Nations and Métis peoples understand soil.

______________________________________________________________________

______________________________________________________________________

______________________________________________________________________

4. Explain how soils are different.

______________________________________________________________________

______________________________________________________________________

______________________________________________________________________

5. Draw and label pictures to show how plants and animals help soil and how soil helps plants and animals.

6. A farmer is complaining about ground squirrels making tunnels in her field. Explain what you could tell her about how these animals help the soil.

7. Look around your community. List what you see that would help make soil.

8. Say you move to a new place in Saskatchewan. You want to find out what you can use the soil there for. Plan how you will find out what type of soil you have.

**9.** Look around your community to see where water is eroding soil. How would you stop this erosion?

**10.** Look at your KWL chart. Are there any questions that you did not answer? What new questions do you have about soil? Research to find answers to these questions.

**11.** Identify how people use different types of soil in your community. Explain how the soil types match the uses.

12. How could you use the way First Nations and Métis peoples understand soil to teach others to take better care of soil in your community?

13. What can you say the next time you hear someone say that soil is just dirt?

## Looking Back

14. List three things that you did not know about soil before you started this unit.

15. Think of how you treated soil before working on this unit. What will you do now to help keep soil healthy?

# Answers to Unit 4 Line Masters

## LM 4-5: Is There Air in Soil?

1. Students' pictures should show bubbles in the water and their answers should include that the air in the bubbles comes from air in soil.

## LM 4-8: 3-2-1 Summary Organizer

| | |
|---|---|
| 3 | **Main kinds of rock particles found in soil:**<br><br>sand, silt, and clay |
| 2 | **Examples of ways particles are different from each other:**<br><br>The size and feel of particles are different from each other. Sand has largest particles and feels gritty. Silt has medium-sized particles and feels powdery. Clay has the smallest particles and feels smooth and sticky when wet. |
| 1 | **Questions I have:**<br><br>Students' answers will vary but could include: Where is soil high in clay found? What does humus feel like? |

## LM 4-15: What Type of Environment Do Earthworms Like?

1. The earthworms went to the side of the box with the wet paper towel. This tells me earthworms need moisture and they will go where the soil is moist. Possible questions students might pose about earthworms include:
   - Why do earthworms need moist soil?
   - What happens to earthworms if the soil is dry or they dry out?
   - After it rains a lot, how long can earthworms stay above ground?

## LM 4-19: How Soil Purifies Water

1. The water appears cleaner than the water that was poured into the top cup.

2. As the particle size gets smaller from pebbles to sand to clay, the size of the spaces between the particles also gets smaller.

3. As the size of the spaces between the particles in each layer becomes smaller, smaller and smaller particles filter out of the dirty water.

## LM 4-21: Why Is It Important for a University Teacher to Understand Soil?

1. Students' answers may vary but could include to name, describe, and decide how to use soil.